Under Ten CMEs

Volume One:
Dugald Drummond to W.A. Stanier
1912-1944

by
E.A. Langridge

Compiled and edited by
John Marshall, Simon Marshall & Bruce Nathan

THE OAKWOOD PRESS

© Oakwood Press 2011

British Library Cataloguing in Publication Data
A Record for this book is available from the British Library
ISBN 978 0 85361 701 3

Typeset by Oakwood Graphics.
Repro by PKmediaworks, Cranborne, Dorset.
Printed by Information Press Ltd, Eynsham, Oxford.

Eric Langridge with his two eldest daughters, Sonia and Jacqueline, at Alport Stone near Ambergate in the late 1920s. *Langridge Collection*

Published by The Oakwood Press (Usk), P.O. Box 13, Usk, Mon., NP15 1YS.
E-mail: sales@oakwoodpress.co.uk
Website: www.oakwoodpress.co.uk

Contents

LMS Hughes 'Crab' 2-6-0s Nos. 13103 and 13105 double-heading an Inverness to Glasgow express *c.*1933. *Kidderminster Railway Museum Trust Collection/Frank Carrier*

Abbreviations

ac	alternating current	cwa	carriage warming apparatus (steam heating)
AEC	Associated Equipment Co. Ltd, Southall	cyl.	cylinder
AEG	Allgemeine Elektrizitäts Gesellschaft, Berlin	D&M	Davies & Metcalfe Co., Romiley
AESD	Association of Engineering and Shipbuilding Draughtsmen	DBHP	Drawbar Horse Power
		dc	direct current
		demu	diesel electric multiple unit
AMIMechE	Associate Member of Institution of Mechanical Engineers	dia.	diameter
		dmu	diesel multiple unit
		DO	Drawing Office
ALE	Associated Locomotive Equipment Co. Ltd, Worcester	DSO	Distinguished Service Order
		Drg	Drawing
ARLE	Association of Railway Locomotive Engineers	EAL	Eric Arthur Langridge
		ED	Engine Diagram
ARPS	Associate of the Royal Photographic Society	EECo.	English Electric Co.
		EP	electro-pneumatic
a/s ratio	Ratio between cross sectional and surface areas of boiler tubes	ER	Eastern Region
		emu	electric multiple unit
		FDL	Fell Developments (Ltd)
ATC	Automatic Train Control	F/S	Factor of Safety, see Appendix 8, Boiler Ratios.
AWS	Automatic Warning System		
BHP	Brake Horse Power	ft	Foot/feet
Bo	Two-axle motor bogie, each axle independently driven.	G&C	Gresham & Craven
		GCR	Great Central Railway
BR	British Railways	GEC	General Electric Co.
BSA	Birmingham Small Arms	GSWR	Glasgow & South Western Railway
BTC	British Transport Commission		
		GHQ	General Headquarters
BTH	British Thomson Houston, Rugby	GIMechE	Graduate Member of Institution of Mechanical Engineers
BUT	British United Traction		
CAV	Charles Anthony Vandervell Co. (traded as CAV)	GNR	Great Northern Railway
		GWR	Great Western Railway
C&W	Carriage & Wagon	HF	Henry Fowler
C(C)E	Chief (Civil) Engineer	HM	His/Her Majesty's
CD	Chief Draughtsman	hp	horsepower
CEE	Chief Electrical Engineer	HST	High Speed Train
cg	centre of gravity	ICI	Imperial Chemical Industries
CM&EE	Chief Mechanical & Electrical Engineer		
		IHP	Indicated Horse Power
CME	Chief Mechanical Engineer	ILocoE	Institution of Locomotive Engineers, formed out of the embryo SLS in 1911 and merged with the IMechE in 1969
CMIB	Central Materials Inspection Bureau		
Co	Three-axle motor bogie, each axle independently driven		
		IMechE	Institution of Mechanical Engineers
Co.	Company		
CPCo.	Crompton Parkinson Co.	in./ins	inch/inches
CR	Caledonian Railway	L&M	Liverpool & Manchester Railway
cu. in.	cubic inch		

L&YR	Lancashire & Yorkshire Railway		NRM	National Railway Museum, York
lbs	pounds		NSR	North Staffordshire Railway
LB&SC	London, Brighton & South Coast Railway		OAP	Old Age Pensioner
LCC	London County Council (trams)		OBE	Order of the British Empire
			OC or O/C	Officer in Charge
LD	Left Driving		od	outside diameter
LDO	Locomotive Drawing Office		ODM	Outdoor Machinery
LDV	Local Defence Volunteers, later Home Guard		P&O	Peninsular & Oriental Shipping Co.
LL	Left Leading		psi	pounds per square inch, pressure
LMR	London Midland Region			
LMS	London Midland & Scottish Railway		PT	Privilege Ticket
			RAF	Royal Air Force
LNER	London & North Eastern Railway		RD	Right Driving
			RE	Royal Engineers
LNWR	London & North Western Railway		RL	Right Leading
			rpm	revolutions per minute
LSWR	London and South Western Railway		R-R	Rolls-Royce Ltd
			RT	Right Trailing
LT	Left Trailing		S&D	Somerset & Dorset Joint Railway
LT&SR	London Tilbury and Southend Railway		SECR	South Eastern & Chatham Railway
M&EE	Mechanical &Electrical Engineers		SLM	Schweizerische Lokomotiv und Maschinenfabrik (Swiss Locomotive and Machinery Co.), Winterthur
M&GN	Midland & Great Northern Joint Railway			
MC&W	Metropolitan Carriage & Wagon Co., Birmingham			
MEP	Mean Effective Pressure		SLS	Stephenson Locomotive Society
Metro-Vicks	Metropolitan Vickers Co., Manchester		SNCF	Société Nationale des Chemins de Fer Français (French National Railways)
MGW	Midland Great Western Railway (Ireland)			
MOS	Ministry of Supply		sq.	square
MPD	Motive Power Department		SR	Southern Railway/Region
mph	miles per hour		Supt	Superintendent
MR	Midland Railway		SVR	Severn Valley Railway
MRC	Midland Railway Centre, Butterley		swg	standard wire gauge
			UCC	University Correspondence College
MTU	Mobile Test Unit (dynamometer car)		UIC	Union Internationale des Chemins de Fer
NBL	North British Locomotive Co., Glasgow			
NCC	Northern Counties Committee (Ireland)		US/USA	United States/United States of America
NELPG	North Eastern Locomotive Preservation Group		VIP	Very Important Person
			WD	War Department
			Wh.Sc.	Whitworth Scholar
NER	North Eastern Railway or North Eastern Region		WR	Western Region
			WSR	West Somerset Railway

Eric Arthur Langridge

Eric Arthur Langridge died on 6th May, 1999, a fortnight before his 103rd birthday. Little known to enthusiasts, until his retirement from BR, Eric became one of the most important contributors to locomotive history, particularly through his monumental series 'Under 10 CMEs', which appeared in the *Journal of the Stephenson Locomotive Society* in 28 instalments between 1973 and 1988. He was probably the last man who had worked for two pre-Grouping railways.

Eric was a Londoner, born on 20th May, 1896, who travelled to school on the Brighton line, but, through family contacts, he went to Eastleigh in 1912 to serve an apprenticeship, nominally under Drummond. Like his near-contemporary E.S. Cox, he had been a classicist at school, and therefore had to start his technical education almost from scratch by night classes at the Hartley University College in Southampton (now Southampton University). But as he won prizes for his work there, his abilities were soon revealed, and he was given extra training beyond the normal programme for a premium apprentice.

Eastleigh locomotive drawing office had an established staff of four, and, when a new design was on the boards, the apprentices who had performed best in engineering drawing at the Hartley were called in to assist. (The drawing office was not on the normal apprentice programme.) Eric's first spell in the drawing office was in 1916, when he did the valve gear for the 'S15' class 4-6-0, and in a later spell he did the valve gears of the 4-6-2T and 4-8-0T.

Despite having given him extra training, the London & South Western Railway (LSWR) had no post for him and, after writing to a number of railways and locomotive builders, he was summoned for interview at Derby, where it had been decided to take in some new blood. He was appointed, and commenced a 39-year-stint in the Midland Railway's Derby drawing offices in 1920.

Although he designed many parts of the locomotive, it was eventually boilers that were his speciality, starting with the spare boiler for the 'Lickey Banker' (which had different staying from the original one) and then the 'G9BS' boiler for the 1925 Somerset & Dorset (S&D) 2-8-0s. His most important work was in the Stanier era, firstly with the class '3A' boiler for what became known as the 'Jubilees': this boiler formed the basis of all the Stanier class '3' boilers, covering the 2-6-0s, the class '5' 4-6-0s and the class '8' 2-8-0. Later he designed the second variety of class '1' boiler for the 'Princesses', with combustion chamber, and the sloping-throatplate class '3A' boiler of the later 'Jubilees'. Finally he did the preliminary layout of the 'Duchess', and then the detailed design of the boiler.

He later became leading draughtsman - new work, and spent a considerable time scheming watertube boilers; any possibility of one being built was finally ended by World War II.

In 1946 he was appointed head of the development drawing office, and was involved with the post-war experimental class '5' engines, and the main line diesels Nos. 10000/1. He became increasingly involved in diesel design, and ended his career as diesel assistant to the chief mechanical engineer (CME) of the London Midland Region (LMR) of British Railways (BR). He retired in 1959.

Very fortunately for locomotive historians, Eric preserved the working notebooks that he had used throughout his time at Derby, together with a large collection of papers, many of them unique. The notebooks are particularly

Eric Langridge with his family, Sonia, Jacqueline, Mrs Langridge, twins Gillian and José and John on holiday at Shaldon, Devon in the mid-1930s. *Langridge Collection*

valuable in dating various stages in the evolution of the Stanier engines and their boilers, but they shed much light on contemporary Derby thinking. For example, it is clear from the time Eric spent in scheming out boilers with round-topped fireboxes, that in 1930/1 there was some uncertainty about the merits of the Belpaire boilers.

These matters were all covered in Eric's articles, but most of the material is now in the Library at the National Railway Museum (NRM), York.

Although many retired BR locomotive men have written autobiographies, most of them graduated into senior management positions, and were far removed from the detailed work of designing engines. *Under 10 CMEs* is unique in being written by a man who stayed close to detailed locomotive design for 40 years, including the early stages of the transition to diesel traction. No other writer has ever recorded in detail how and why locomotive designs evolved.

Eric was a keen reader of the *SLS Journal* and often corresponded with the Editor, until well past his 100th birthday. He was also an enthusiastic supporter of the Friends of the NRM, and frequently contributed to their newsletter. He had a distinctive style of writing, well suited to his highly cynical view of some of the machinations of higher management.

Eric was a valuable source of information for the authors of the Railway Correspondence & Travel Society *Locomotives of the LMS* series, and to anyone interested in the details of latter-day LMS and BR locomotives. In retirement, Eric lived firstly in Hastings and then in Polegate, East Sussex. After his wife's death in 1982, he moved into a flat, and finally lived with his twin daughters, retired nurses, who took great care of him. He remained active well into his 102nd year, taking a daily walk, and always being ready to talk trains. In the Autumn of 1998, he was interviewed by *The Professional Engineer*, the journal of the Institution of Mechanical Engineers, which discovered that he was their longest-serving member, having been elected in 1919. The resultant article showed the liveliness of his brain. Eric was a talented musician, and played piano duets with a friend up to the last year of his life. He died peacefully after a short period in a nursing home. The funeral took place at Polegate on 18th May, 1999. It was a pleasure to know him.

A.F. Cook

Introduction

Eric Langridge originally wrote the material which forms the basis of this book in the form of a series of articles which appeared somewhat spasmodically in the *Journal* of the Stephenson Locomotive Society (SLS) between November 1973 and the November/December issue of 1988. Additional articles on Eastleigh drawing office, published in the May 1967 *SLS Journal*, the London Midland & Scottish Railway (LMS) diesel-electrics Nos. 10000 and 10001, published in the April and May 1969 editions, his experience in the LSWR outdoor machinery department, published in the February 1970 edition, and on the LMS '7F' 0-8-0, published in the January 1971 edition, have been blended into the main narrative, while various items of correspondence in the *Journal* arising at the time have also been added where appropriate. A series of five articles by Langridge published in the June to October 1997 issues of *Steam World* magazine (by which time Langridge was 101!) has also been checked for additional clarification of details, blended in where relevant, and we are grateful to the editor of *Steam World* for permission to use this. Much of this latter material was first published in *Steam World*. We are also grateful to the editor of the *Model Engineer* for permission to incorporate material from an article by Langridge on the 2-6-4Ts, published on 15th September, 1967 and to Special Interest Model Books for permission to use material from Langridge's contribution to the book *The LMS Duchesses*, MAP, 1973.

It was clear that this account offered the serious enthusiast an unusual glimpse into the inner workings of the locomotive design world, but as *Journal* articles they have remained less than ideally accessible. When, around 2003, I suggested to my father, John Marshall, that the SLS should 'do something' with these articles in the way of publication in book form he agreed that indeed 'we' should, giving me an object lesson on the advisability of keeping one's mouth shut!

My father set to work on this project with great enthusiasm, and we agreed that the best solution was simply to retain as much of Langridge's original material as possible, only making changes to smooth out the narrative or to correct any errors or add up-dates which had subsequently been identified. Langridge, like most engineers, had a strong tendency to resort to abbreviations, some of which appear almost unintelligible to those outside the industry, especially after the subsequent passage of time. A list of abbreviations was therefore prepared by my father, some items requiring quite diligent research. As a general rule we have tried to apply the full wording where first used, the abbreviation being used thereafter. The inclusion of an index, too, is seen as a vital addition for the book format.

However, by late 2005 it was apparent that my father's health was starting to fail and so latterly the burden of the job has fallen largely on the shoulders of Bruce Nathan, at that time editor of the *SLS Journal*, Ian Kennedy of Oakwood Press and myself. One of the largest tasks has been finding copies of all the photographs which accompanied the original articles, with the preparation of appropriate captions. Most of the original illustrations have been found, but in some instances alternatives have had to be used. We have also incorporated some additional pictures, largely from the collections of the Stephenson Locomotive Society and Kidderminster Railway Museum, which we hope will be of interest. Owing to the long time interval over which these articles originally appeared a certain degree of repetition crept in to the narrative. We have tried to cut this out as much as possible, blending text where necessary. However, it is very probable that some duplication may have slipped through our net, especially arising from the additional material, for which we apologize, and hope that these can be accepted as simple recapitulations.

Starting work on the LSWR it is perhaps inevitable that Langridge came to view the Great Western Railway (GWR) as a hated rival, a view which was by no means diminished on his transfer to the Midland, and was then probably magnified after the trials of *Launceston Castle* on the LMS! To those of us who view things copper-capped in middle chrome green livery with some affection this may jar a little, particularly when he is crowing about having abandoned all Stanier's GWR features, this from the drawing office which produced the rather disappointing Stanier 2-6-2Ts. If only he and his colleagues could have swallowed a little of their pride and produced an updated version of Churchward's brilliant little '45XX' 2-6-2T their success would have been assured! Also it seems a trifle unfair to try to blame the GWR for the failings of the early 'Jubilees' when Euston had in fact produced an under-boilered 'Patriot'! However, in order to maintain Langridge's slant on this matter we have kept all his remarks concerning the GWR and its works exactly as he set them down and simply added editorial comment where there appeared to be factual discrepancies.

One curious feature of the writings of both Langridge and his near contemporary, E.S. Cox (published by Ian Allan in the 1960s) is that they barely mention each other such that it has been suggested that there may have been some sort of enmity or rivalry between them. The paths of Langridge and Cox must have crossed first of all when Cox moved from Horwich, where he had been in charge of the dynamometer car, to the drawing office at Derby in 1926 and Langridge mentions Cox in connection with the drawings for the 2-6-4T bunker and tanks. Cox states that these drawings were the last production drawings he produced in his career. From January 1931 to the end of 1934 Cox was at Euston working with Lemon, then Stanier, so Langridge must have been fully aware of his contribution. After a short time in Derby works, Cox resumed working as personal and technical assistant to the CME, either at Euston or at Derby. From 1946 he was back on locomotive testing, using the Mobile Test Units (MTUs) which Langridge had helped design, yet at this stage Langridge makes no mention of Cox, while Cox only refers to Langridge in passing as development assistant under T.F. Coleman in his book *Chronicles of Steam* (Ian Allan 1967). As a result we believe there is much new information in this narrative adding to, rather than duplicating, Cox's accounts.

Clearly Derby drawing office had a great pride in the job, which is also reflected in Langridge's refusal to acknowledge any design as being based on another unless it was virtually an exact copy, the story of the 'Lord Nelson' drawings at North British being a case in point. The only exception to this appears to be when describing the design of the LMS '7F' 0-8-0 as a replacement for the London & North Western Railway (LNWR) 'G2', where he shows how the two designs had no more commonality of parts than did a 'Black Five' and a 'Hall', yet he presents the '7F' as being a direct development of the 'G2'! Nevertheless this account of a working life in two leading locomotive drawing offices, then later through the changeover to diesel traction, gives a unique insight into the human aspects involved in the design of many well known locomotives and rolling stock, and goes some way towards explaining why things ended up the way they did. What also comes across, compared with a modern engineering design office, is the lack of job security in those days, together with a lack of respect for the individual, bordering on contempt. Whilst E.S. Cox describes how Stanier involved himself with the design proposals at the Euston Headquarters, it also becomes clear that Stanier, unlike Churchward, had very little day to day contact with his far-flung works drawing offices and as a result probably his engineers and draughtsmen adopted fewer GWR features than may hitherto have been supposed. Indeed, the issuing of instruction 'from on high' probably led to an inevitable sense of scorn among the likes of Langridge! We must be thankful that Eric Langridge lived to such an active old age to complete this account and furthermore was still able to discuss intricate details of locomotive matters well past his century.

As well as those mentioned above we also owe thanks to David Postle at Kidderminster Railway Museum for help and encouragement, Phil Cheesewright, Paul Fathers, Brian Oldford, Dai Price and Pete Simpson of the Severn Valley Railway (SVR) for assistance with some of the more obscure abbreviations, operating and other details, Dr Trevor Turner, also of the SVR, for help with metallurgical notes, SVR boilersmith Graham Beddow for advice on boiler construction and maintenance, Neil Simkins and John Forrest with help on boiler ratios, Richard Watkins of LNWR, Crewe for information on the preserved 'G2' class 0-8-0, Andrew Forster of the West Somerset Railway and John Moorhouse of the Midland Railway Centre for information on the preserved S&DR 2-8-0s, Jim Jarvis and Bob Essery for help with photographs, Phil Atkins, formerly Librarian at National Railway Museum, York for much help and encouragement, Jack Kirby, Collections Interpretation Manager at 'Thinktank', Birmingham Science Museum, for a diligent search after Langridge's Bassett Lowke model, Mark Higginson of Derby Industrial Museum for information concerning the Derby drawing office (DO) valve gear model, Laura Lipner at the library of the Institution of Mechanical Engineers for career details of Lt Col L.F.R. Fell, Adrian Tester for his valuable contribution on the technicalities of dynamometers.

Sources and a bibliography appear at the end of Volume Two of this work accompanied by appendices and an index.

Simon Marshall,
Loughborough

Chapter One

Dugald Drummond

My first chief mechanical engineer was Dugald Drummond. That was in 1912 and in those days anyone not having relatives in the LSWR employ had to get an introduction before being taken on as an unindentured premium apprentice. Fortunately my father was in the London Office of the then very prosperous San Paulo Brazilian Railway (there was a staff of six!) and had contacts with their Consulting Engineers and suppliers and so was able to obtain the necessary recommendation: the LSWR had supplied many engineers to the then British-owned South American Railways in the course of time. For myself, having chosen to become a locomotive engineer rather than a bank manager, I would have preferred to join the London, Brighton & South Coast Railway (LB&SCR) at Brighton, for since 1905 I had travelled up and down to London Bridge to school and had formed a sentimental attachment to it. However, I am pretty certain now that I was lucky to go to Eastleigh: the experience I gained was wider and, ten to one, if I had gone to Brighton, I should now be lying in the fields of Flanders of World War I. As a matter of fact, L. Billinton, who had just taken over the Loco. Dept. from Earle Marsh, wrote in January 1912, that he only had a vacancy for a pupil at £150 per annum, thus pricing the LB&SCR out of my family's reach, who had already one son at Cambridge University. Dugald Drummond accepted an apprentice 'from outside' for one fee of £50 and suggested I finish my term at school. I had been brought up on the Classics side - Latin and Greek and so on - but when my future appeared to lie in engineering I dropped that for Machine Drawing and extra time in the school workshop. St Olave's was fortunate in having a good wood and metal workshop supervised by B.G.E. Knight, who started up the Crossley gas engine by swinging himself on the flywheel; an awesome sight!

It was thus September 1912, after passing the company's doctor's examination (in Wandsworth Road London Offices), before I paid my first visit to Eastleigh: Charlie Prescott, a relative of my guarantor and already employed on the running shed, took us down to the CME offices where in due course we were ushered into 'Tosh' Harrison's office. Tosh - of course I did not know his nickname until later - was Urie's chief clerk, a very pleasant man, slightly ginger with a light beard, anxious to make us feel at home. R.W. Urie was works manager and I think next in seniority to the CME, for I believe that Douglas Eve, the running assistant to the CME, was lower down the ranks. So, in the absence of Drummond, father and I were taken in to meet Urie who appeared to be a most fatherly sort. He gave us a long talk on the works, the procedures

Dugald Drummond

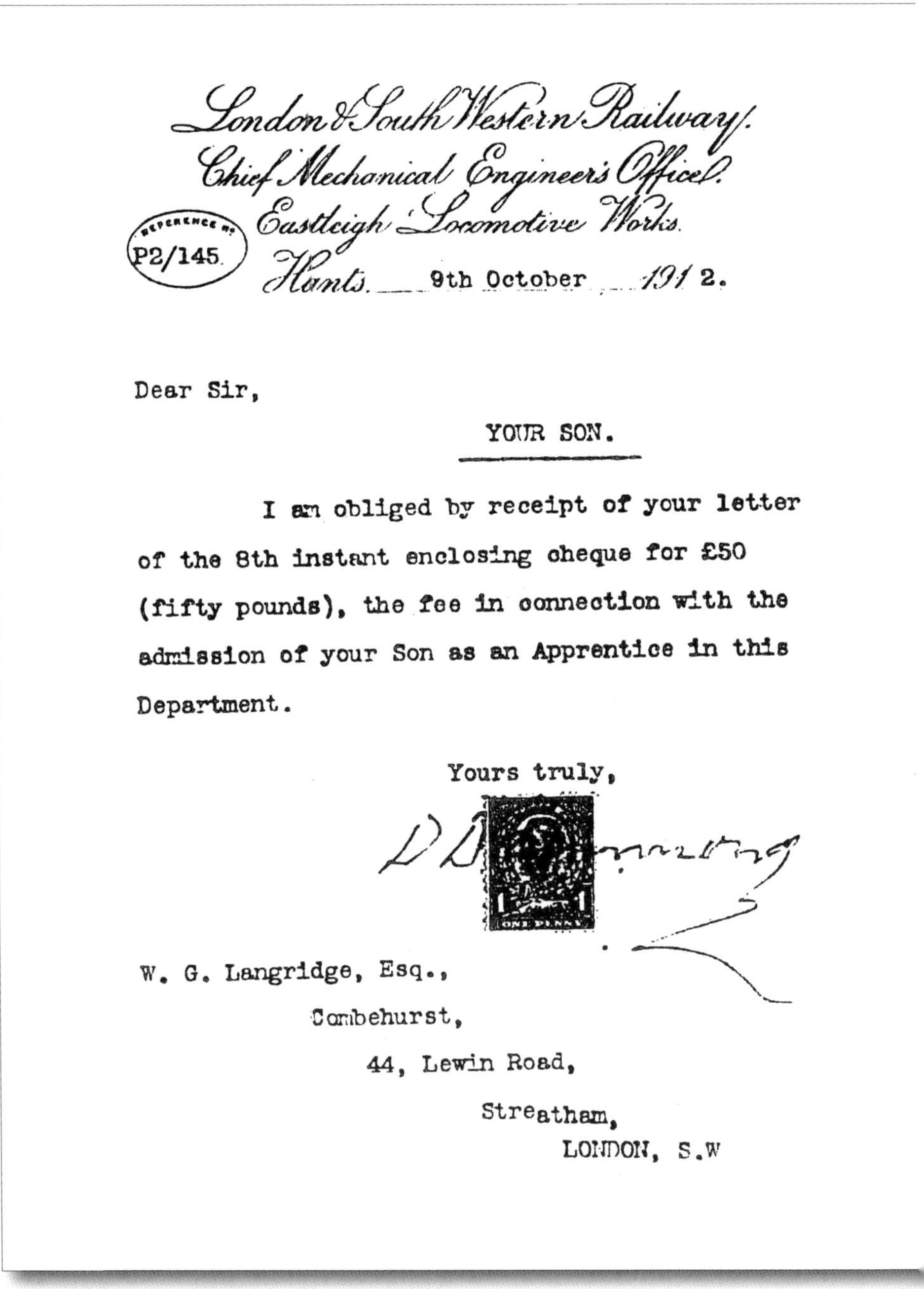

London & South Western Railway.
Chief Mechanical Engineer's Office.
Eastleigh Locomotive Works.

P2/145.

Hants. ___ 9th October ___ 191 2.

Dear Sir,

YOUR SON.

    I am obliged by receipt of your letter of the 8th instant enclosing cheque for £50 (fifty pounds), the fee in connection with the admission of your Son as an Apprentice in this Department.

Yours truly,

W. G. Langridge, Esq.,
    Combehurst,
        44, Lewin Road,
           Streatham,
             LONDON, S.W

The LSWR acknowledgement of the fee paid by Langridge's father for his apprenticeship at Eastleigh.
Langridge Collection

and so on and put me wise to what I - obviously a raw school boy of 16 - should find in the workshops, the procedure and so on. Remember, the only working men I had seen were those leaning up against the walls of shops, etc., in Tooley Street, SE, waiting to earn a few shillings should the gates of Hays Wharf, or the others, open. When they did open occasionally there was a mad rush across the road - Tooley St - to get in first: no fear of getting knocked down, for all the drays (and LCC trams!) were horse drawn, the only danger came from slipping on the cobbles covered by horses' droppings! R.W. Urie made quite an impression on me as being a conscientious employer and although my personal contacts with him were few I retained that feeling all the time I was on the LSWR. Charlie Prescott took us round to choose my 'digs' and so I came under the care of a very good driver's widow and Cranbury Road came to be 'home from home', on and off, for the next seven years.

I never met the great Drummond face to face, the nearest being an occasion when we were streaming from the shops at the dinner hour and the 'Old Man' was hobbling across the tarmac from his little 4-2-4T 'Bug' to the office block only about 20 yards away. We gathered that he was recovering from an operation on his leg - some said an amputation - but evidently unwilling to give in - although he was 72. But within a fortnight, on 8th November, 1912, he was dead. He was buried at Brookwood, the cemetery alongside the railway near Woking: on the afternoon of his funeral the warning bells throughout the Eastleigh Loco. shops rang and all work stopped. The chargehands in the machine shop pulled out the switches and stopped their sections of belt-driven machinery: in the two minutes quiet that followed a few 'wags', as you can guess, 'tolled the bells' by a few taps on connecting rods or the like. It was all over quickly: no one in the shops worried: railways were for ever secure weren't they? - whoever was CME!

Drummond's 'Bug'. SR (LSWR) 'F9' class 4-2-4T No. 58s (formerly No. 773) inspection saloon in Eastleigh works.   *Kidderminster Railway Museum/L.W.T. Sharp Collection*

Eastleigh station in the early years of the 20th century with an unidentified outside-cylinder LSWR 4-4-0 present.   *Kidderminster Railway Museum Trust Collection/Wilsteed of Southampton*

LSWR '0135' class 4-4-0 No. 312 (No. 0143 until 1913) standing withdrawn at Eastleigh works. This was one of the first of William Adams' 4-4-0s built by Beyer, Peacock in 1880. The earlier number can be seen on the cabside underneath the later number. The tender has been detached.
                        Kidderminster Railway Museum Trust Collection/H.C. Casserley

Drummond was a very good leader, obviously, for he had transferred his shops from Nine Elms to a new site at Eastleigh: he had put in turret lathes, milling machines, wheel lathes, etc., of the latest design. He had staffed his shops in the main with Scottish foremen and had seen that the workmanship was first class. A little town had been built on the west side of the main London/Southampton railway with sloping road and bridge over the line at right angles and just about big enough to take two horse-drawn grocer's carts, to supply 'Spike Island', a string of houses mostly inhabited by shed personnel. Spike Island divided the new shops from the new running shed. He also reduced the working hours to 7 am-12 noon, 1-5 pm Monday to Friday, with 7 am-12 noon on Saturdays, a 50 hour week with no breakfast break or 6 am start as was usual in engineering shops. True it meant the apprentice got 4s. 8d. instead of 5s. 0d. a week! The remains of the old shops at Nine Elms have disappeared now, but, until the 1960s, a bay of the erecting shop with the track for overhead cranes was to be seen from the down trains just after crossing Wandsworth Road SE.

In regard to his locomotive designs I am unable to say how much he laid down the details. He had learned in the hard way from a varied experience but seemed to have a strong leaning to Stroudley practices - tidiness, simplicity and standardization. In his later years J.A. Hunter, a real Aberdonian, was his chief draughtsman and one of the Urie boys had a lot to do with his latest designs, for his style of drawing and printing is unmistakeable. It is, however, notable that the design of Drummond's first inside-cylinder locomotives was so good that it lasted right through to the end of the LSWR. His design bore no relation to that of Adams, his predecessor on the LSWR, and improved on that of Stroudley for whom he was works manager for many years. Whoever designed the 18½ in. x 26 in. inside-cylinder block with its two small slide valves per cylinder was certainly far-sighted for it could be used for 0-4-4T, 0-6-0 goods, 4-4-0 passenger and even the first lots of 4-cylinder 4-6-0 locomotives ('330' class).

Similarly, boilers and fireboxes of two sizes sufficed up to the days of the '463' class 4-4-0s and the 4-6-0s. Motion and coupling and connecting rods were also standardized so that interchangeability of parts amongst something like 250 locomotives was achieved. The dimension of 10 ft 0 in. between driving and trailing axle centres on all 4-4-0s after the first 10 was considered verging on the 'risky' at the time: it allowed a deep 7 ft 4 in. long firebox to be used giving about 24 sq. ft of grate. No unusual bending of coupling rods took place - they were flat rectangular section as advocated later by the Great Western Railway. Drummond boiler fittings were simple and economical in use of material and maintenance, e.g., safety valves, steam valves, inward opening firedoor and injectors. One could perhaps criticise the combined brake ejector and driver's valve for being heavy - it was a Gresham & Craven fitting. The costly things were the steam reversing engine and single and duplex feed water pumps fitted to later locomotives. And the most 'cussed' fitting was the bronze feed water pipe inside the smokebox tubeplate, the clackbox being outside. Stripping these was a nightmare job, but things like unwheeling a locomotive or changing a spring or adjusting brakes were child's play compared with Adams' locomotives. One often reads that Drummond bearings were skimpy. However, all engines, whether LSWR or any other inside-cylinder design with Stephenson gear, had the

LSWR 'M7' class 0-4-4T built at Nine Elms in 1900.   *SLS Collection*

SR 'B4' class 0-4-0 dock tank No. 88. This was an Adams design, but Drummond built some
similar locomotives.   *SLS Collection/W. Clark*

'M7' class 0-4-4T No. 249 in Southern Railway livery at Waterloo, December 1937
SLS Collection/R.F. Roberts

'M7' class 0-4-4T No. 30109, in BR livery and fitted for push-pull working, stands at Bentley with a Bordon branch train.
SLS Collection/R.F. Roberts

Drummond '700' class 0-6-0 No. 30350 at Eastleigh shed, 5th September, 1953.   *Bruce Nathan*

LSWR No. 443, one of the last of Drummond's 6 ft 7 in. 4-6-0s on a down West of England express.   *Ken Lea Collection*

same dimension between tyres - about 4 ft 5⅜ in. - between which the engine frame and projections - such as axlebox guides - had to pass when unwheeling and so were in the same boat. In that space the designer had to provide for axlebox bearing, crank webs and big end pins, four eccentric sheaves; so 8 in. was about the maximum bearing anyone could get in. The LSWR oil pads could have been better perhaps, but the oil grooves were off-centre in the best approved style and the oil good in those early days. Originally Drummond used bronze axleboxes, but later had forged steel boxes with fitted brasses, case-hardened faces to case-hardened axlebox cheeks. Obviously, this arrangement would not get rid of the heat so quickly and may have added to the risk of hot boxes. Naturally, with his Scotch sense of economy Drummond did not plaster everything with anti-friction white metal as did, for example, the Midland Railway (MR). And he laid down rules against 'thrashing' his locomotives and ran a coal bonus scheme for engine crews to encourage economy.

In his time, an experimental boiler with one large flue and cross tubes was fitted to an ordinary firebox; cast-iron bushes in coupling rods were tried and one 4-6-0 (perhaps No. 458) was given an extra superheater element in a copper flue tube 3½ in. dia. running from front tube plate to the firebox wrapper - it had a right-angle bend to get in there.

Of his less run-of-the-mill locomotives the 4-cylinder uncoupled 4-4-0s seemed to be his way of doing what Webb had done less successfully on the London & North Western Railway in his uncoupled compounds. One driver at Nine Elms, named Geary, had a reputation for doing wonderful things with No. 720, one of the large-boilered 4-2-2-0s.

As with most people who designed 4-6-0 express passenger engines (except LNWR), Drummond found getting them to run at high speeds difficult. The '330s' of 1905 - ante-dating 'Claughtons' by about six years - were probably more economical than the latter but would not run fast and soon got demoted to hauling Royal Navy coal from Wales to Portsmouth. They were probably considerably over their estimated weight also. The next five did better, although crippled by having 6 ft 0 in. diameter 'drivers', but were lighter. The last Drummond 4-6-0s were considerably better with 6 ft 7 in. 'drivers'. These came out in 1911/12 - contemporary with LNWR 'Claughtons' - and had 9 in. piston valves for their 15 in. cylinders - a very generous proportion - outside Walschaerts gear also working inside valves by rocking levers, plus 31.5 sq. ft grate. To hear one of these come into the side platform at Eastleigh with the 8.18 pm to Waterloo (from Bournemouth) with duplex feed pump ticking over and cylinder safety valves just easing the cylinder compression reminded one more of marine work than locomotive work.

As on other lines - Great Central Railway (GCR), and LNWR and Caledonian Railway (CR) - the 4-4-0 seemed to be able to beat all the others and this was the case with the Drummond '463' class. To get an extra 1 ft 0 in. of firebox length, the rear had to be raised to clear the trailing axle - as the 10 ft 0 in. coupling rod was adhered to. But the cylinder (inside) design was quite new; and having Walschaerts gear - thus requiring only two eccentrics and giving more room for axlebox bearing - and piston valves on top of cylinders - made them unique. The exhaust steam feed-water heating arrangement in the tender and duplex feed

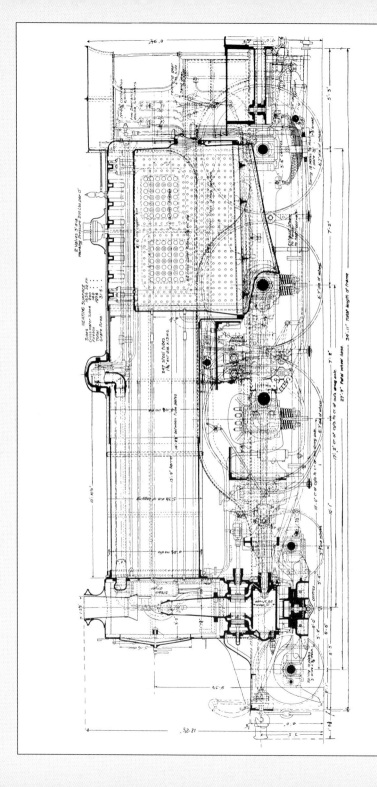

General arrangement of a Drummond '443' class 4-6-0. When designing the 'Coronation' motion, Langridge avoided copying this layout.

pumps on the locomotives were standard for express locomotives and some tank engines; the tenders were also to Drummond's usual pattern on bogies with inside bearings on the axles. This frame-less design meant that the bogie centres were riveted direct on to the tender well: inevitably looseness developed and so they became like the old-fashioned horse-drawn road water carts, whence they got their nickname.

The entrance to the carriage works was in the Bishopstoke Road: the old bridge over the railway was a deep girder affair with a sharp right-angled meeting with the Allbrook-Winchester road and the Junction Hotel squeezed in between the road and the station entrance. The up signal gantry was a heavy one across the through and platform lines with home and distant signals high up and repeaters below. The usual thing was for Portsmouth trains to use the far side and the Southampton trains the inner. The near side platform was

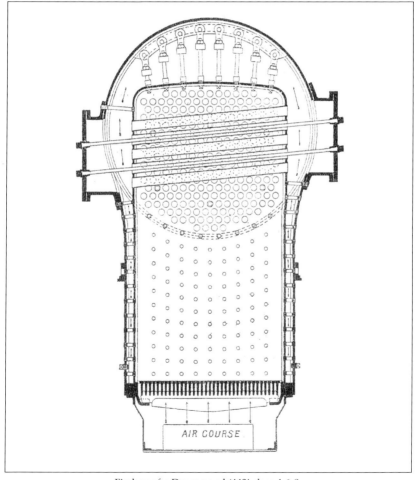

Firebox of a Drummond '443' class 4-6-0.

Drummond 'K10' class 'Small Hopper' 4-4-0 at Waterloo, 1948. *Ken Lea*

LSWR Drummond 'F13' class four-cylinder 4-6-0 No. 331 at Eastleigh shed.
Kidderminster Railway Museum Trust Collection/V.R. Webster

normally used by the Romsey trains but the 8.18 pm fast London train always used it - one of the few Bournemouth trains that stopped at Eastleigh. It was always worth while seeing, for it was a Nine Elms turn and had a 'big-un' on, often a 4-cylinder 'Paddlebox' 4-6-0. They were to me very impressive engines, standing there with their duplex feed pumps ticking over and their high-pitched boiler. I remember one night the driver was a shortish fellow. Standing on his driver's stool he swung the downward hanging regulator handle right across and then half way back. One would imagine that sort of thing on a Bulleid would make it slip like blazes, but not the Drummond 4-6-0. Evidently the driver knew its ways for it went off on the curved exit without a murmur. That train did not stop at Eastleigh on Sundays but you could hear it pass through after a whistle as you sat in church listening to the evening sermon. All up Portsmouth trains came in on this Romsey platform; they came in at a fine pace making a great clatter over the crossings at the lower end of the station. Actually it was a far sweeter way into that platform than to the other as there was no reverse curve. Off the main line in the opposite direction was a leading turnout to the shed and works. It seemed strange to me that a facing point to a by-road should be allowed here as through trains did anything up to 75 mph through there. It is also strange that the station was never rebuilt; there were some very ancient bits in the up platform if you liked to look for them.

Having come up the hard way Drummond knew his men: his lectures on how to drive and handle his locomotives were published in 1907: he was an active president of the LSWR Engineering Club. His address in the proceedings of 1911, which I possess, contained an outright condemnation of the Atlantic (4-4-2) design! Thus, although he may have been well paid in the end (around £5,000), he earned it, more perhaps than some other CMEs, in looking after 900-odd locomotives, the shops, sheds and outdoor machinery and the staff attached thereto. An extract from the 1911 proceedings is appended at the conclusion of this chapter.

I see I left myself in my digs: there the regular routine commencing with a 6.15 am rise started: signing the LSWR Book of Rules in the works time office. Collecting my number disc, 775; meeting Mills, the machine shop foreman (Scotch of course); 'Punch' Cook (proper Cockney), the chargehand of the screwing section, were the preliminaries to a few weeks on the nut tapping machine. 'Punch's' machine screwed long stays, etc.; his two mates turned up horn stay and cylinder studs galore from black bar. The newcomer's job was to feed blank stamped-out nuts on to three vertical rotating spindles and pull down the check to hold the nuts as the rotating spindle and tap formed the thread. The days were long and sometimes frustrating to the ex-school boy: but next to him were the two other members of the gang, also apprentices, Owen and Surrey Warner's (the C&W supt) son. Their jobs were to face up the tapped nuts and deal with others brought across from the erecting shop for thinning down: occasionally a case-hardened one would creep through and make a mess of the cutting tool! So there was someone of one's own ilk to pass the time of day with. One advantage of the lack of walls between machine, erecting and boiler shops. was that, from our machines, we lads could see the latest products being carried down the length of the erecting shop from the New Works gang

Eastleigh works erecting shop showing locomotives under repair.

Kidderminster Railway Museum/John Fairman Collection

Eastleigh works erecting shop on 7th June, 1924 with 'F6' class 0-4-4T No. 1 undergoing repair. Although after the formation of the Southern Railway, the locomotive is still in LSWR livery. Its wheels have been removed and they may be amongst those in the foreground.

Kidderminster Railway Museum Trust Collection/H.C. Casserley

Eastleigh works erecting shop with several locomotives in the foreground including a small 0-4-4T and 'Schools' class 4-4-0. Tenders are under repair In the two most distant bays. This would have been after the author's time but would have looked much the same in his day.

Kidderminster Railway Museum/John Fairman Collection

The Drummond fitting shop at Eastleigh works. Several connecting rods are on the nearest bench and several more stacked on the floor.

Kidderminster Railway Museum/John Fairman Collection

Eastleigh works boiler shop with fitters at work on the nearest boiler.

Kidderminster Railway Museum/John Fairman Collection

to the exit doors to the yard. They usually had had a coat of grey paint on already and it was impressive to see No. 458, the last 4-cylinder 4-6-0, and one or two of the '463' class 4-4-0s being carried slowly over the centre road clear of the locomotives on the side roads under repair.

As the weeks went by one learned accepted practices: cleaning down your machine at 11.45 on Saturday mornings, having a sandwich (your elevenses) about mid-morning on the toolbox against the wall behind your machine, finding out the least objectionable urinal, etc. These latter necessaries - and the accompanying 'bogs' - seem to have been tacked on the works walls in odd places as an afterthought. No smoking was allowed on works premises so men - if all about was quiet - would nip in for 'two draws and a spit' - or more - besides using them for their intended purposes. They were 50 per cent open to the sky, just as well to let out the smell of 'thick twist', etc. It was a really bad feature in a modern building. The two in the erecting shop, which had to serve the fitting and machine shops as well, were pretty foul: the least unpleasant was in the paint shop, so if the need arose I risked detection for being in illegal area and went there. There were four or five stalls - no doors of course - with the main sewage pipe passing through with holes and wooden seats. One of the lads thought it would be a good idea to shift some of the tardy occupants: so he lit a ball of paper, popped it through the first seat hole and ran for his life while the burning paper floated down with the moving water under the posteriors of the occupants who shot up with singed pants or worse!

The other trying thing was lack of heating of any sort and steel can be very cold on a winter's morning. Heating of the shops was not considered necessary, Drummond must have said, 'Working will keep them warm'. Artificial light - from first Monday in November to ditto in February - was by carbon-arc lamps, no individual lights were provided - the old smoky oil lamp had to suffice in the erecting shop pits. A plentiful supply of simple cylindrical air hoists were provided in fitting and machine shops doing away with manual lifting. Time keeping was strict: no one left his machine until the 12 o'clock hooter blew, then Punch would shut down the motor and there was a scramble across the yard, up the steps and 'home'.

One had to obtain privilege tickets forms from your shop office - again the size of the old telegraph form - fill in the station you wanted to get them at and where you were going to and give them in to the foreman's office. He was empowered to initial them over Drummond's stamp and you collected them later. If you were attending Southampton Tech. you kept a note of the ticket number and in due course sent in the statement to the foreman's office and eventually collected the refund in your pay tin. It was 3d. return to the docks station at the privilege rate but although that might sound small it was worth collecting in those days. Thus the foreman was a power in the land. It was not so many years since foremen had actually employed their men. I imagine he still had a say as to whom he would recommend taking on but the onus and consequences on employing men - insurance etc., then rested with the company. Lloyd George's National Health scheme was not very old and you could 'opt out' of it to a certain extent if you were willing to forego some of the long term benefits, which I did.

Eastleigh works electric journal wheel lathe with a set of locomotive driving wheels minus tyres in place. *Kidderminster Railway Museum/John Fairman Collection*

The front of Eastleigh works showing the large storage area and LBSC 'Terrier' 0-6-0T No. 2653 in background. *Kidderminster Railway Museum/John Fairman Collection*

We were all paid weekly on Thursdays after the 5 pm finish: it took over half-an-hour to complete and when your shop - they went up one in rotation - was at the end of the queue you wondered if your 4s. 8d. was worth waiting for. However, it bought the luxuries - Cut Golden Bar at 4d. an ounce - while my father paid the 'digs' at 15s. a week. Privilege Ticket (PT) fare Waterloo return 2s. 10½d., a pass once a month, a three-speed push-bike on which to explore the lovely surrounding country. Reg Preece had a bike and he took me by road down to 'Town', i.e. Southampton, and showed me round the town and into the docks which seemed quite open if you liked to go in. They were getting near their peak then. All the big lines came in: North German Lloyd, Cunard, etc. A sight on Saturday afternoons was the departure of two Union Castle boats: one like the *Edinburgh Castle* was going non-stop to Capetown while the smaller one like the *Garth Castle* had come round from Tilbury in the morning to pick up a few more passengers, for it was cheaper to travel on a stopping boat as she was. Just round from the quays were the dry docks: the big one to take White Star's *Olympic* had just been completed. It was a wonderful sight in those days to see the many liners' funnels towering over everything and visible from much of the town; perhaps even more impressive was to hear the *Olympic's* hooter sounding her departure - it was said you could hear it in Eastleigh. So there was plenty to do outside the works and one's vision and education was widening rapidly - all at 16½ years of age.

The railway CME department ran two series of technical classes for their apprentices, a senior one and a junior, each in the morning in the company's time once a fortnight. They covered quite simple mechanical and heat problems and all apprentices were expected to attend. A prize in the form of books chosen by the apprentice was awarded to the one who gained the maximum number of marks for the homework - a write-up of the previous week's lecture - he submitted. I am afraid it was very unfair on the boys who had not had the education of the sort that the outside usually had had; however, orders were orders and we privilege ones had to attend and usually took the prizes. These classes were usually taken by D.C. Urie until he left to take up the job in Ireland, then Chard the leading hand in the drawing office took over.

Charlie Prescott introduced me to the LSWR Engineering Society: the President was naturally Dugald Drummond and the membership covered all grades on the railway. Papers were given by people from all departments and from some outside engineers responsible for supplying specialized equipment. I particularly remember one by a Ross pop safety valve representative who spoke about 'spheroidal' water running along hot plates - the connection being that sometimes water refused to turn into steam and so could build up in a boiler side and cause water to come out when the safety valve lifted and so keep the valve open and drain off the water to a dangerously low level. I have not myself seen this happen but have been told authoritatively of it happening to an Lancashire & Yorkshire Railway (L&Y) 'Crab' in my LMS days. The society held visits in the summer and I remember going to the dry dock and the Otterburn pumping stations and a long distance trip to Derby, of which more anon. The following is typical of the society's proceedings and rounds off this chapter on Drummond:

Extract from Address to LSWR Engineering Society

Things to know and avoid in the Design and Management of the Modern Locomotive Engine
by D. Drummond, Esq., MICE, MIME (President)
Read: 27th July, 1911

There are at least three problems to be seriously considered by the Chief Mechanical Engineer of a Railway: (1) The contour of the railway; (2) The description of traffic to be worked over it; (3) Haulage distance, and the types of engines best suited to equip the same; all of which are important factors.

A few years ago the minds of many gentlemen responsible for the management of the railways of Great Britain were unduly alarmed at being considered outclassed by American methods in railway management, overlooking the fact that the conditions were entirely different, and required to be dealt with by means best suited to meet each case. It, unfortunately, directed the attention of foreign railway companies, who had had their rolling stock and other, equipment supplied almost exclusively by British manufacturers, causing them to consider seriously their position when the British companies practically admitted American superiority.*

Orders for locomotives were placed and supplied by American firms for several English railways, but the result proved conclusively the superiority of the English engines, from every point of view, over those imported from America.

A few of our railways are continuing the use of an American type of engine known as the 'Atlantic', They are, in my opinion, the most unsatisfactory engine that has been introduced into English practice, owing to the disturbing effects on the permanent way and bridges, compared with the four-cylinder, six-coupled modern express engines. I am of opinion the wear and tear of the permanent way and bridges should form a very important factor in the design of the locomotive engine.

Superheating of Steam

It is important that all waste heat escaping into the atmosphere should be utilised as far as possible without complications. Superheating the steam in the smokebox on its passage to the steam chest ensures dryer steam. I have had a number of engines running with a simple method of superheating for the last eight years with good results. I am not an advocate of superheating from 500 to 600 degrees Fahrenheit. The difficulty in guaranteeing the working surfaces being properly lubricated, which is a most important factor in locomotive practice, or high-speed engines, should not be lost sight of.

The men who are in charge of marine engines are educated mechanics, and can understand and intelligently deal with all questions that are likely to create trouble, and so prevent them arising; but locomotive drivers, while capable and intelligent men, have not been so educated as to expect from them the same degree of intelligence to prevent accidents 'taking place through overheating'. These are all factors that must be taken into account in dealing with questions of this character, and nothing in locomotive practice should be adopted that you cannot hold the driver responsible for in the performance of his duty.

We have tubes giving 125 square feet of heating surface for superheating the steam, which makes three passes through the superheater before it reaches the steam chest. The superheating of steam up to a high temperature is not obtainable by the heat of 600 degrees in the smokebox, unless by means which become complicated and expensive to maintain in working order. I consider it safer to keep the superheated steam well below the point that affects and impairs the proper lubrication of the piston and valves. In my opinion the temperature in locomotive practice should not exceed 450 degrees Fahrenheit.

---

* Drummond must be referring to Baldwin and other American built 2-6-0s.

Inside Crank Axles

During the last six years all inside crank axles used on the London and South-Western Railway have been built in nine separate parts, the webs of the crank arms are so designed as to avoid the use of balance weights in the wheels. These cranks have been in use a sufficient time to warrant my recommending their adoption in preference to the solid forged crank axle. I recommend several parts be put together by shrinkage in preference to hydraulic pressure.

Shrinkage allowance per inch of diameter .0029 in.

I have provided drawings showing how they are designed to prevent the parts from shifting, should heating take place in any of the journals. Without such precautions they are liable to get out of position.

Bogie Engines

The oscillation of bogies at high speeds is considerable, and is due to the centre pin of the bogie being central between the leading and trailing axles. To obviate this difficulty I place the pin two inches out of centre, and by this means secure a steady running bogie, and practically do away with the oscillation and side hammering on the rails, and the lurching of the engine when passing round curves.

Automatic Cylinder Drain Valve

These valves ensure the cylinders being kept free from water or a vacuum being formed in the steam chest or cylinders, preventing the hot gases in the smokebox from being drawn into the steam chest when the engine is running without steam.

It entirely does away with the use of cranks and rods as at present in use, which have to be operated from the footplate.

Regulator

The regulator spindle-box doing away with the stuffing-box, makes a clean front plate free from drip, and does away with packing. You will observe the spindle is made of brass, with a hollow square boss inside to take the iron spindle connected to the regulator valve-rod for working the same. The boss of the brass spindle is tapered to an angle of 62 degrees. A slight recess is made in the spindle and packed with asbestos cord; the inside of the socket for carrying the spindle is also tapered for the spindle to work into. The steam pressure keeps the spindle steam-tight. This arrangement makes the opening and shutting of the valve an easy operation.

Piston Valves

The piston valves fitted to the London and South-Western Railway engines have now been in use for three years with entire satisfaction. When last I examined them they showed no appreciable signs of wear, the cylinder and piston rings had a fine polished surface.

The piston valves adopted by some of the Companies are, in my opinion, too small in diameter. To secure efficient elastic piston rings, the valve piston chambers should not be less than 0.6 the diameter of the cylinder, or one-third its area.

SR 'L12' class No. 421 on Brighton-Plymouth train at Southampton Central, August 1939. This
was a Drummond 4-4-0 superheated by Urie.   *SLS Collection/R.F. Roberts*

SR 'T14' class 4-6-0 No. 444 on an up Waterloo express at Bournemouth West, August 1936. This
was another Drummond design modified and superheated by Urie.   *SLS Collection/R.F. Roberts*

Chapter Two

R.W. Urie

My second CME was R.W. Urie. Before the death of Drummond in 1912 the LSWR had appointed their CMEs from 'outside'. This had resulted in a new set of standards being set up and although they chose a man from 'inside' to succeed Drummond (Urie, the Eastleigh works manager, had been associated with him for many years), a revolution in design and standards actually took place. As I have previously written, he gave me a talk about the works and men and routine in Drummond's absence. With his shock of white hair he struck me as a very sincere person: when I read somewhere of a writer referring to him as 'Bob Urie' it seems quite out of keeping with the man and his actions as I came to know them in the next few years. He lived in Hill Lane, Southampton, a few hundred yards up from Southampton West station as it was then called. The River Test came right up to the old station walls (which were then on the water-side of the present island platform) and there were no buildings or approach on that side: the main road came along Western Shore, past the power station, over the level crossing to Four Posts Hill. Hill Lane was a high class area with large houses, very pleasant before the bombing of World War II and the subsequent rebuilding and motor roads. Apparently the LSWR authorities could not forget that Urie had been an assistant as they took away the former CME's private engine-cum-coach - the 'Bug' - for use of VIPs generally and drawings or pictures of Urie locomotives in the press appeared as 'produced by permission of the General Manager'. 'RU' travelled by ordinary trains to and from Eastleigh and in later years could be seen from the drawing office windows (then upstairs at the south end of the present block of buildings) walking with dignified, steady gait and umbrella by the lineside to the station just after 4.00 pm thus keeping up the status of his position. It is remarkable that the up platform at Eastleigh station is almost unaltered in its higgledy-piggledy state now after 60 years: the Smith's bookstall still faces the entrance stairs as it did when I bought my railway magazines in 1912.*

Following his own promotion, Urie moved J.A. Hunter up from chief draughtsman (CD) to works manager and brought in an outsider to fill the CD position. This, although he had two sons in good positions in his department, the older assistant works manager with office sited on the job, in the erecting shop: the younger in the drawing office. Perhaps it was his deliberate policy (perhaps a Scotch one, too?) to push people away to gain experience, but anyhow son J.J. went to Chile and D.C. to the Midland Great Western Railway of

Robert W. Urie

Ireland (MGW). The man he appointed as CD was J.J. Finlayson: he was no railwayman as such but had been chief estimator at the then biggest locomotive building company, the North British Loco. Co., Glasgow, the famous 'Combine'. To have served a term as a draughtsman there was considered to give one an 'Oxbridge' degree: as an example I could quote from a letter from James Clayton some years later when I applied for a job on the South Eastern & Chatham Railway (SECR) to the effect that he would recommend I got some experience first in design at the North British Loco. Finlayson was familiar with all sorts of designs for abroad and particularly those for the Indian Railways Standard Locos. The appointment turned out to have a very big influence on locomotive design, one could almost say it started off the outside 2-cylinder 4-6-0 fashion in this country.* The 'leading hand' also appointed from outside, E. Chard, was on the contrary, very much a railwayman: from an apprentice on the Somerset & Dorset Joint Railway at Highbridge, he came via the MR, Derby drawing office; North British Loco. Co.; the Great Northern Railway (GNR), Doncaster drawing office; to Eastleigh, thus being the widest experienced man on the drawing office staff of four.

Under the new set up, little change appeared in the works for some months and when the new drawings of the bits and pieces arrived they gave the older men a bit of a shock. It seems pretty certain that the basic ideas in the Urie designs came from the man himself, although by the time I reached the drawing office in 1916 he seemed to have detached himself from all detail design.

However, it was some time before I became wise to all this and in the meantime winter brought on the evening classes at Hartley University College, Southampton, then situated in High Street, about 10 minutes walk from the Docks station or as it then was called Southampton Terminus. This entailed a quick tea and wash-and-change at the digs to catch a train about 6.15 pm which used to come swinging round the curve from Romsey across the through road to the down platform just before the London-Bournemouth express was due to pass. We bought our PTs (at 3½*d.*) return, took the numbers, and got a refund on presenting a statement at the time office at end of term. The Hartley Certificate helped towards a degree or AMIMechE. The Principal, Professor Eustace, took heat engines; Mr Ford, who, I think, recently retired from the Southampton University (which succeeded the Hartley), the mechanics class and a Harland & Wolff draughtsman called 'Tremelling the Drawing'. Tremelling gave us marine examples at first, but when he found that he had a railwayman in his class he got some LSWR engine details which were as strange to him as his stuff was to me, so we both broadened our minds. They were all good teachers and when you are young you can still soak up knowledge 7-9 pm after a long day in the shops. Walking back to the station at 9 pm along the narrow streets around Holy Road, one soon realised that this was a seaport: even at this early hour (but of course pubs kept open any old hours), there were quite a few merchantmen rolling about the footpaths in peril from the trams which took up 90 per cent of the road space and more on the sharp curves at Orchard Street. Back at the digs supper and a mug of my good landlady's special cocoa, bed at 10.30 pm, ready for the start next day at 6.15 am. Three evenings like that, a bit of homework to boot, kept one out of mischief in the winter!

---

* *Compilers' Note:* In the interest of balance it should perhaps be pointed out that the GWR under Churchward had completed one or two outside 2-cylinder 4-6-0s of their own by this stage!

That autumn (1912) Prescott went off to South America to take up a job on the San Paulo Railway. I went down to see him sail off and met a friend of his, Whitton the pattern shop foreman, there too: which I remember as I got in a second class compartment with him on the return train to Eastleigh and blow me if the ticket inspector did not come along and checking tickets noticed that I had a third class one. Second class privilege tickets were not granted to shop floor staff, and that was my classification. I thought Whitton might have paid the difference but no! Poor Langridge had to find it! Prescott had given me many years' *Railway Magazines* which I valued and kept for years.

Christmas was approaching and a scarcely veiled remark that he smoked a lot of cigarettes led in due course to a present of Player's Weights (five a penny) to chargehand Punch Cook. Soon I was moved down the machine shop to an old machine working on my own turning up the rough forgings for big end bolts which I had to fit as a light driving fit in Adams' strap and solid box big-ends. This machine, like nearly all lathes was belt-driven and in the middle of the turret lathe section: so by keeping one's eyes open and having a walk round the nearby shapers and the big planers and millers (with individual motor drives) one got a good idea of machine practice. There being no dividing walls one might walk (with a businesslike gait!) through the nearby wheel shop, boiler shop and even peep into the separate power house fed from Lancashire boilers next door.

Diesel power first raised its head to me when at Eastleigh, around 1913. I joined a party to look round the newly-installed diesel-electric generating plant in the carriage & wagon works. The party was taken round by D.C. Urie, who later held high positions in Ireland, the Highland Railway and finally the LMS. We were told the engines would run on coal-dust! Rather amusing when one thinks of the dust-free atmosphere now insisted upon by diesel fuel-pump manufacturers! The next contact I had with this growing child was on the LMS 0-6-0 shunter No. 1831, but more of that later.

Mills, the foreman, transferred me down his shop after some months facing up nuts and turning collar bolts on an old bigger lathe where one turned up big-end bolts for the strap type big ends. This was all on repair work of course but as the holes for the bolts were slightly tapered turning the bolt to get a nice tap-in fit required a fair amount of patience, for it would not be passed unless it fitted all the way through. This machine was near a set of turret lathes - quite new at that date - and some planers which were the only machines with individual motor drive, so by keeping your eyes open you learned what could and could not be done by machines - useful when you became a draughtsman.

The custom at August Bank Holiday was for the works to close down for a week (without pay to the men, of course) and as the end of my first year's apprenticeship drew near I began to wonder if I ever should last out my five years. Anyhow at my year's end in September 1913 I was moved to the fitting shop. Any inclination towards hand-work was quickly stifled by being put on filing drawhooks and polishing them with emery paper! A poor way of learning how to file a level surface. Bedding down flat regulator valves with scraper also seemed boring although the leading hand - old Harrison - had been at it for years. For him the high-spots seemed to flatten out in no time. Then we had the fitting of brass inserts to Adams' single bar crossheads one of which fell off the bench and squashed my big toe. The subsequent telling-off by Cowley, the foreman, for not reporting it seemed unfair to me then: but I expect he had got a nasty back-hander from the works doctor whom I had to see later. The lighter side of life appeared on the squad setting boiler safety valves by a hydraulic hand pump. The spring adjustment was made by altering the thickness of shim under the spring fixing, mounting the valves on a water tank and slowly depressing hand pump lever and reading pressure gauge. A sharp push on the lever would spray water high in the air and around obviously giving the lads a chance for a bit of horseplay. Another job for the lads was to hang on the end of a long spanner tightening up the nut fixing on the Drummond (and Urie) pistons. There was not much doubt that the piston rods were pre-stressed after some 15 stone lads had jumped on the end of a 10 ft spanner!

There wasn't much hand-fitting done in the so-called fitting shop: the motion parts were mostly lapped on grinding machines. There was a little cotter fitting and taper pin fitting on motion parts: the brass work was all dealt with in the brass shop enclosed in a 7 ft wood partition. One interesting section was the marking-off table: situated just inside the smith shop (although part of the fitting shop staff), nice and warm compared with the rest of the unheated shops, it gave one a chance to work to drawings for the first time in my apprenticeship. You whitened the faces to be machined: set up the particular part on the table: scribed the finished face line with a surface gauge and lightly pop-marked the lines. Sometimes the forgings or castings were untrue and had to be sent back to the smith to have the inaccurate arms or whatever it was re-set: sometimes they had to be scrapped. The presiding chargehand was a well known character, T. Clyde Britten, who served the LSWR, and the Southern Railway/Region (SR), in comparatively humble positions for an ex-pupil, for very many years. He was Chairman of the Committee of the LSWR Engineering Society at Eastleigh, hob-nobbed with lots of VIPs yet seemed quite happy to remain a 'working-man', a sort of 'gentleman foreman'. I believe 'Clyde' as he was known everywhere actually finished his career in SR days as foreman of the fitting shop: he was certainly an enigma: he stayed while others went on! I don't believe he joined any of the 'learned' institutions: I can see him walking with his characteristic lope along Leigh Road to his house even now.

Being situated in a corner of the smithy, one had a chance to see smiths making smaller forgings under light power hammers or on the anvil. Across three or four sidings was the forge with two heavy steam hammers where you could watch connecting rods, etc., being forged out of the blooms. The men had a few templates covering the vital sizes to work to: they were the lords of creation and shook the ground with their hammers. Another Scot, Starkie, was officer-in-charge (OC) here; he wrote many articles on his craft in the old locomotive magazines. Next door under the same roof-line was the pattern shop under Whitton: machines were just creeping in here to supplant the craftsman also. Next in this block came the iron foundry - but I will write of that later.

Incidentally it is strange how one Scot brings along another: the cycle shop in Leigh Road was also run by one: he was reliable and odds and ends that I required for my trusty BSA 3-speed bicycle were supplied by him including a steel rim in place of an aluminium one on the back wheel. Many miles did my BSA and I cover in the country around Eastleigh. The outskirts of town finished northwards at the Romsey railway line, eastwards at the cemetery, southwards just beyond the works' bridge and eastwards at the carriage works (now sold off) so one was in lanes right away. Chandler's Ford was a delightful hamlet of a few houses around the station and the main road thence to Southampton through woods - up the hill marked and known to us cyclists as 'Tenez-la-Gauche' - lots of loose gravel on it to Bassett - no houses then - down through the common to the docks.

The nearest I have been to cruising was having lunch with some friends who were going off to South Africa in 1913. Their boat - the *Garth Castle* - was delayed by fog on her run from Tilbury (she was on the Union Castle's 'stopping' run) so the shipping company gave us free lunch on the *Kinfauns Castle* - a posh new four-funnel fast boat awaiting loading up - both boats were lost in World War I. We had a good look over her and some of the P&O's - like the *Avon* they all had names commencing with 'A'. Most of the Eastleigh-trained men went abroad for experience and there was a close tie with the South American railways, being British-owned and equipped by British products.

It was impressive to look at liners propped up resting on chocks in the largest dry-dock in the country: the engine house with centrifugal pumps to empty the water from the dock was deep down alongside and Adams's little 0-4-0 shunters with classic names squeaked around 2 chain (?) curves.

My stay at the marking-off table working in almost 'white-collar' conditions - even electric filament lamps (reading lamp types) were provided - came to an end and back I went to filing and scraping. But not for long! On 23rd July, 1914, I was transferred to the erecting shop, the place of hard labour.

Just before, the Engineering Club had organized a trip to Derby MR Loco. Works. We left Eastleigh on the 10.05 pm - always an Adams 'Jubilee' class 0-4-2 turn - arrived Waterloo 12.15, walked across to St Pancras and after calling at the coffee stall at the foot of the steps caught the 'Paper Train' 2.40 am. Nearly everyone talks of the winds from the north as they go into St Pancras - at 2 am they seem to come straight from Blea Moor. Paper trains from London terminii were amongst the fastest bookings then and the 2.40 was no exception, arriving Derby 5.10 am. There G.W. Wooliscroft of the Derby Society met us, took us to the Insititute for breakfast and in parties round the works and shed. It seemed a scattered place compared with tidy Eastleigh, but, of course, had much more history buried in its walls. We finished at the famous '4' Shed, spick and span: grass plots outside - no walking except on footpaths and *around* the turntables inside. The first '4F' class was here, only out a few months, No. 3835. The MR men seemed inordinately proud of their new 0-6-0: couldn't see any point in the LSWR's '486s'! Little did I know that fate was to send me to the MR in a few years' time. We caught the 3.25 pm back to St Pancras. It was one of the Manchester trains that stopped at Cheadle where the locomotive uncoupled, fetched a coach from siding that had come from Liverpool, re-coupled and was off, all done at the trot in typical MR style. The '700' class 4-4-0s did most of the work north of Derby: I doubt if Compounds were allowed over the Throstle Nest Bridge outside Manchester Central then.

Well, as I have said, if you like hard exercise the locomotive erecting shop was the place for you. I was posted to Brown's gang where they stripped down and repaired the smaller variety of locomotives. You were a sort of fitter's mate at first and getting Adams' 0-6-0T No. 238 ready for lifting was a good introduction. Struggling with 4 ft spanners to move reluctant nuts on spring gear, taking the weight of rods as pins were knocked out, levering off the whole set of side rods to crash on to the floor - all was part of 'heavy engineering', now enjoyed only in preservation railway workshops. Lots of other bits and pipes have to be disconnected - hammer and chisel are the most useful tools and a left-hander like myself soon gets the awkward jobs - as well as the right-hander's - passed to him.

Adams' 4-4-0s (Adams Express we called them in the shops) got double bars and crossheads in early Urie days. I helped put up a set about 1915. It meant a new back cylinder cover with face and studs to take the lower bar and likewise an extra foot on the motion plate. I think this was a built-up affair as it was before the days of welding. Incidentally some of Drummond's 4-6-0s got built-up outside motion plates due to castings being supplied with blow holes under the surface. I think we re-used the old top single bar on the Adams, but my memory is a bit hazy on that point. I was told that the double bar arrangement was introduced because of fractures of the piston rod with the single bar, but I can't see the connection myself. No other class of Adams' engines were altered so far as I know. A lot of his engines got Drummond-type boilers as renewals were required in his time: they had barrels with lap joints instead of butt-straps and the familiar safety valve and backplate fittings of Drummond's. I remember that bedding on Adams' water gauges was the very devil to do: they had four ½ in. studs that broke off like carrots if you put the slightest weight on them. Drummond's were ⅝ in. diameter.

The fitting of Drummond boilers and Urie slidebars seemed to be quite spasmodic: a case of as and when required and possible. Of course there was a war on and Eastleigh had more important things to do.

When you come to design yourself, you remember all the awkward corners if you are any good; for instance we spent all one afternoon trying to get the nuts off a spring link. Obviously they had not been used for months so why not have a simple link with pin hole, as later Drummond engines had? I remember Maunsell (of the SECR and SR) saying in his Presidential address that a ¾ in. nut should be the minimum size used on locomotives: I doubt if his staff carried it out. Decent sized pins in spring gear and ashpan and cylinder cock are appreciated by the erector - and running shed fitter. They don't get greased from the day they go in until the day they come out - and by that time the small ones will have worn zig-zag fashion and be the deuce of a job to drive out. Removeable horn cheek guides were another time-saver: trueing-up the faces by handfile was exasperating and expensive. You could go on about umpteen details: any car-owner who does his own maintenance knows what chumps they still have in drawing offices. Perhaps it's only the 'Stylist' who runs the show. Stripping smokeboxes could well have been a job for Dickens' famous chimney sweep -

except that he would have needed a hammer and chisel to split every nut and to dig them out of the cement often used to seal the smokebox bottom. People who designed steam regulators in boilers to be way down in an unremoveable dome - Drummond's had a completely removeable one - want dealing with by Gilbert & Sullivan's 'Ko-Ko'.

Standardizing of details in Drummond's designs were a help in getting engines repaired quickly: much of his motion work and rods were interchangeable on half-a-dozen classes and with my next chargehand, Jackson, we had a good variety of 0-4-4s, 0-6-0s and 4-4-0s going through our hands. He had one or two 'big 'uns' allocated to him too, but didn't like them as the 'balance' or 'bonus' was small. Others told me of artifices to make things pay - polishing heads of hornblock or cylinder fixing bolts and booking them as 'changed', taking off cross-water tube doors on Drummond fireboxes also paid well - in any case they never made more than 20 per cent on a repair that may have stood on the gang for weeks. A 'T14' 'Paddlebox' firebox made a nice room for your morning lunch seated on a firebar carrier invisible to all! The chargehand erector didn't get very dirty: he had to decide on whether to rebore cylinder and face up valve chests, check lining-up slideboxes, etc., and get any gauge of exact parts across to machine and fitting shops, 'chivvy-up' jobs. He was a progress-man, form-filler substitute and general manager for his little gang of maybe half-a-dozen - not more - all for 42s. a week. In the Office - level with the overhead crane and shaken by them dwelt Harvey, the foreman, Charlie Biggs, the assistant - a much respected man who died c.1914 at Eastleigh at a great age - and below was 'Oly' issuing oil, grease, gauges, special tools and 'waste' if he were in a good mood. A fire risk not worrying them at all, I suppose. One oiled up one's hands to loosen the grime, washed it off with paraffin and again if you were lucky with soft soap and hot water-heated on the traveller riveter's little hand blown forge. But there was quite a happy mood in the shop. Of course when wheeling a repaired locomotive came along it was a case of all hands on deck and the chargehand would wave his instructions to the crane drivers up aloft. We used the two heavy cranes for this job: the hooks of one under the buffer beam, and under the dragbox for the other. Then after bolting on the horn stays the cranes would lift the engine clear of all others and carry it down to the end just inside the shop doors. Then it was hauled round to be weighed and the springs adjusted to give a nice distribution. I think I worked on most classes of Adams and Drummond types in the course of my time on Brown's and later Hunt's and Jackson's gangs.

At the top end of No. 1 bay was the new work gang under Bill Marshall: the only gang where any reference to drawing took place. Everywhere else you used gauges or templates or your little 6 in. rule. I suppose if a replacement con. rod or the like were required a drawing would be fished out, but there was no elaborate shop drawing or office copies of tracing organization (as I found later at Derby). Marshall's gang turned out a fine job: at this time in 1914 he was building '486' class 4-6-0s, the first design of the Urie period.

World War I had started just at commencement of the works' summer holidays. The first effect I found was trying to get back from my holiday in Torquay: the train that eventually left Exeter Queen Street was about 20 coaches-long hauled by a couple of 'Grasshopper' 4-4-0s, stopping at all stations to Salisbury and Eastleigh. The works lost their Territorial and Service Reservists - my landlady's son amongst them - and we were soon working evenings until 9 pm in the shops on repairs to our own locomotives and 'foreigners', at apprentice's rate of about 10 shillings a week. We got a lot of old Adams 0-6-0s ready for shipment overseas to Egypt and Turkey but not much purely military work. We had the loan (!) of some GNR 0-6-0s, from which we learned of the poor quality of workmanship at Doncaster. I always remember the appalling condition of the cylinder joint faces to the covers - long ago they must have abandoned getting a decent metal to metal joint as we were brought up to use on the LSWR. Their joints were made with a piece of copper wire running round the stud line. Consequently the faces had eroded away - the dropping of smokebox ash when the smokebox door opened helped the trouble - and it was a nightmare to try to get a joint that would not blow. It made one proud of our own LSWR products! Another time I took down and re-assembled all the motion work on a Drummond 0-4-4 tank with the help of a few wooden 'sprags' by myself - no labourers being available and I being a bit of a fool really! However, I still have my 10 fingers although I ought to have had one chopped off by 'feeling' whether the holes were true or not before slipping in the motion pins. Another occasion I well remember was when having 'bedded-on' an axlebox on its journal, I then got a labourer to hold it upright while I tapped in the axlebox keep underneath and slipped in the securing spring hanger pin. This man - an elderly son of the soil - had been taken on in the works like a lot more as they were short-handed and he, for his part, thought 30s. a week plus five nights' overtime better than farm labouring at Chandler's Ford. I slid the axlebox on to the journal, turned it upright, and told him to hold it there - as all axleboxes are 'top-heavy' on their own - and moved the supporting table away so that I could tap in the keep below the axiebox. There was a sudden flash as the 'box' turned turtle and landed on the shop floor within a half-inch of my foot. The old boy had no idea of how easily the box would slip out of his light grasp - he had no mechanical and precious little other 'know-how' - and stood there amazed. I am afraid I never had a good flow of curses - far better to thank my lucky stars once more! He was a harmless, willing sort, just completely out of his element.

One repair about this time was to a Urie 4-6-0 that ran down the hill and derailed at Andover spreading its load of cattle in trucks over the countryside: Tommy Lyle in the Outdoor Machinery (ODM) Dept said that pigs were running over the line when he got there to help clear things up.

At Eastleigh CME works the ODM staff had a bench at the end of the fitting shop and came under the fitting shop foreman, a man called Cowley, but they were very much their own masters. Their chargehand - was his name Mills? - was alleged by some of his mates to be an imposter as they reckoned he had not 'served his time' and so was not a fitter! The standard wage at that time was 38s. a week. A job on a turntable or other gear in the far West could mean a pleasant few days out of reach of trouble. The all-stations pass was a piece of pink paper about the size of a £5 note. Many years later we rented a converted coach-bungalow backing onto the line at Instow, by which time Drummond 'M7s' rattled our back door in place of the old Adams-Beyer, Peacocks of 1913. Lastly, just after World War II at Braunton, Bulleid's 4-6-2s, one at each end, were taking trains down to Ilfracombe. Now I gather it has all gone and I don't want to go and see the cemeteries, thank you!

Evening classes at Hartley College, Southampton kept going and there was also a weekly works class (two grades) for apprentices, tutored by D.C. Urie before he left the company and then by E. Chard. The former were thoroughly technical of course, whereas the latter dealt with more general engineering work and covered a wider ground in general terms suitable for trade apprentices in the main.

Putting things back on the locomotives was a more satisfying job. The axleboxes would have come back remetalled and bored to suit the axles (which might also have been turned down if badly scored) and faced on sides to suit horngaps and also with keeps fitted. The erector 'bedded' them on the journals, scraping the white metal to suit, oiled them up, fitted pads in keeps, hangers and springs below ready on the middle road for dropping the locomotive on with help from the 30 tons travelling crane. So it would go together again, not forgetting that the erector also refitted boiler mountings, smokebox gear and ashpan. After wheeling, the motion had to be coupled up and pipes and brake rods below axles. It was the practice to get this done, if possible, before the locomotive was hauled out and shoved into the paint shop, otherwise the paint shop foreman chewed you up for 'chipping' his edges. Pistons and valves were left out (and cylinder front covers) until the engine had been finished painted, and adjustments to spring hangers made when it was on the weighing machine, then on a side road in No. 1 bay, where also the mysterious process of valve-setting took place. The Eastleigh valve-setter was an ex-Crewe man, very secret about how he decided how many 'shim's' should he put in between eccentric foot and sheave or how much the rod should be 'jumped' on the Stephenson-geared locomotives at 1 in 10 slope of motion. Finally, the locomotive was taken outside the erecting shop, lighted up and steam raised. Then the unique practice of 'blowing-out' the cylinders took place. A shunting engine pushed and pulled the locomotive up and down a few yards whilst the driver of the repaired locomotive opened and shut his regulator. So you had clouds of steam around: the intention being that any loose bits - split pins, etc., that had lodged in the cylinders got blown out. Then we put in valves and pistons, coupled up to rods, put on covers, saw to any leaking fittings. Next day or so, the locomotive would go a trial run up the Romsey-Salisbury line to Dean or Dunbridge (the long siding, pleasant lanes and pub are still there) but of course only the gang's chargehand or leading fitter were allowed on such jaunts. Any necessary alterations would be made on the return to the shop yard and that was another off our hands and perhaps a little 'balance' in our pay packets in a week or two.

For 'number takers' information I had clocked up a good variety of locomotives - Nos. 494, 671, 323, 505, 286, 238 on Brown's gang: Nos. 405, 695, 532, 0123, 0484, 688, 150, 126 on Jackson's gang. My next chargehand was Hunt: that was February 1915. The war was supposed to have finished by Christmas 1914, of course but it didn't; and so things looked less cheerful and scarcities and a little censoring of railway news crept in. Hunt dealt in the 'big 'uns'. I am afraid the only number I have kept recorded is 462, the last 'Paddlebox'. Amongst the items one couldn't help noticing loose rivets in stretchers on the earlier 4-6-0s and the funny upside-down motion (outside Walschaerts) of the '330s'. One thing about them all was their 1¼ in. thick frames, must have been unique for locomotives of that era.

The man who appeared to 'progress' apprentices through the shops was the works manager's chief clerk, 'Tosh' Harrison. Trade apprentices stuck to their own one shop but the outsiders - the 'premium' ones - were treated more generously although nothing was down in writing as to their training. 'Tosh' was ginger-haired and slightly bearded, but a very courteous gentleman, known by umpteen apprentices and pupils as their friend and adviser, occasionally reprimanding the wilder ones. So I was greatly surprised in November 1915 to be called into his little office and told that I was to report to the ODM foreman at Nine Elms wharf in three days' time, how to find his office in the goods depot (recently demolished but platforms still visible) and that the hours were 6.00 am to 5.30 pm (as compared with 7 to 5 at Eastleigh!). However, it meant I could live at home and it broke the frustrating labouring in the erecting shop. It also meant the end of the Hartley, Southampton evening classes and the Eastleigh ones too. For the latter I had (with my friend Barnes) received a Directors' Prize of £5 for 1914 session: D.C. Urie who ran the class took us into the Directors' room in the old Waterloo, York Road Offices where Hugh Drummond congratulated us and presented us with the books we had chosen. We went across the road and 'DC' provided us (by contrast!) with lunch at the ABC Café! I was not to meet 'DC' again for many years: actually when Josiah Stamp held a send-off party for Riddles & Co. who were taking the 'Royal Scot' train to America: that was a rather better lunch than the ABC's and I was a humble London Midland & Scottish Railway draughtsman!

I will only add that, seeing the writing, as I thought, on the wall, I tried to get into the Army under the Derby scheme. Appalling losses in manpower were taking place in the army and conscription was being called for by some of the press. The outcome was the Derby scheme, whereby one attested and was called up in age groups. The railway gave one no instructions as to what to do, beyond the general idea that railwaymen were in a reserved occupation, similar to munitions workers. However, here was I aged 18 and fit, so I thought the best thing was to join up. Accordingly I went to the office in Streatham and got my armlet, collected army form W3194, 3291, etc., and sent back to work by Lieut Jermingham. That was as far as I got to active service, although I was called up for medical examination at various times later as the reserve of cannon fodder got less and less. Those forms are mere curiosities now, but serious then when, next day, I met a crowd of fellows going off for training from Vauxhall station and many of them to their end at Passchendaele. Such is the 'luck of the draw', or not, isn't it?

An advantage of being an apprentice in the CME Dept, at Eastleigh was that, although the £50 premium (required to get a lad, who had no family connections working on the railway) legally only allowed him to work in machine fitting and erecting shops, in actual fact, if he behaved himself and looked at all promising, he would get a chance to spend some of his five years' 'time' in other departments. One of these was the Running Dept, another the outdoor machinery department.

Nine Elms had once been a little hamlet at the junction of the Wandle and the Thames. In 1915 it was a densely-populated, closely built-up, shoddy area - of character though - cheek by jowl with gasworks, loco sheds, wharves and so on. The LCC trams rattled along picking up the 'juice' via a 'plough' whose tail ran in the 'conduit' between the rails and contacted the 'live-rails' there. Goods and freight were moved about on the roads by horse-drawn drays.

The goods sheds were, of course, on the site of the old terminus station at Nine Elms and hydraulic jib cranes were fixed all down the platforms to lift out merchandise from rail wagons to platform or to dray as required. To move wagons hydraulic capstans were sited at strategic points. The entrance for road vehicles was through gates from Nine Elms Lane. Also situated alongside the sheds was the hydraulic power station. Boilers were the old Lancashire type and the engine a two-cylinder compound direct coupled to hydraulic ram-pumps with a fly-wheel mounted centrally. Water power is unique in many ways : mechanical movement at the cranes is made by a cylinder being put in communication with the hydraulic main (maybe at 1,000 psi) when water enters and pushes out a ram. Exhaust disconnects the cylinder and discharges the volume of used water. So all the power house has to do is to keep the mains full of water at the working pressure. A cushion between the engine pump and the crane cylinder is provided by an 'accumulator', which is simply a heavily-weighted piston in large cylinder working on a similar principle to a gas-holding cylinder. It is allowed to rise and fall a determined distance thus providing a pressure head in the system. As it falls so it opens the steam regulating valve to the main pumping engine which thus restores the quantity of water under pressure to the system. On rising it cuts off the steam supply. Normally the engine is working in a series of bursts of speed alternating with periods of quiet. 'Speed' must be interpreted at a low figure though, not more than 100 rpm, the stroke of the cylinder and ram being about 30 inches.

Across Nine Elms Lane was the wharf. About eight hydraulic cranes, each on four legs and moveable (by hand gear) along rails laid on the edge of the wharf, were provided to deal with merchandise coming up the river in barges. This, in 1915, was mostly grain, i.e. in sacks. These were lifted up, six at a time, the men looping a chain deftly over each corner of a sack, the other end of the chains being fixed to a common ring hung on the crane hook. These cranes had separate lifting, luffing and turning hydraulic cylinders. All were controlled by levers in the driver's cabin fixed to the crane post. The cylinder rams all had pulleys at head and tail with chain fixed to drum to be turned at one end and to cylinder body at the other. As the ram came out the operating end was forced to move like a Weston pulley block. The hydraulic capstans were more complicated. Above the surface of the base casting only the drum for the rope and the foot-operated plunger projected. On one side of the base casting, which was about four-foot square, was a liftable steel loop through which one put a sprag and hung on to tightly while a sunken square key was rotated on the opposite side. The base was pivoted at the edges at right angles to the sprag and key and turned turtle to expose all the working parts mounted on its underside. The pivots also carried the water pressure and release supplies through their centres. On the upturned base were three single oscillating cylinders, their piston crossheads bearing against a crank arm attached to the rope winding drum pivot: all very neatly laid out. The menace to a new fitter was the fact that the balance of weight was all in favour of the capstan turning itself upside down with a bang once the retaining key was turned. Still, I never heard of anyone getting their limbs broken during my time on the wharf. Besides the cranes on the wharf and in the goods sheds there were the hydraulic lifts to the platforms at Vauxhall station - then a tremendous milk-churn collecting centre - and the engine turntable in Nine Elms running shed. Yet again there were lifts at Waterloo station, although the small turntable there was hand-operated. All machinery at outdoor goods yards on the LSWR down to Woking came under the ODM Dept and several of the goods collecting centres situated in those days in various parts of the city and Southwark likewise.

The staff to run this motley lot were one foreman, who could never be found in his office away at the far end of the goods shed, one chargehand fitter, one fitter (of course, they were really millwrights), two labourers, the greasers, and one who acted more or less as fitter's mate, and two apprentices. The power house had its firemen and engine driver, too. It is a tribute to the reliability of hydraulic machinery that these few could keep the whole outfit going - probably the lot cost less than £20 a week.

The work was extremely interesting after being cooped up in the locomotive shops with dead steam engines. Although the water pressure was miles above steam boiler pressure a burst merely meant that there was a beast of a mess but no danger. Capstans wanted most attention. The operating plunger valve soon wore its seat away with constant water hammer at 'on' and 'off' and we made unit replacements of these when they leaked too badly, taking the old valve to the little workshop. Then we cut (by hand) a new seat and ground the valve in again. New seats on the valve had to be done on the lathe at the locomotive shops. The oscillating cylinders had leather washers U-shaped to fit the trunnions and these were made by squeezing a ring of leather between male and female dies. After a few days the leather - wet before being pressed - was stiff in its new shape. U-shaped washers and brass rings between them were the standard method of sealing any rotating hydraulic joint. Small brass slide valves operated by hand lever, with something like 20 to 1 leverage, were used on crane work.

Board of Trade regulations required chains to be changed once a year for the large sizes. All chains were sent to Eastleigh for examination and annealing. We had no wire ropes except for an odd sling or two for outsize or special jobs. The 'Bear', being an old seaman, was very proud of any 'splicing' of wire ropes he was called on to do. If you have been lucky enough to see a man splicing a rope with about a dozen wires around the central hemp core you will not forget it. Strong wrist and fingers and a lifetime's 'know-how' go towards the neat interlacing of wire within wire, cutting ends off to length and wrapping the whole joint neatly with tarred string in the finish.

Changing the chains on a luffing crane was a pleasant Sunday job: we did them in the summer. You roped one end of the new chain to one end of the old one in its working position, carefully removed the anchoring clip. The other end of the old chain was tied to another rope which passed through an anchored guide pulley to a capstan. Making sure everything was taut, the other fixing anchor was removed and slowly and carefully the old chain was pulled off and the new one came into its place. The labourers did most of the work and they knew the technique from A to Z, took their time and care that no green 'uns like me got my fingers taken off by trapping them in the chain links!

Other regular maintenance meant constant oiling and greasing of moving parts of machinery and gland packing. All glands were packed with plaited hemp soaked in tallow. The labourers would spend an afternoon occasionally plaiting hemp ropes into square or rectangular shapes to suit the size of gland concerned. Occasionally pipe joints would leak - all joints were made with gutta-percha rings which we made ourselves from plain rope, just melting the ends and sticking them together. Horrible sticky stuff is gutta-percha: like plasticine when hot and melting but very effective as a joint.

Apart from hydraulic details we had outstation cranes and chains to maintain. I remember spending most of a pleasant day up the top of the fixed yard crane at Weybridge measuring up and calipering pin diameters for a replacement pin and pulley. Old Pete, the labourer, knew the location and all about the crane. He could well have done the job - but he wasn't a 'skilled man' as I was! He accompanied me on several odd jobs and knew the back ways into Vauxhall and the labyrinth of arches below platform level at Waterloo. Females had not penetrated the ranks of railwaymen in 1915, at any rate lower than clerical staff! My first experience of working alongside a 'live' third rail was at Waterloo. The turntable had to be reached by crossing the lines at the end of the platforms and itself was rather too near the 'juice' for my fancy. On the other side was the Necropolis station - very thoughtfully placed, perhaps, in case of accidents. Looking back I think there must have been a table on the Windsor side but I never visited it. There was a workshop in the arches under the platforms which was used by the ODM men: more useful to some of them was the full-sized bath with hot water laid on. Paddy the labourer told me he used it regularly. It was a real warren under the Waterloo platforms; I could easily have got lost down there. Another set of people who knew their way about these dungeons were the English Electric Co.'s engineers who might be called in about failures on their equipment. I did not find this out until I was working for the LMS at Derby when I was talking about old times with one of their men. You must remember that only five of the new platforms were built at this time and the dungeons seemed to extend right under these and the entrance road. No doubt there was a private way in from York Road if you knew where to find it. Vauxhall was a very busy station for milk churn transference. The Windsor platforms bore the brunt of it and all the lifts were hydraulic and maintained by the ODM people on the wharf.

Nine Elms goods shed was on the north side of the main line: on the south side, opposite, were the remains of the old locomotive shops. Very noticeable was the old erecting shop, with the supporting piers for the overhead cranes. Some of this floor space was used as goods sheds; above were the office staff.

The turntable in Nine Elms Loco. was in almost continuous use and the only time we could do any maintenance was first thing in the morning. So for one of us and a labourer the regular thing was for us to walk across from our little workshop (and signing-on point on the wharf) to the turntable near the locomotive entrance gate - a good ¾ mile - with 4 ft spanner and tube to tighten up the centre pivot bolts. If nothing else wanted tightening these bolts always did. Turning 100 engines a day and being 'bumped' as each came on and off rattled the nuts down half a turn. Why no attempt was made to fit a locking device I cannot say. It would not be too easy as the forces were pretty severe.

A by-product of this early morning 'ramble' was a cup of tea in the shunter's hut alongside the turntable, and the smoke of a homemade 'gasper' by my 'mate'! The turntable was in such heavy demand that a shunter was employed full time to operate it. In those days the crew who had worked their train into Waterloo also brought the locomotive back to the shed and 'disposed' of their engine; latterly, a spare crew worked locomotives in and out between Waterloo and the sheds thus saving main line men's time and wages.

The little gang on the wharf got on pretty well together. The leading, or chargehand, fitter was a slightly superior sort of character. The next man was a real little cockney, self-opinionated and much more forceful than the chargehand. The 'Bear', whose tobacco was the thickest of 'twists', had the rolling gait of the seaman. His outer clothes would have stood up straight on their own, so well greased and tallowed had they become. I suspect the inner layers were not too clean either, for I don't think the underground bath at Waterloo came within his perambulation. Open air and up the luffing cranes were his preferences.

The apprentices had some fun: it seems incredible that on one occasion there was a kind of paper-chase - including a crossing of Nine Elms Lane - only trams and horse-drawn drays then - when we had a visitor in the person of Joey Light. He was a short-sighted lad whose 'leg' was easily pulled; he had borrowed someone's tools without permission and that started the lads on the run. I remember Falconer, who later became CME of the Argentine Railway, chasing Joey Light across Nine Elms Lane one day. A more serious but joyful event was the passing of a collier bringing coal from Newcastle to the gas company's wharf just above our railway wharf. The papers - no wireless in those days, remember - had told us that this boat coming down the East Coast had sunk a German submarine by fire from her reargunner. The wharf, and indeed the rest of the embankment where possible, was lined with men cheering this brave boat as she slowly sailed up-stream.

This year, 1915, was also the time when the Zeppelin airships floated across at night and dropped their bombs pretty well at random. Although the raids did little damage, bombing was a thing a British population had never before experienced. The eerie, almost silent, approach of the airships and the seemingly inadequate defences against them rather shook people. For myself, living at home with my parents at Streatham, the most exciting time came one night after I had been to a Queen's Hall Prom. concert. We found the trains at Victoria, LB&SC, without lights and very few on in the station itself. No one told us what was afoot, but we guessed 'Zepps' were about. So we went out in the dark, safely over Grosvenor Bridge - non-stop to Streatham Common station. It was about 11.45 pm as I was walking home, then, after a bite of supper I went to bed. The others had already done so, and within ¾ hour came the little purr of the 'Zepp's' engines, then some bangs shook the house and from my attic window I saw a few flames spurt up northwards. Curiosity made me get up and put on a few things. A fire engine going down the road made me walk down to the railway station and sure enough a bomb had flattened two houses opposite the down platform of the station and put out most of the station glass on that side. Actually, about eight bombs fell in a straight line at ¼ mile intervals, from Streatham Common station to the 'William IV' public house at Kennington and the Borough High Street. A few weeks later I saw one 'Zepp' coming down in flames, again from my attic windows and heard the cheers rising from the unseen hundreds who must have likewise been watching in the dark.

When one is young one can quite well work long hours and yet go to a prom. concert in the evening. My routine was to be up at 4.45 am, make a cup of tea and catch the 5.18 am from Streatham Common station, which consisted of the old Stroudley 4-wheel stock and was crowded as badly as, and smelled rather worse than the 8.15 am, commuter trains of today. I got out at Battersea Park and walked along Stewart's Lane to the Nine Elms Loco. entrance where you could pick up a large 1*d*. mug of tea. Then through the yard, across the lane to the wharf shop. The shop was about the size of the 'through lounge' in the modern semi-detached. It boasted a bench and two or three vices, no machine tools of course.

During the summer months I often cycled from home to work. No motor traffic worth speaking of made cycling pleasant. Greasy woodblock paving was taking the place of cobbles: that and the slot between the running rails for the trams electrical pick-up 'Plough' were more nuisance to the cyclist. In

SR 'T9' class 4-4-0 No. 115 on a Portsmouth-Cardiff train of GWR stock at Southampton Central, August 1938. Another Drummond design superheated by Urie.

SLS Collection/R.F. Roberts

comparison the crush on the 5.25 train was incredible. All workmen started at 6 of course then and many used the cheap workmen's fares available at that time; money was valuable in those days. I had done a lot of exploring of Hampshire on a bicycle during my past two years at Eastleigh and now I could explore London on my bike during the dinner-hour. Lunch on the edge of the wharf on a sunny day was as attractive as office workers find it in Embankment Gardens today. Breakfast, 8.15 to 9.00 am, was 'taken' at one of the little coffee shops in Battersea Park Road. I was introduced to this one by Charlie Monk, the apprentice who was already at Nine Elms when I arrived. He was a fascinating character, monk-like in his dark, ascetic appearance; very otherwise in his language, everything being bloody … or worse. There was no need to keep the conversation going, Charlie would carry on his bitter but amusing comments on all and sundry *ad lib*. Our host's busiest time had passed by 8.15 am; his lady at the raised transverse counter at the rear of the shop had time to join in the chatter with us. All the woodwork in the shop - no chrome-plate vulgarity, then - was clean as a new pin, there were about four 'stalls' each side of the centre gangway. Our attentive host would shout out our orders for 'two rashers and two rounds of toast twice' and they would come in a minute or two. Food was good and still fairly cheap in these homely working class conditions.

However, my last period of 'living at home' was coming to an end. I received a surprise on 13th October, 1916 on being told to report to the CME Drawing Office at Eastleigh the next week.

With some regrets I left Nine Elms ODM. I never went back: but after World War I the goods shed and wharf were re-equipped with electrical machinery and the old hydraulic power station abandoned.* What happened to all the men with whom I worked I never knew: it was another of those happy periods we all experience as we pass through life, and I was truly grateful to Perry and the gang for their help and companionship for almost 12 months' stay on the 'Wharf'.

Now, 50 years later, with the anti-railwayites in charge for the last 10, and bulldozers to hand, all vestiges of the goods and running sheds are being stamped out and relics of industrial history destroyed. I am glad to be living by the seashore out of sight of my old haunts. The waves still roar on the shingle as they did before the peace of Nine Elms was disturbed by the first traders.

---

* *Compilers' Note:* In the April 1970 *Journal* P. Hay wrote: Not all the hydraulic machinery was removed after World War I, however, and some of it was still in active use in the 1950s. The original London & Southampton Railway terminus building was still in use in 1957 and as well as the machinery Mr Langridge mentions, it was the home of an unusual hydraulic 'bridge' which could be raised to connect the loading platforms on either side of the building. The space between them was a roadway but would, I expect, originally have been carriage sidings if the common pattern for early stations was in fact adopted at Nine Elms. The bridge was raised by two hydraulic rams acting from below and of course presented a complete barrier to motor vehicles using the shed to deliver traffic to the trains. For this reason it was not often used, and its presence was advertised by white painted rectangles along its side girders and an overhead notice. This old shed was full of interest to any historically-minded railwayman and its low, slate-covered roof contrasted greatly with the more modern buildings around it. I remember in the adjoining shed, probably of the 1880s, contained at least one working hydraulic platform crane which was liked because it was possible for the operator standing beside it to exercise a precision of control - almost a lightness of touch - that never seemed possible with electric cranes.

Chapter Three

Eastleigh Drawing Office

On 19th October, 1916 I reported to the CME Drawing Office: the training of premium apprentices was 'Machine Fitting and Erecting Shops' and here was I being transferred to a 'white-collar' job where, being of military age and in the army reserve, I was only kept in 'civvies' by agreement between the army and the railway authority.

It seemed that the chief draughtsman wanted some extra men to complete detail drawings for the new 4-6-0s (the 'N' & 'P15s'), so another fellow and myself got called in. Presumably records of modest achievements at Hartley College (Southampton) and the railway's classes had made him think us not to be 'duds'. Nevertheless I had done no drawing or technical work for the last year whilst I was at Nine Elms ODM.

The drawing office at Eastleigh at that time occupied the south end of the first floor of the office block to the left of the main works entrance still extant alongside the Southampton main line. I still remember asking Forrest, the porter (a character with a wonderful memory down the years for people's names and faces), the way and presenting myself to T.S. Finlayson, the chief draughtsman. There was a continuous table built against the outer walls so as you worked you looked into the light, not very comfortable. The pleasant aroma of tracing paper, the quiet, the cleanliness after the shop floors, all made me feel the whole thing was unreal. However, 'TSF' passed me over to Chard, the leading hand, who worked on a board just outside the CD's office window. I met the other staff, Johnston, Cummings, Shaw, the draughtsmen; Eley, who was called 'the clerk', had a little desk at which he would copy, longhand, TSF's few letters, write out PT forms, do a bit of tracing of drawings on a drawing board alongside his desks, print, up in the loft, blueprints off tracings - those on cloth were rolled up and used as 'shop copies', the tracings themselves were used as office copies. He was withal a strong member of the Railway Clerks' Association! He was a very willing fellow and became a well-known delegate in later years. Shaw and Cummings were elderly and seemed to potter about on odd jobs on tenders and tank tracings, although Cummings got married and fathered an heir at over 65 years of age! Johnston and Chard had joined the drawing office staff at the same time as Finlayson, i.e., when R.W. Urie became CME and J.A. Hunter, the former chief draughtsman, got promoted to works manager, the usual way up the ladder in those days. Johnston was rather a dour Scot with little to say, worked steadily at his frame and pipe-and-rod drawings: always carried an umbrella! Chard had served his apprenticeship at Highbridge, S&D, and had come to Eastleigh drawing office via Derby (MR), where he did the frame drawing for the Deeley 0-6-4, '2000' class tank engines, North British Locomotive Co., Glasgow, and then to GNR Doncaster drawing office. Thus, his experience was wide and the number of people he had met pretty vast: he became my guide, philosopher and friend in many ways. Finlayson was very good to me, too: he was essentially a practical rather than a

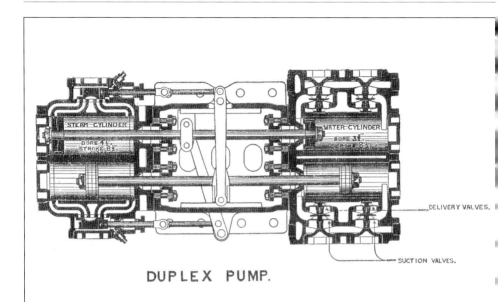

DUPLEX PUMP.

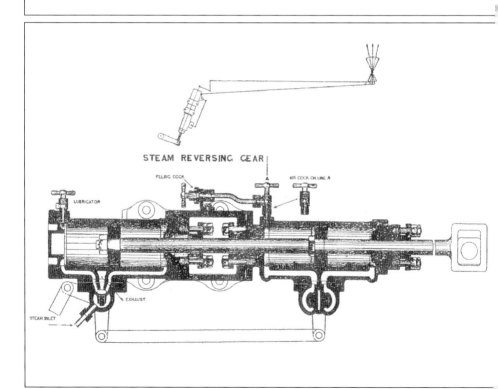

high-brow mathematical man who would point out the 'whys and wherefores' for good production. It was easy enough for someone else to do any abstract sums: his 'know-how' and 6 in. slide rule was sufficient for him and there wasn't much beating about the bush. If you showed a bit of promise and got on with the job you soon got interesting tasks and had to stand on your own feet - a wonderful training that stood me in good stead. Sandboxes for the 'N15s' were my first job: they were to be cast-iron ⅜ in. thick, to hold 2 cu. ft, fixed outside the frames, front of drivers, to be easily attached and get-at-able. So one just drew down the 'juxta', i.e., all the bits and pieces around the area in plan, elevation and end view that had already been designed on the frames, and schemed out your sandbox on a tracing paper overlay. TSF reminded you not to waste volume in empty air space, remember the angle of repose of sand, arrange for the parting face of the wooden pattern, the 'chaplets' to support the core and so on - quite a lot of practical points to be remembered even in a simple job. Having decided on the most suitable design you drew it in on the main drawing, stretched some tracing cloth, chalked it, and traced the drawing in ink. Then with titles and quantities required '1 of' etc. - what class it referred to - 'N15' 'P15' and 'LSWR' and so on in the bottom right-hand corner, all was ready to enter up in the drawing register, for TSF to check, Eley to get a blue print by daylight, upstairs in the attic, and to send it downstairs to the works manager for issue to the shops.

There was no elaborate system of recording or ordering; all very economical and satisfactory where only one works just across the yard was concerned. Nothing involving heat engines or strength of materials came my way but Chard, on quiet days, would get one interested in centre of gravity calculations (cg) of proposed designs and traction problems that might come up. The old *Mechanical World Handbook* and the *Locomotive Magazine Diary* contained most of the information the practical designer would require.

The standard Urie design made a complete break with the Stroudley-Drummond era, in which fine fitting and craftsmanship played so big a part and which really had its basis in marine engineering where the engineer on board ship would walk round his engines feeling bearings, adjusting trimmings and polishing up all his fittings. Thus the little 8 in. x 8 in. axleboxes with hand-fitted brasses, the duplex boiler feed pumps, the steam reversing gear and the multi-cylindered locomotive with steam dryer in the smokebox (where also were housed brass feed-water delivery pipes under full boiler pressure!) gave way to a simple big 2-cylinder engine with cheap brass 9 in. x 12 in. bearings, plain injectors and high superheat. Drummond's engines had always had 1¼ in. frames, notably thick amongst contemporary designs, and this feature was retained with strong cross-bracing. The marine type big ends gave way to the simpler, but heavier, square split brass with strap, cotter and two bolts and the introduction of 5 in. steel flue tubes requiring the manipulation of big tube expanders meant the omission of another Drummond feature, the cross water-tubes in the firebox. (Incidentally, these gave little trouble with leakage.) The boiler shop foreman, like many of Drummond's men, was a Scot who had strong opinions and turned out a beautiful job. Features like the Drummond sling stays were retained, but the normal firehole ring was replaced by a much wider forging

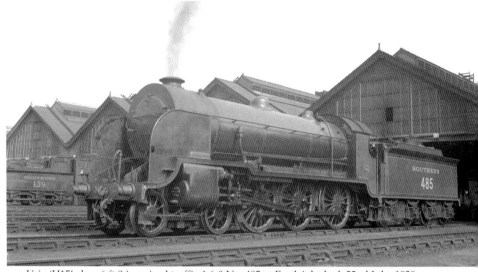

Urie 'H15' class 6 ft 0 in. mixed traffic 4-6-0 No. 485 at Eastleigh shed, 22nd July, 1938.
Kidderminster Railway Museum Trust Collection/A.N.H. Glover

Eastleigh works drawing stores with member of staff posed at sliding window hatch.
Kidderminster Railway Museum/John Fairman Collection

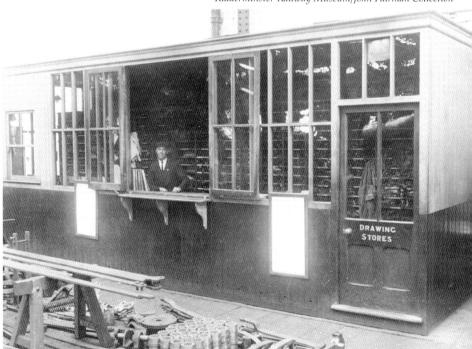

which kept the rivets away from the opening, where the heads always burn away, and provided more metal to cope with the wear from the fire-irons. The simple and effective inward-opening door of Drummond pattern was retained. Around 1912 J.G. Robinson, CME of the Great Central Railway, had a great advocate in Blundstone, editor of the *Railway Engineer*, and in some ways created a fashion in GCR practice. In this way the 180 psi boiler pressure adopted by Finlayson came about. Injectors were fitted behind the footstep and all joints on delivery pipes were made with 4-bolt flanges, a notable improvement on the previous union nuts, a practice dating back to the Adams era.

The valve gear design was typical of NB Loco practice: the expansion link being carried on a 'motion girder' bolted to the motion plate at one end and a platform support at the rear - a design to reappear in the LMS 'Scots' etc. A 22 inch cast-steel piston head working in a cast-iron cylinder supported by a crosshead with spigoted cast-iron slippers and a tail-rod bush at the front end of the piston rod would seem to be asking for trouble, particularly as the piston rings were ⅜ in. square with no supporting slipper of the Midland type, but none came! A generous 11 in. piston valve also had ⅜ in. rings which required loose end pieces as it was impossible to 'spring' such stiff rings into position. The large 5 in. diameter valve spindle supporting bush was another 'contract shop' idea: in fact, throughout the design very little 'shaping' was required, emphasis being on the much cheaper 'turning' on lathes. The coupling rods were plain flat parallel sections with no fluting. The crosshead was formed on the end of the piston rod forging, thus eliminating a cottered joint and the weighty article of a separate crosshead. The valve-setting broke with LSWR practice, for the travel in full gear (80%) was 5⅜ in. with a lead of ¼ in. This, with a Walschaert type valve gear, which gives no increase in lead as the gear is 'notched up', provided a large port opening to steam as there was only 1 in. lap. The big piston valve diameter provided some 36 sq. in. opening to exhaust.

Forced lubrication was provided by a 'Detroit' displacement lubricator, thus again avoiding auxiliary machinery, like pumps, with moving parts. The oil fed into the main steam pipes and was licked off the spoon-shaped end of the nozzle by the passing steam, thus creating an oily atmosphere. The valves and pistons kept notably free of hard carbon deposits so common with pump-lubricated locos. Direct loaded adjustable spring links were also provided - to appear later on some LMS designs. These allow an engine to be dropped on to the wheels, with axleboxes and springs already mounted, and the loco to be pushed onto the weigh table with a minimum use of overhead crane time. The practical result of this new design was an enormous increase in mileage between repairs compared with Drummond engines. The standards of cylinder arrangement and large bearings remained for the Urie regime.

It should be mentioned that the tender attached to these locos was also a brand new design. Incredibly the Drummond bogie tender had remained unchanged in the method of attaching the bogie centres to the tank well during his time as CME although it was well known that the rivets into the water space loosened and leaked, the tender spraying water onto the track like a water cart. It had the merit of being frameless and therefore a light design. The new tender had a separate frame supported on carriage type bogies with separate tank

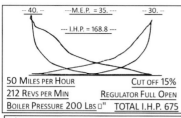

-- 40. -- ---M.E.P. = 35. --- -- 30. --

--- I.H.P. = 168.8 ---

50 Miles per Hour Cut off 15%
212 Revs per Min Regulator Full Open
Boiler Pressure 200 Lbs ▢" Total I.H.P. 675

1½ Mile Post -- Left Outside -- Level

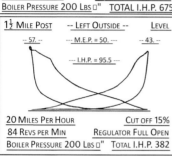

-- 57. -- ---M.E.P. = 50. --- -- 43. --

--- I.H.P. = 95.5 ---

20 Miles Per Hour Cut off 15%
84 Revs per Min Regulator Full Open
Boiler Pressure 200 Lbs ▢" Total I.H.P. 382

4 Mile Post --- Left Inside --- 1 in 334 Up

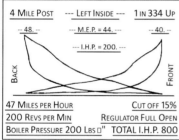

-- 48. -- --- M.E.P. = 44. --- -- 40. --

--- I.H.P. = 200. ---

Back   Front

47 Miles per Hour Cut off 15%
200 Revs per Min Regulator Full Open
Boiler Pressure 200 Lbs ▢" Total I.H.P. 800

2 Mile Post --- Left Inside --- Level

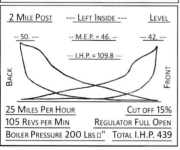

-- 50. --- -- M.E.P. = 46. --- -- 42. --

--- I.H.P. = 109.8 ---

Back   Front

25 Miles Per Hour Cut off 15%
105 Revs per Min Regulator Full Open
Boiler Pressure 200 Lbs ▢" Total I.H.P. 439

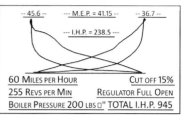

-- 45.6 -- -- M.E.P. = 41.15 -- -- 36.7 --

--- I.H.P. = 238.5 ---

60 Miles per Hour Cut off 15%
255 Revs per Min Regulator Full Open
Boiler Pressure 200 Lbs ▢" Total I.H.P. 945

64 Mile Post --Right Outside-- 1 in 251 Down

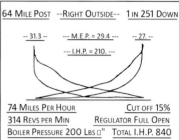

-- 31.3 -- --- M.E.P. = 29.4 --- -- 27. --

--- I.H.P. = 210. ---

74 Miles Per Hour Cut off 15%
314 Revs per Min Regulator Full Open
Boiler Pressure 200 Lbs ▢" Total I.H.P. 840

24 Mile Post --- Right Inside --- 1 in 326 Up

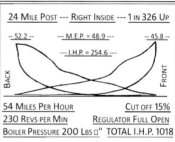

-- 52.2 -- ---M.E.P. = 48.9 --- -- 45.8 --

--- I.H.P. = 254.6 ---

Back   Front

54 Miles Per Hour Cut off 15%
230 Revs per Min Regulator Full Open
Boiler Pressure 200 Lbs ▢" Total I.H.P. 1018

92 Mile Post ------- Right Inside ------- 1 in 176 Up

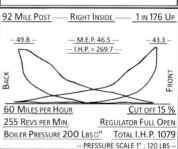

-- 49.8 -- --- M.E.P. 46.5 --- -- 43.3 --

--- I.H.P. = 269.7 ---

Back   Front

60 Miles per Hour Cut off 15 %
255 Revs per Min. Regulator Full Open
Boiler Pressure 200 Lbs ▢" Total I.H.P. 1079

-- Pressure Scale 1" : 120 Lbs --

-- INDICATOR DIAGRAMS 446 ENGINE . CLASS 4-6-0. --
-- TAKEN BETWEEN LONDON AND BOURNEMOUTH OCTOBER 6TH 1911.
-- LOAD 10 BOGIE COACHES --

-- 2 P.M. EX WATERLOO --   -- L.S.W.R. --

-- MECHANICAL ENGINEERS DEPT. --
-- REDRAWN FROM DRAWING No. 10499 -- -- EASTLEIGH LOCO WORKS --

superimposed. It was heavier, but trouble free, and bearings and springs were all visible and extremely accessible.

Having got the engine into service some indicator diagrams were taken and fuel measurements made in 1914. The figures for a gross weight (train and locomotive) of about 500 tons at an average speed between London and Salisbury of 55 mph came out at about 2 lb. coal per ihp hour with a steam consumption of about 18 lb. A more practical figure of coal per mile from the posted records at the shed of 36 lb. seemed to prove that the engine was as economical as the best Drummond 4-cylinder locomotives.*

Referring to Mr Lewcock's letter I regret that I have no copy of the motion readings for Drummond 4-6-0 No. 446. I have a line diagram of the outside motion, but unfortunately it is too faint for reproduction. However, from this I can quote the salient dimensions as follows:

Centre of pins in combination lever (or lap or lead lever), 32⅜ inches bottom to valve crosshead pin: from that to top pin (radius rod) 3¹¹⁄₁₆ inches. Remembering that the gear had outside steam admission, one can get the lap plus lead figure. The valve travel and lap on Drummond's big 4-4-0 built a year or two later I have recorded as 4¾ inches and so I think one could take the same figures for the 4-6-0. The connecting rods were 11 ft 0 in. outside and 6 ft 6 in. inside. Unfortunately the diagrams reproduced above were taken at different points in the journey. She had 9 inch diameter piston valves - remarkably big for a 15 inch cylinder diameter in those days; but the feeling of that school of

* *Compilers' Note:* In July/August 1988 *Journal* Eddie Lewcock wrote:

Mr Langridge makes reference to some interesting indicator diagrams from LSWR engine 446. I took the opportunity of checking with some LMS Class 5 indicator diagrams on D.R.S. No. 5673 taken in January 1949 and which, at a speed of about 50 mph, gave the following figures at 15% cut-off:

	Speed (mph)	Boiler pressure (psi)	Indicated horsepower	
a)	50	205	643	
b)	55	205	675	

These compare with the LSWR locomotive figures as follows:

c)	50	200	675	
d)	47	200	800	(4 mile post)
e)	54	200	1018	(24 mile post)

At a speed of about 50 mph, the short valve-travel Drummond engine comes out remarkably well, particularly Curve e) - possibly because the engine had warmed through nicely by milepost 24 - although the horsepower variations do seem rather wide between Curves c) and e). As most short valve-travel engines were notoriously bad performers at short cut-offs, it will be very interesting to hear further details about the valve gear on engine 446. Possibly Mr Langridge could comment more about these tests at moderate speeds, where the Drummond was equalling and out-performing the Class 5, on power output (but probably not on thermal efficiency!). The problems of short-travel valves are shown up, however, at milepost 64, at 74 mph, when the limitations of power output at high speed are clearly seen.

designer - like the LNWR - was to give the travel on the steam side and so keep up the 'top line' of the diagram rather than concentrate on keeping the 'bottom line' down - the Swindon practice. The LSWR diagrams certainly seem to show a low exhaust line. I remember that you could drop a bolt down the blast pipe and it fell straight into the cylinder exhaust chamber - no bends on the way.

At about this time there appeared the Urie stove-pipe chimney. Although commented on adversely by many who particularly object to it on the famous Drummond 4-4-0 engine No. 120, there are good functional reasons for its design. There are no expensive cores to be made for the casting; the metal thickness is fairly uniform with an extra reinforcing thickness where it is wanted, at the rim.

All engineers disliked paying royalties on superheaters, and the next step was to design the 'Eastleigh' superheater, first fitted in 1915 to engine No. 335 - a Drummond 4-cylinder locomotive which had been lying for a few years with a broken frame. The old boiler was used with a new tubeplate and minus the firebox cross water tubes. The invention consisted of separate top and bottom cast-iron headers with cast-iron bridge pieces, the top entry to these being saturated steam and the bottom superheated. The elements were straight double return pipes pushed through the bridge piece with a nut and washer at each side. An illustration appeared in the *Locomotive Magazine* in April 1915. The whole arrangement was quite simple, but being cast iron was also weighty. Nevertheless, superheating went ahead on the Drummond engines having piston valves. The next step was to try out superheating on Drummond engines having flat valves and outside admission. This put the valve spindle packing under the influence of high pressure steam. The first engine to be treated in this way was No. 421, the engine involved in the famous Salisbury derailment of 1906. The success of this led to a gradual extension of superheating to all

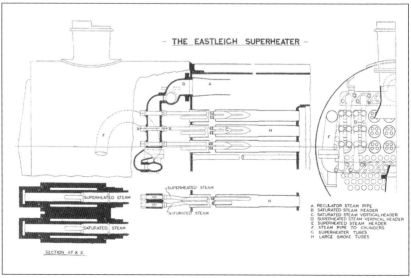

- THE EASTLEIGH SUPERHEATER -

A REGULATOR STEAM PIPE
B SATURATED STEAM HEADER
C SATURATED STEAM VERTICAL HEADER
D SUPERHEATED STEAM VERTICAL HEADER
E SUPERHEATED STEAM HEADER
F STEAM PIPE TO CYLINDERS
G SUPERHEATER TUBES
H LARGE SMOKE TUBES

SECTION AT X X

engines in the passenger class and provided what I thought for many years was the only example in this country of flat valve superheating. However, in the August 1967 *SLS Journal* the noted L&Y historian, Eric Mason, advised that some LNW 'Precursor' and L&Y 4-4-0s were so fitted, and although I worked for 30 years or so with men from Crewe and Horwich I had never heard mention of it before. The MR fitted a few 0-6-4 'Deeley' tanks and '3F' Goods 0-6-0s experimentally in the 1920s, but they were short-lived efforts not perpetuated. The point I wished to make about the LSWR flat valve superheaters was that they were so successful that they were fitted to nearly all Drummond flat valve engines and lasted throughout the life of the locos through SR and BR eras. The cost of alteration was small compared with the rebuilding with piston valves as done by many railways and it was almost a case of getting something for nothing!*

Returning to the drawing office in 1916 I had, of course, come back to my old digs at Eastleigh. That there was a war on was evident as a sergeant from the Royal Army Medical Corps was now occupying the best bedroom! He was a 6 ft man, a good age, aparently called up from reserve. Quite a pleasant fellow, apt to be talkative and to lecture us on 'joints and fractures': worked 9 to 5 and appeared to be doing well. The remount depot at Swaythling spread out in the fields either side of North Stoneham Lane - now part of the Southampton University Campus, saved from becoming the appalling mess on the other side of the railway called Southampton airport. The remounts were mules - four-legged ones - for the 1914 Army still relied on animal power to haul their artillery. Meeting these unawares in the narrow lane on a bike with shaded headlamp made you think you had reached Never Never Land.

My dear old landlady - to whom I was 'Arthur', she couldn't get her tongue round 'Eric' - surprised me one day by asking me to read to her a letter from a daughter: I could not believe it, but the, fact was that she could neither read nor write. She had been a country lass in an Essex village by the Blackwater; married an LSWR engine driver at Nine Elms who transferred the family to Eastleigh, and had been left a widow with four capable children. None of them being at home now, and having taken me under her wing, she made me her 'scribe', Indian fashion, but I did it sitting on a chair and not on my haunches. Her eldest married daughter lived at Mansfield - nicely placed then for door-to-door transport from Eastleigh on the through GCR train by Oxford, Banbury, Leicester and Nottingham. I amused them on one visit by rigging up my 'O' gauge Bassett-Lowke steam engine *Black Prince* (which I hope is now at Birmingham Museum) in Cranbury Road back garden.† The old lady's eldest son was firing from Eastleigh shed: the second one was a carriage builder (wood in those days) and the third - the same age as myself - a territorial in France but normally a locomotive shop apprentice. Fireman Alf Preece, Reg's son, asked if

---

* *Compilers' Note:* Once again Langridge seems blind to developments on the GWR, where superheating of slide valve locomotives was commonplace, presumably the low degree of GWR superheat being well suited for the purpose.

† Despite a detailed search by the museum, no reference to a locomotive model matching this description could be found. If the model had entered the museum for more than a very brief period, it should have been possible to find some trace of it on the files; it is therefore considered unlikely that it ever went there.

I would like a trip with him on the footplate, so one dark evening I joined him and his driver on an Adams' 0-4-4T at Eastleigh station for a run to Portsmouth ('Pompey') and back. We had a light train and the trip was unadventurous. I thought the engine was rough riding with solid thumps on the cab floor, which the driver put down to her being low on the springs. Cranbury Road, like others around, consisted of terrace houses, four bedrooms and a bath upstairs tucked half-way into a recess of one bedroom, but no hot water supply. So you lugged buckets of hot water up from the copper downstairs for your tub.

Across the recreation ground, being further from the works, the houses were better. Driver Greening lived that way and gave me footplate rides on No. 707, a 'T9' 4-4-0. He was in the express link at Eastleigh shed and was a friend of the Preeces, his wife looking after me when Mrs Preece had a holiday visiting her daughter in Mansfield. No. 707 had steam reverse and was as originally built: when we were doing 60 mph down to Basingstoke the indicator pointed to 10 per cent, back! That was typical of how the steam reversing indicator - a light sectioned steel rod - could get bent and give false readings. Of course a good driver knew by the feel of the sounds and riding of his engine whereabouts his gear was. Later in life I thought that a good argument for the MR's practice of putting only 1, 2, 3, 4 and no degrees of expansion on their reversing indicator plates. You could see that the trailing hornblocks were 'working' in the frame too from the oil marks. But at about 70 mph she rode sweetly and without much rattle, far better than Alf's 0-4-4 Adams tank on the Pompey runs.

Back in the drawing office Finlayson sent me up to Nine Elms to measure up brake blocks and other 'consumable' gear on a GCR 2-8-0 Standard WD locomotive. It seemed that drawings and spares were hard to come by and that sketches would allow castings to be made if not fully machined. The GCR built heavy beasts: no wonder they had a long life, but really the LSWR had little traffic that really suited them. Anyhow, the job kept me busy for a few weeks and was good practice. Another day he told me to go in the yard and measure up a boiler going for scrap and give him the weight. That took most of the day; when I gave him the sizes he just scribbled down a few figures and said, 'Is that the weight?' And of course, having been chief estimator at North British before coming to Eastleigh, it was just about that!

I should have said previously that my pal Barnes was keen on joining the Institution of Locomotive Engineers. He was much more of a polite go-getter than I was: so we both got elected as Graduates in 1916 and attended a number of the Saturday afternoon meetings at Caxton Hall. At one meeting the outdoor supt SECR, A.D. Jones, gave us a private lecture on how they got the British Expeditionary Force to France in record time. Barnes later gave a paper himself and won a prize. Life seemed pleasant and promising: the wages office below the drawing office had recruited a few girls to take the place of men called-up - book-keeping and wages slips, &c., were all made out longhand. Inevitably the few young men upstairs came to walk to the station with the young ladies and some sort of social life grew up with local get-togethers and concerts to provide money for comforts for the troops. At one of these at Eastleigh we were a bit late and my pal and I thought we had better see the girls safely in the train to Southampton - most lived in that area. One was getting off at bleak St Denys and no male seemed to offer to escort, so I acted the Sir Galahad! Next day, Finlayson called me into his office and, in his best Glasgow tongue, asked if I were going home to London that weekend. On being told, 'Yes', he said, 'Ye needna pey yer fare - here's a free pass fo' ye!' Delightful of him, wasn't it? It was his daughter that I had seen safely into the parental home!

By this time America had entered World War I and our railways were allowed a quota of American steel to build some badly-needed locomotives. The LSWR put their allocation into the 'N15' class, which was a larger-wheeled version of the '486' first batch of 4-6-0s. To keep up the tractive effort the cylinder diameter was increased to 22 in., but at the same time tail rods were abolished. At one time in the Eastleigh DO a general arrangement drawing in pencil existed showing the proposed engine with 7 ft 1 in. coupled wheels and a sharply-tapered boiler.

There was a rooted objection to leading 2-wheeled trucks in the DO and thus when a goods engine was required the same basic 4-6-0 design appeared. When this set of standards was applied to a hump shunter it became a 4-8-0 and to a tank engine for outer suburban work (the inner lines being electrified) it became a 4-6-2. The heavy standard chassis and large bearings made it necessary to spread the wheelbase of the latter in order to meet the engineer's loading curves, particularly as through running to Brent was involved. Finlayson had strong objections to the express tank engine of the other southern lines, maintaining that they were unstable at speed and expensive in upkeep. Judging from subsequent events he would appear to have been right.

There were periodic comb-outs for the Army and it looked improbable that young men would be allowed to stay in drawing offices for long. So on 2nd April, 1917, with 3 or 4 inches of snow on the ground, back I went to the erecting shop and the 7 am start. A trip on the footplate of No. 313 shook me back to realities. Then I got transferred to the wheel shop: building up crank-axles and pressing on wheels were the most interesting jobs there. My job was to fit rectangular keys in the wheel boss and axle: the key was forged on the end of a long bar with a doublehead so that you could flog the key in and out again after trying the fit. Foreman White seemed a suspicious sort of fellow: when 'Tosh' Harrison (the aforementioned chief clerk) gave me a few days' holiday I put in a single PT form for a ticket from Marlborough to Cirencester to his office for signature. He had me in and asked how I was going to get to Marlborough; I said, 'By bike and I'm riding all the way back!' Maybe he thought me awkward: incidentally I had not travelled that lovely road through Savernake Forest from that day until an OAP (BR) outing last summer. No time, unfortunately, to see that wonderful pumping engine on the Kennet canal and ride and walk over the Cotswold country again. Anyhow being technically out of 'my time' on 24th September and entitled to 'Improver's' wage (24s.) I was sent back to the erecting shop first, on Hunt's gang and then to Kilpin who erected the steam heating on locomotives in the erecting shop. I managed to see a bit of valve setting done as we were doing our stuff: the chargehand was very secretive about it all, of course. He was the only Crewe-trained man I came across in the shops, the rest were Cockneys and a very few Scotch skilled men. The spasmodic air raids were still going on so a weekend at home was not always a rest-time although my family had returned to London.

Disappointment at the progress of the war, shortage of food and general malaise started up labour troubles. The first I saw of it was when Maitland, an ex-apprentice, got on a box in the erecting shop and started telling us to down tools: nothing much happened after he had got his speech off his chest but it was a new situation for Charlie Biggs the assistant foreman, whom everybody liked, to have to deal with. Foreman Harvey was not so popular: he was rather a withdrawn figure. He happened to be in front of me at the time office one day and he picked up five golden sovereigns as pay, I suppose, for the week. However, there was serious trouble at the running sheds and Hunter, the works manager, asked us apprentices and improvers if we would be willing to help out. So friend Barnes and I went down nightly on the 8.30 pm to Bournemouth Central shed to help Elliot, the foreman, keep his stud workable as far as possible. Once again one appreciated get-at-able design: brake block adjustment on a Drummond locomotive was simple as the nut with right- and left-handed threaded ends simply pulled up the rods on rotation. With Adams' one thread-cum-pin-hole nut, you had to sprag up the blocks, withdraw the pin, drop the rods and adjust nut, and vice versa to finish the job, really a two-man task. One night the phone rang and a signalman down the line said a troop special was coming along and the sergeant had complained that no heating was coming through. Would we have a look at it if he stopped it on the through road in Central station? In due course he came in and I clambered on to the footplate. The carriage heating valve was jammed on its seat and, being under boiler pressure, there was no way in which we could move it, so the train had to go on with no heat, poor chaps. I wondered where they were bound for. On another night we found a side-control bogie spring broken on one of the four '463' class (big 4-4-0s) allocated to Bournemouth for the London expresses: not having or being able to get one from Eastleigh, Elliot had a look underneath and decided to let her run - a bit risky I thought, but he was a fine railwayman and knew what could be safely chanced. We heard no adverse report on her running for the next 10 days: after all the propelling of bogie coaches without side control at high speeds today seems to be accepted so perhaps we were in advance of our time! However, we didn't enjoy the time at Bournemouth: the noise of the train rattling down the cutting into Central station can still cause me a nightmare. True the cab of an Adams radial tank provided a snug corner for a little bit of 'shut-eye' about 5 am before getting a cup of tea and sandwich, with luck, and the 8.10 am home to sleep. We seemed to pick a compartment with commuters dealing in precious stones, but got no hints as to how to get rich quick: still we got about £10 for that fortnight's work.

In three weeks the strike fizzled out and we 'boys' were given a week's leave. Rather than go back to the works where our reception might not have been welcomed, we were sent to other sheds: my next job was again on night work at Guildford as 'joint-maker': you had to deal with joints reported blowing on boiler and fittings. The locomotives at Guildford that came my way were mostly old crocks, badly maintained: trying to get a decent shop job done on dome covers whose faces had been ruined by copper wire joints, some with four or five broken studs, was pretty frustrating. I stuck it for a month and found I was merely labouring and had no time to continue my swotting. The only relief came in being able to attend ILocoE meetings at Caxton Hall on Saturday afternoons. Late arrival from one of these led to a row with foreman Mitchell over rotten shed organization and the end of that job. I wrote to R.W. Urie and by a stroke of luck and good will on the part of Urie I got back to Eastleigh on a job in the iron foundry. In this way I got an insight into actual moulding and casting. Most casting went according to plan but one big cylinder set of moulds blew back just after pouring the metal from the ladle had commenced. Some sand had become detached when the mould was being baked apparently, and had blocked the main vent: the white hot metal blew back in little blobs high in the air. No one got burned but the casting was a 'waster'. In that block of buildings the iron foundry pattern shop and heavy forge were housed so that one could see some of the finest crafts being practised. Alas, they are practically extinct now, and man the worse off.

Yet again the wheel turned and I was back in the drawing office! This time it was April 1918, and drawings for the 'S15' 4-6-0 goods engine were being made. As the standard Urie outside cylinder and motion were adopted there was no great technical design required: it was a case of simple mathematics in getting the positions of motion bracket and reversing shaft to suit an incline of 1 in 24, compared with 1 in 36 on the 6 ft 0 in. 4-6-0s 'H' and 'K15'. Finlayson gave me the job of doing this and drawing out the new steel castings. Calculating the size of crescent in the coupled wheels meant an exercise from W.E. Dalby's textbook on balancing. The proportion of reciprocating weight to be balanced was calculated on Finlayson's North British Locomotive Co.'s practice, i.e., weight of locomotive divided by 400 unbalanced. In steel castings he was keen on having half-beaded edges which means that, for example, a simple hollow biscuit tin would have the edges beaded on the outside only, thus enabling the corebox for the inside to be easily withdrawn from the mould, whereas the pattern for the

Urie 'S15' class 5 ft 7 in. heavy freight 4-6-0 as BR No. 30504. *Ken Lea*

outside could contain all the beads and 'prints' and, being parted in halves, be likewise easily removed from the mould before the insertion of the corebox. Similarly the rods for the valve gear were machined flat on one side, fluted on the other, the loss in moment of inertia compared with a double fluted rod being small and the saving in weight of forging and amount of machining being considerable. I thought I would go one better by incorporating the shape of the outside angle in the motion girder casting but although Finlayson thought it all right, R.W. Urie turned it down on the score that the finish of the casting would not be good enough and would spoil the look of the nice long outside running angle. 'R.W.' never came into the drawing office himself and it was only occasionally that Finlayson would venture into his sanctum. Shortly after building the first 4-6-0s with Schmidt and Robinson type superheaters the Urie type was introduced and patented. No. 335, the so-called rebuild of Drummond's 4-cylinder 4-6-0 (only the boiler shell was re-used) was the first locomotive fitted, as illustrated in Loco. Mag. It consisted of top and bottom header with bridge pieces (all cast iron) receiving sleeves attached to straight element tubes. Being heavy, it required a cast-iron slab to be added at the footplate end to bring back the centre of gravity to the old position when fitted to 4-4-0s and others when superheated. Another feature contributing to success (and simplicity) of Urie locomotives was the use of Detroit sight feed lubricators. Drops of oil were fed into each steam pipe at entry to steam chest and wear and carbonisation were minute. The piston valves had two Ramsbottom type rings but the smaller Drummond locomotives, when superheated, retained their flat valves without change. When I came on the MR later, to see the elaborate mechanical lubricators, check valves, air relief valves, etc., I was appalled at their complications - and you had to drive out the piston valves with flogging hammers withal!

Another year was well on the way: the war seemed no nearer finishing in the spring of 1918: air raids were still going on in London and people finding temporary country homes if possible. But life in Southampton district seemed normal, live theatres staging their usual Gilbert & Sullivan operas and Martin Harvey plays, etc. When one has a 9 to 5 white-collar job there is time for pleasure in various ways: being within 10 minutes walk of the office I had time to play a movement from a Beethoven piano sonata in the dinner hour as well as get a meal at the digs. Cycling round the Isle of Wight at a weekend, the 8 am boat to Cowes on a Sunday morning down Southampton Water before the days of oil refineries and Marchwood power station gave one a trip in pre-industrialized England - or in the New Forest cycling kept one fit. However, before the wheel of fortune turned again I realised that the future had to be thought of seriously. The Inst. Loco. Engineers gave one a small standing but membership of the Inst. of Mech. Engineers seemed to be the thing to aim at. I had failed my London Matriculation in Classics at school so this time I leaned to the engineering side for the two optional subjects. I took up a correspondence course with a man named G.P. Knowles who, I believe later founded the University Correspondence College (UCC). My idea was to get London Matriculation, which would excuse me half of the AMIMechE examination and also help to a B.Sc. (Eng.) degree.

The 'wheel' turned with a vengeance in late summer as the war clouds gathered and I was back in dungarees 7 am to 9 pm as a fitter in the erecting shop. Variety came in acting as relief fitter at Salisbury and Nine Elms sheds. It also provided valuable experience of the right kind - and my first 'All Stations' pass - a bit of pink paper the size of a postal order. The leading fitter at Salisbury would tell tales of goings-on in Drummond days when his early 4-cylinder 4-6-0s were there operating both to Exeter and London, both on pretty fast schedules: the Exeter one was a real racing ground with a saw-tooth profile. The Drummond edict was that the locomotives *had* to run to schedule, so hot big-ends, etc., had to be dealt with *'tout-de-suite'*, or he would he on the carpet. Salisbury shed separated by the main line from the hateful GWR one across the way seemed to ooze character. A straight dead-end shed with a few poky offices along the far wall had a set of sheer legs for lifting jobs. You could just about get a driving axle out of a 4-4-0 if you packed up under the cab buffer beam and hoisted her up at an angle by lifting at the front end: Drummond steel boxes with removable fitted brass gave you a bit more room than solid brass boxes as you could wangle the brass out without taking out complete axle. What a game though - even preservation societies seem to have wheel drops now! They ran a coal saving bonus scheme on the LSWR: a large board on the shed wall recorded all the top link engines and their lb./mile consumption. I took down the figures: most were under 40 lb./mile, believe it or not! One amusing thing happened to a saddle tank for which a replacement set of eccentric sheaves had come across from Eastleigh. They were cast in pairs - a fore and aft together- and there was discussion as to which was left and right as either way they sat quite nicely on the axle. Well, of course, we got one set the wrong way round and when the regulator was opened gently after getting up steam the tankie took two-thirds of a rev, forward and then one back! Nine Elms shed was much bigger and I got only uninteresting jobs during the day when I was there. Anwell was shed foreman in those days: a well-known railway name. Years later in the diesel era I met his son, a Crown Agents' man, at a diesel conference.

On one of my free days I thought I would use my all stations pass to go to Yeovil to see how my friend Falconer was getting on as temporary shed foreman (no divisional locomotive superintendents in those days). A 'Paddlebox' 4-6-0 was hauling the fast from Salisbury but, at high speed beyond Semley, we ran into half-a-dozen cows strolling across the line. She kept on the road but the third and fourth coaches each had a bogie derailed and there was a nasty mess of bits of cow about. With no prospect of getting much further, some of us walked back to Semley where after an hour or two an up express stopped to pick us up for London: so ended my day out. The rest of that 'leave' was spent sitting for the London Matric. Exam. at the Imperial Institute: this time I got through OK. A bit more swotting and was through the AMIMechE exam, and elected GIMechE at first go.

My generation will remember how the big German advance to Paris in 1918 was suddenly unexpectedly halted by the Allies who this time didn't go back; rather the reverse. This seemed to put hope into industry and - lo, and behold! -some of us apprentices and improvers were called back to the drawing office and took off our dungarees for the last time. Of course, financially we were worse off: a temporary junior draughtsman, didn't get the wages of a fitter-improver, and we knew there was little chance of getting on the staff: the LSWR just didn't do that sort of thing.

Finlayson said that two tank engine designs were proposed: the 4-8-0 had been agreed but the 4-6-2 was still not settled due to weight restrictions on the West London Extension and other lines it was intended to run over. Chard had to get out the diagrams and I was given the 4-8-0 motion to do first off. Again we were using the Urie standard cylinder and valve gear layout, so questions of strength scarcely arose. I swung the '486' motion round to the new incline of the cylinders; calculated the new centres vertically and longitudinally and found a convenient position for the slidebar bracket and reversing shaft. As the side tanks came well forward I had to cast onto the slidebar bracket the supports for the expansion link and also carry the front end of the side tank there. The motion done for the 4-8-0, it was child's play to do that for the 4-6-2 tank, now that its wheelbase had been settled, in similar fashion and draw out the castings and ordering sketches. Chard did the boiler, a variation on the Urie standard, Johnson the frames and pipe and rod and Cummings and Shaw the tanks. Two or three other lads were doing details, of course.

The wheels for the 4-8-0 presented a few problems when it came to the balance weights. The size of axle, journal and wheel boss and rim section were all to be to Urie standard '486' sizes - some weight! But the small 5 ft 1 in. diameter wheels meant there was little room for the balance crescent-shaped weight. I should say that there was no motion model and no balancing machine at Eastleigh: you could lay out the valve gear and get the readings laboriously for the parent '486' design; those following with shorter or longer rods would not vary from the original greatly and were considered to be 'near enough'. The schedule for the balancing is set out below: 40 per cent, reciprocating mass was balanced, being the maximum we could get in the small wheels.

Balancing of tank shunting engine 'G16' 4-8-0

Reciprocating parts.

Piston, rod and nut and crosshead	667 lb.
Crosshead arm	18 lb.
Half conn. rod	229 lb.
Total	*914 lb.*

Forty per cent of No. 914 to be balanced, distributed equally as far as possible in each wheel. NB - 60 lb. only could be put in driving wheel.

Reciprocating parts	111	60	111	111
Half conn. rod	-	299	-	-
Coupling rods	117	274	274	117
Wheel boss	190	190	190	190
Crank pin to conn. rod	-	44	-	-
Crank pin to coupling rods	29	36	29	29
Return crank	-	85	-	-
Total (all at 14 in. crank radius)	*447*	*988*	*604*	*447*

SR Urie 'G16' class 4-8-0T No. 492 for hump shunting at Eastleigh, 19th June, 1938.
SLS Collection/W.A. Camwell

It is then a matter of trying out various sizes of crescents and calculating their centres of gravity so that the moment of the crescent by its centre of gravity is equal to the weight to be balanced by its centre of gravity (i.e. its crank radius). The depth of the crescent is fixed by clearances to coupling rod and main frame of locomotive and the weight, 0.28 lb. per cu. inch (7850 kg/cu. m or 7.85g/cu. cm). Allowance for spokes (usually about 12 per cent) has to be made where they pass through the crescent and so are ineffective as balance weight. A plarimeter is used to obtain area of crescent.

Another thing the small wheel did was to limit the length of spring link from buckle to axlebox. The hornstay had to have a gap to allow the jaws of the buckle to pass and also a 'set' to allow the spring pin to be removed: so it was an ungainly steel casting. But it worked all right, I believe. Yet again, layout of the 4-8-0 wheelbase diagramatically on a 7 chain curve (all at 1½ in. = 1 foot) showed that the rear coupled axle must have about ⅜ in. side play each way. I assumed that it would necessitate a vertical fork at the next coupling rod joint but, No! Finlayson was quite happy to leave the coupling rods without vertical joint and allow ⅜ in. extra slack on the crankpin journal - which seemed a poor bit of design to young me! I tried to sell the idea of an independently sprung bogie to him, too, but he turned down my design: he disliked separate springs (particularly the coiled ones, *à la* GCR, I had shown) both from cost and good running points of view. So we stuck to his standard long-wheel-based (7 ft 6 in.) 4-wheel bogie with equalizing beams, and I went on learning the pros and cons of designing.

The sun would pour through the drawing office windows on summer afternoons (there were no partitions dividing the big office until the Maunsell era) and one afternoon about 2.30 all was quiet apart from persistent scratching: suddenly Finlayson appeared at the door of his private office, pipe in hand (smoking was not allowed in offices then) and shouted across to a young man, 'Ke-ayton! A little less scratching out! Use a bit more elbow grease!' Poor Cayton had been diligently removing an unwanted line on his cloth tracing. The chief retired to his desk within: all was deathly still: perhaps one or two of the older heads could be seen to nod.

The GWR worked the Didcot-Newbury line from Southampton Terminus and one of their trains - 12.36 from Eastleigh - provided a chancey connection at Winchester, if you ran most of the way from their Chesil station up the hill to the LSWR one, with the 'fast' Southampton-Winchester-Waterloo train ahead of the slower 12.53 Eastleigh-Waterloo semi-fast. Falconer and I often did this - although the GWR ticket collector at Chesil was apt to haggle. One day we stuck just short of the platform at Chesil and precious minutes were ticking away: so Falconer opened the carriage door and I followed with our bags, through the goods yard (gate open fortunately) and dashed up to the LSWR station just in time - I can't remember if we shut the carriage door: you remember that old GWR doors had no latch only a positive right angle turn. Anyhow, no one reported us!

I must hurry through my last few months under R.W.U. While general discussions were going on as to who would own and run the various individual railways a new post on the LSWR was created and M.F. Ryan from the S&D (Highbridge) became Asst CME indicating that Urie would retire shortly. No posts were available for the few temp. junior draughtsmen so we divided up likely employers - contract shops and railways - and wrote around for a job. One went to Barr of Stroud, another to Beyer, Peacock, and then Ryan called me in one day and said he was leaving to become CME of the Central Argentine Railway and would I like to go out to the drawing office there. He also invited one or two others: my personal ties made me turn the offer down. As things have turned out - our loss of Empire and railways owned in South America - I am glad I did, for if you retire on pension you can't take it out of their country and are condemned to finish your life on foreign soil. After a good many 'No vacancy' replies I eventually got an interview with the chief locomotive draughtsman of the MR. Although he could not offer me a staff job then the chances of getting one shortly, when re-grading of his other young men had been completed, were very bright. I was, in fact, replacing an established man, T.B. Smith, who was leaving to join his family timber business. Chard had worked at Derby, in Symes' time as experimental draughtsman, and could put in a good word for me and so I came to pack my bags and leave Cranbury Road digs for the last time. My last weeks in the Eastleigh drawing office were occupied in scheming out the superheater for Drummond 0-4-4T and 0-6-0 goods engines. To get the superheater headers in above the inside cylinders forced up the height of the boiler and the extra weight at the front end had to be balanced by a heavy cast-iron block under the cab floor. The proportioning of the flue and tube areas followed the usual Schmidt recommendation - about 50/50 and their standard size of tubing and flue were used. With these small boilers the mean hydraulic depth ratios were practically equal (*see Appendix Eight*).

The feeling at Eastleigh in Urie's day was 'Cut down supplementary machinery on locos.' Hence Drummond's feed pumps, steam reversing gear and any idea of mechanical lubrication was taboo. The LSWR must have saved themselves a lot of money by cutting out shop costs on such fancy things: hot water injectors, screw reverse and sight feed lubricators were pounds cheaper. Likewise Urie locos had no snifter valves – another expendable item! There was a drifting mark on the regulator which was much cheaper and kept the piston valves clean. The 'N' and 'P15s', Nos. 736 to 740 and 741 to 745, were built in the Urie era, before I left Eastleigh. Also the 'S15s', I think Nos. 493 to 497, came out before his 4-6-2 and 4-8-0 tanks. It was after these that Maunsell's versions appeared with GWR ideas from Holcroft and MR cabs from James Clayton - a curious mixture of personalities that appears never to have coalesced. Fortunately, Urie had provided a solid basis of design which enabled the type to run reliably up to nationalization.

Saying 'Goodbye', after eight of one's formative years spent in happy surroundings is a bit painful. I had been lucky to have such a good training in a job I was very fond of: it prevented me, I hope, from becoming biased pro this or that later on, in dealing with a variety of men who became my chiefs in the drawing office or even as CMEs. Many times I was to be told on first meeting them that I did not know the first thing about design but in every case, I think, we ended up by being good friends. J.A. Hunter, the Eastleigh works manager, who lived well on into his nineties, remarked to me on leaving that he thought 'the steam engine would last my time'; he was right, but only just! On Finlayson's board lay a proposal for an outside-cylinder 4-4-0. It materialized in Maunsell's time as the 'Schools' class, having picked up an inside cylinder with Drummond '463' inside Walschaerts gear in the meantime. Some of the personnel carried on for many years, Finlayson himself spent another 15 years as CD, Eastleigh, and his staff increased greatly in numbers. In LSWR days his drawing office was a fine place to learn the elements of loco design. There was thus a tremendous chance for apprentices who were brought into the office

Urie 'H16' class 4-6-2 tank No. 517. *Ken Lea*

temporarily to gain experience quickly under some of the best designers in the country. They found themselves - I was one myself - quickly doing valve motions, steel castings and so on which would never have come their way in the bigger offices. However, design appeals to a minority: most of the railway trained men preferred outside jobs, of which there were ample in the days when this country had an empire and many dependencies. The British-owned railways in South America drew many men from the LSWR. The practice of not keeping on their men was fairly general except for the case of craft apprentices. At any rate LSWR influence did not die on the Southern, and I carried it to the MR and LMS.

894 Ex.
1195

Telegrams:
"LOCOMOTIVE, ASHFORD."

J.C./ER

South Eastern and Chatham Railway,

Telephone No. 32.

PLEASE REFER TO

IN YOUR REPLY.

R. E. L. MAUNSELL,
Chief Mechanical Engineer.

LOCOMOTIVE, CARRIAGE AND WAGON DEPARTMENT.

CHIEF MECHANICAL ENGINEER'S OFFICE,

DRAWING OFFICE, ASHFORD,

KENT.

October 27th, 1919.

Dear Sir,
　　　　Yours of the 25th. inst.
　　　　I regret that we have no vacancy in our Drawing Office at present for a Draughtsman, but your name has been filed for reference and will have consideration when the first vacancy occurs.
　　　　May I suggest that an application to Messrs. Beyer Peacock & Co., Manchester or the North British Loco. Co., Glasgow, would most likely be successful. If you choose you will be at liberty to mention my name in connection with your application.

　　　　　　Yours truly,

　　　　　　J. Clayton .

　　　　　　Personal Ass't to C.M.E.

Mr.E.A.Langridge,
　　44, Lenin Road,
　　　　Streatham. S.W.16.

A letter from James Clayton of the South Eastern & Chatham Railway in 1919 advising there was no vacancy for a draughtsman.　　　　　　　　　　*E.A. Langridge Papers*

Chapter Four

H. Fowler (Midland Railway)

There was little formality or paper work on joining the MR. No signing on the dotted line or medical examination: S.J. Symes, the chief draughtsman, hoped I would settle down and be happy; rang for the leading hand, Jock Henderson, who took me down the long office (one felt the gaze of inquiring eyes!) showed me my bench alongside his, introduced me to Willie Armin on the bench on my other side and there I was!

The locomotive drawing office was on the top floor of the famous block under the clock tower: it was old (1893) being an additional floor on a building dating back to the 1860s. You can read and see pictures in J.B. Radford's interesting book, *Derby Works and Midland Locomotives* (Ian Allan, 1971). Thus, the amenities compared with Eastleigh (built 1911) were atrocious - I should think worse than any other locomotive concern. The pedestrian approach to the block of offices is over the long bridge from the station platforms (or the car park since the station became a 'closed' one) wide enough to take two large gentlemen (like HF!) abreast and open to all weather. The staircase up is just about wide enough to allow two people to pass: how it came to pass any fire insurance regulations, goodness knows! At the top of the flights of stairs the general drawing office was to the right: it dealt with the CME's fixed plant (including sheds and electric power stations). To the left a passage led to the locomotive drawing office: a door to the left here opened into the chief draughtsman's office, a door to the right to a small room with washbasins and urinal. At the end of this dim passage a glass-panelled door opened to the locomotive drawing office proper. This end was the top of an L-shaped office: first a little parted-off clerical section with Harold and Croxall, his assistant (who had found some digs for me in Charnwood Street) with files concerning personnel and office work. The only female there in 1920 was the office girl: the locomotive drawing office had its office boy; also a great character in the person of Richardson who wrote up the drawing register in beautiful copperplate style, got out drawings if in a good mood, shouted round the office if he couldn't find them, and growled at the draughtsman who had them. For anything more serious than passing water one had to go down an iron spiral stair from the shop drawing stores (entered through a fireproof (?) door beside my drawing bench), down, through two floors of millwright's shop out into the open for a few yards, turn left through the archway which had a railway serving the old historic No. 1 shed (round which the office block had been built), where one found a dozen or so obscured glass doors behind which stood a

(Sir) Henry Fowler
SLS Collection

69

lavatory pan! Being like the entrance to nether regions artificial light had to be provided by incandescent gas; yet this was the only place where smoking was permitted and the older hands took down their morning papers and lit their pipes and puffed away to add to the stink, quite untroubled by rattling of wagons being shunted a few feet from where they sat. I should add that there was a washbasin in the locomotive drawing office near the base of the L-shape: this could cause pandemonium to the tracer nearby when a bit of horseplay took place, as on the occasion when Jimmy Rankin tried to get D.W. Sanford's head under the tap - or it might have been vice versa. Anyhow, water got splashed about much to Johnny Brigg's (the tracer) real annoyance. I omitted to say earlier that hats (everyone wore bowlers or trilbys), coats and umbrellas were put on a row of hooks in the entrance passage - very unpleasant on wet mornings!

In charge of the shop drawing store was John Smith. He was one of those too willing fellows who practised what he preached - he was a well-known local preacher in surrounding villages. On the quiet he made a cup of tea for the older draughtsmen: I suppose it had been going on for years and was 'winked at'. At the far end of the store, which was a false floor in the millwrights' shop rafters, it was quiet and well hidden for Edward Whitton and one or two others to have their 'elevenses', and John couldn't refuse to help them. The office hours seemed long to me after Eastleigh's 9 to 5, they were 9 to 5.30 with 1¼ hours lunch break, 8 to 12 on Saturdays. There was no entering or leaving five minutes before time: everyone stood at attention at their benches until the clock struck and then there was a rush to get down on the bridge. The floor of this was simply cross-timbers some of them loose: goodness knows how spiked heels and fancy shoes would have coped with the slots. There was another way out - at the foot of the office stairway you turned right to (the lower yard and left through the works gate under the low narrow bridge into Siddals Road alongside the civil engineers' offices. Here was a cycle shed: cars were almost non-existent, certainly not allowed here except for Harry Fowler's and S.J. Symes'. These were garaged (and probably maintained) here by people who had to do with works trucks, etc. Rather amusing to remember a notice sent round by Fowler a few years later deploring the fact that some of the staff were buying cars, so encouraging road transport and ruining their own livelihood.

From my drawing bench with just a blank wall behind me I could look up the office and see all that was going on. Most of the benches were end-on to a window, however, giving a nice side natural light but we all had two movable pedestal lights as well. One's board was on the left-hand half, the other half you used for reference drawings, while below were the office copies in numerical order, a hundred to a drawer. Method and system was a great god. You can read of it in James Clayton's paper to the ILocoE in 1917: he took it with him when he went to the SECR at Ashford in 1914 but whether it survived into C.S. Cocks' day in the Bulleid era, I doubt. From my years of working with that sometimes impatient gentleman in the 1950s at Derby, I guess not. Each draughtsman had a number of fibre tablets with his number on - mine was '11' - and the drill was, that he put one in the appropriate slot in the drawer of the drawing he had taken out for reference. Every drawing was supposed to be put away on a Saturday morning and so poor Richardson had a busy time rushing around, puffing and blowing, for it was his job to do the tidying up. The office copies were true to scale, black and white, canvas-backed sheets to MR sizes 40 in. x 27 in., etc., mostly coloured up. Even the World War I drawings of guns, etc., that were part of the Midland Railway's war effort were just as elaborately finished.

There were 11 staffed draughtsmen in 1920, two staffed male tracers, four unstaffed men returned from the Forces, six junior draughtsmen in the office: compared with the four staffed and 2 or 3 pupils or apprentices at Eastleigh made me wonder what on earth they all did! Of course the MR had some 3,000 locomotives against the LSWR's 900-odd but even that didn't seem to justify such a large staff. Gradually I worked it out and it seemed that Jock Henderson had five men and two juniors (Jock being the 'leading hand') on new work and big alterations: Tommy Hall and three juniors dealt with ex-London, Tilbury & Southend Railway (LT&SR) matters; Jimmy Doleman and W. Woore dealt with the everlasting rebuilds of 4-4-0s and 0-6-0s details, kept the boiler book and diagram books up-to-date: H. Chambers had one man and some juniors on experimental work: Sanford and J. Sutherland were the mathematicians. The two tracers and Richardson and young Joe, the office boy, were really under Jock's control, too. A few months after I started another outsider appeared: Jimmy Rankin who had served his time at Andrew Barclay's, Kilmarnock. It was said that J.E. Anderson had recommended him. He was a likeable fellow full of energy but didn't stay in the locomotive drawing office for long. This completed the staff except for a few additional juniors, locally trained, up to the 1923 amalgamation. Tracings were all stored in the photographers section down the yard where Scotton, an ARPS, was head with Panton (whose son came into the locomotive drawing office for a time before going east with an oil company) and Kirkman assisting. Radford (a nephew of a later photographer) says in his book that all the negatives they took are still in existence but presumably the tracings have unfortunately been scrapped. Of all these people only two of us ended up on the drawing office side. The others got out to other departments where there was more money!

When he took me on Symes said he wanted to build up the office with some new blood. It had a great tradition: the MR had a well-merited reputation for being 'scientific' in Johnson's and Deeley's time and the reports and records of experimental and testing work and the visits to International Exhibitions between 1905 and 1911 show that it was well deserved. They had a few Whitworth Scholars (Wh.Sc.) and one notable character was Percy Parr, whose articles in *Engineering* in 1911 on the design of connecting rods were as notable as those of Rowlands of the GCR in later years. They also had Moulton, a Wh.Sc., whose conscience led him to leave MR in World War I because of its armaments work and become a cobbler. Another senior man Symes had taken on, W.L. Armin, came from Manning, Wardle's just before World War I. Things petered out during the war and the L&Y assumed supremacy in testing with their new dynamometer car. The LNWR also had one of course, but it was little more than a pull-and-speed-meter. Nevertheless in 1920 the place seemed lacking in drive after Eastleigh locomotive drawing office.

Possibly the main cause was J.E. Anderson's character: like other Scot engineers he had served his time up north at the small Great North of Scotland Railway, gone through a few big contract shops and got a job in the MR locomotive drawing office. Evidently he impressed his personality on the place and people were apt to sit back if he didn't lead. When Fowler was away at Farnborough during World War I hob-nobbing with Army VIPs and sitting on committees and councils of learned societies, J.E.A., was acting CME running the show at home. Jock was very happy to stamp up the office with his iron-tipped boots should Symes ring for him: and 'Buff' Campbell told you in a whisper that you couldn't have more than 3¾ in. valve travel or you would land in purgatory! There was a feeling of unsettledness - returning soldiers don't take easily to confined offices -

James Edward Anderson, acting CME of the MR during Fowler's absence in World War I.

what was going to happen to railways generally and so on. No wonder Rankin got down in the works manager's, Ensor and Bramley to the Running Dept and even Campbell left for BTH, Rugby, having been presented with a 10 in. sliderule by us, his colleagues, rather reluctantly. 'Buff' was back at Derby just after amalgamation to stay for good.

In the matter of initialing drawings, in the absence of any 'drawn by, checked by', etc., plate these are apt to give credit for design to the man who gave the drawing a casual lookover, clocking that dimensioning was OK. The majority of the drawings of the so-called standard bits and pieces we used in 1920/23 bore J.E.A.'s. All the arrangement drawings for the MR '2000' tanks also carried his monogram for he was chief draughtsman on J.W. Smith's departure (not to be confused with W.M. Smith of 'Compound' fame) from 1906 to 1913, the last three of which also included being works manager. Rather strangely, J.E.A. appeared to dislike the social side of his job and the learned societies, thus being in complete contrast to Fowler. Even when pushed into the Presidential chair at the Inst. Loco. Engrs. his Address on election was a half-hearted affair with Fowler following with a paper on his favourite hobby, metallurgy. Sir Henry Fowler never appeared in the locomotive drawing office in my MR or LMS days. I wanted some time off in 1922 to sit for a London University Examination and was told to see him at 8.30 am (!) one morning. I appeared with waistcoat buttoned one hole high: that stuck in my memory more than what Fowler said in the two minutes I was with him. His chief clerk, preventing access to Fowler was Pratt: a character and chronicler well described elsewhere. It was said that Fowler had been known to go up to London twice in one day: evidently he liked to hit the headlines in person. His photograph beside the 'Royal Scot' locomotive *Boy Scout* seemed typical.

One committee he was on concerned the Association of Railway Locomotive Engineers' (ARLE) 1918 efforts to produce standard designs. Of course, J.E.A.

was in the backroom advising and the locomotive drawing office produced the MR suggestions for 2-6-0 and 2-8-0s. In the Derby records were long arguments on valve gear between MR and SECR. For the latter James Clayton put forward the sort of thing he used on Maunsell's 2-6-0s - a long travel - whereas the MR favoured the short one. All this again seemed to point to the fact that J.E.A.'s nominee to follow him as chief draughtsman in 1913 was the more amenable Symes than Clayton who came on to the locomotive drawing office via Cecil Paget's monstrosity. It is also interesting in passing to note Clayton's conversion to long travel ideas so quickly after joining Maunsell's ex-Swindon Holcroft, Pearson, etc., set up. In spite of indicator diagrams and graphs of port openings, the MR failed to be convinced that a long travel gear had any advantages for a freight locomotive. After his return from the Army, D.W. Sandford became Fowler's feeder on ARLE matters, but anything like standard locomotives was forgotten and buried. There was no lack of information at Derby as to what was going on in the locomotive world here and abroad: it was all filed by one of the tracers, Mitchell, in cases or folders, some 100 or more of them. A lot must have been collected for the Lickey Banker schemes and earlier still in regard to the Compounds. The old loft was full of magazines again strictly filed and kept in order by a man graded as 'labourer'.

The first drawing job given me by 'Jock' Henderson was to redesign the well-known MR boiler fitting combined steam valve and clack box reducing the wall thickness from ⅜ in. to ¼ in. That didn't take me long but just when I was going to dimension the drawing up, lo and behold Jock said in his good Scotch brogue - 'I dinna think ye had better make it so thin - try it oot at 5⁄16 in.! ' Typical Jock, was that attitude: it brought some sharp repartee from the ex-soldiers. However, I held my tongue and re-drew the thing, and, I think, I traced it: it became 20-9400 and was used up to Stanier's days: I had made my mark! Then followed the same thing to produce a new standard sanding and blower valve. There was a passion for using flanged plates instead of flat ones with angles about this time, so all tender plates and splashers were re-drawn to suit: my part was to try and find a standard bent plate for all the different guard-irons, cropping its ends and using packing pieces to suit the different frames. A little more interesting was making drawings of a steel centre piston head with cast-iron bull ring riveted on for the Compound's cylinders, an idea J.E. Anderson had brought back from his recent trip to America: a very pointless idea which didn't last long. Then came the scare of coal strikes and we got our arrangements of oil tanks on shunters and Compounds. No decent work seemed to be in the offing, and a stock job that was on various boards was a proposed 2-6-0 in which no VIP seemed to take an interest. I fiddled about on the cylinder and smokebox saddle drawings for months getting no decisions. A bit better was putting a boiler on two Beyer goods engines for Turkey that the LT&SR had picked up cheap years before and - a forerunner of the future - Drawing S-3800 20 in. piston with narrow rings copied from a Doncaster drawing. Amongst my other jobs before 1923 Amalgamation I see, a new boiler with longitudinal stays instead of gussets for the banker, screw reverse in place of steam for engine Nos. 995 and 1000, and fitting of an exhaust steam injector on a class '4F', a '700' class and a '990' class locomotive. I can't say I was very happy at this sort of work after doing motion arrangements at Eastleigh: however, I was staffed and graded at II,

Midland Compound 4-4-0 No. 1042 on an up express of typical Midland Railway stock.
Bruce Nathan Collection

The north end of Derby station frontage in 1921. This would have been around the time that Langridge arrived at Derby. *Kidderminster Railway Museum Trust Collection*

Up Manchester express at Elstree headed by Midland Railway '700' class 4-4-0 No. 749.

SLS Collection

£300 per annum along with the other juniors: I had hoped to be higher than that! Symes gave me a fortnight's holiday after only six months' service and I took my bike across to Bettws-y-Coed by the wonderful North Staffordshire Railway (NSR) through train, Derby to Llandudno, and rode 100 mile circuits for the next seven days. The next year, 1921, another fellow and I exploited our free pass facilities to get to France and Belgium: Zeebrugge was still in a mess from World War I and we photographed the Mole and the Block ships sunk in the famous St George's Day raid.

Life seemed too easy, there was no call for technical expertise in the locomotive drawing office, so to keep my brain working, I started an Inter-B.Sc. course at Derby Tech., then handily placed in Green Lane. There I met two first class teachers in Bill Fearn and A. Record for Maths and Electricity. Record arranged a trip to Settle to see the total eclipse on 29th June, 1927. We nearly missed the show as a sleeping car special conveying the Astronomer Royal's party broke a coupling near Bell Busk just in front of us, and so we had to practically run up the hill above Settle station to take up our stand. It was about 6 am and a cloudy day, but we were lucky to see the total eclipse which a lot of people elsewhere missed. It was funny that the LMS people didn't catch on to the idea of people wanting to go and see the eclipse until the last week before: typical of so much of their outlook in those days.

One advantage of having jobs on various classes of engines was that I found out some of the MR peculiarities of design. All main frames were in two pieces on 4-4-0s, three pieces in the case of the Compounds. The only apparent reason was economy on plate sizes: a big lapped joint at the motion plate seemed queer to me. The extra piece on the Compounds ran from front buffer beam to cylinder where there was another lap. It seems that this was the subject of a W.A. Smith's patent so the first Deeley Compounds to 0/2998 had an awkward angle piece across the top of the cylinder instead of the plain flat fork used before (and after by LMS). Record has it that Deeley suggested to his Board that he should negotiate with Smith, so as to use his style of lap but it appears that he went ahead independently to build 40 in all. A strange thing on the '700s' was that the connecting rod had a ½ in. set in plan, the cylinder centres being ½ in. less than the crankaxle big-end centres. The use of thick linings of white metal everywhere would have horrified the economical LSWR: likewise the expensive manganese-bronze axleboxes. It was interesting to note that Johnson had used drum-head tubeplates and sliding firedoors and graduated ashpan quadrants all of which were to come back, replacing MR style, in Stanier's time.

Midland Railway 0-6-0 No. 2314 at Derby in 1920. It was a Kitson-built engine, rebuilt by
Johnson and modified by Deeley.   *SLS Collection/H.C. Casserley*

Midland Railway 4-4-0 No. 526 on an up express passing Mill Hill.   *SLS Collection*

Midland Railway Deeley 0-6-4T No. 2022 in original un-superheated form with round top firebox at Derby, 5th August, 1921. *Kidderminster Railway Museum Trust Collection/H.C. Casserley*

LMS ex-Midland Railway 0-6-4T No. 2020 on a down passenger train near Ambergate, May 1923.   *Kidderminster Railway Museum Trust Collection/W. Potter*

An up express emerging from Milford tunnel north of Derby in the early 1930s. LMS ex-Midland Railway '2P' class 4-4-0 No. 350 is piloting ex-MR '3P' class 4-4-0 No. 741.

Kidderminster Railway Museum Trust Collection/Frank Carrier

LMS ex-Midland Railway '2P' class 4-4-0 No. 557 piloting an LMS Compound 4-4-0 approaching Ambergate on a Manchester-St Pancras express, *c.*1931.

Kidderminster Railway Museum Trust Collection/J.H.L. Adams

The less said about the MR crude brake ejector lever the better. I had come across their driver's brake valve incorporating a steam brake piston on Adams's LSWR locomotives but there it was neater. The driver had the vacuum disc valve on his side of cab and the fireman the steam brake portion: of course they were cross-connected so that the driver had control of both steam and vacuum but not vice versa.

Midland Railway CME employees seemed to have a penchant for patents. The royalties from Silvertown lubricators, understood to be a Fowler/Symes patent marketed by Greshams & Craven, must have been considerable. Then there was Fowler/Anderson by-pass valve, the superheater element fixing, sold to the Superheater Co. and possibly Smith's collapsing piston valve on Johnson's locomotives. I am not sure whether Sanford put through his double-ported piston valve and (with Stanier) his variable cut-off gear. Geach (on the motive power side) had a constant flow oilbox idea. H.G. Ivatt apparently missed a patent on the 10,000 bogie layout due to publishing drawings in advance of the application, worse luck! One or two of us might have collected a few American dollars. Besides taking over the LT&SR, which resulted in the departure of the colourful R.H. Whitelegg to the Glasgow & South Western Railway (GSWR), the MR also owned the Northern Counties Committee (Ireland) (NCC). Being a different gauge and across the water the CME there remained. B. Malcolm had some two-cylinder (inside) compound 4-4-0s of which Derby held the drawings. In fact they built a few more before providing us in the locomotive drawing office with a bit of interesting designing of 4-4-0 simple 2-cylinder locomotive for 5 ft 3 in. gauge. The NCC had a leaning towards inside Walschaerts valve gear: I think the only other railway to use it was my former employer the LSWR on Drummond's '463' class. This was copied for the SR 'Schools' - designed at Eastleigh - and by the writer for the LMS '9500' class 0-8-0s.

Before going on to the 1923 Amalgamation and the consequences on formation of LMS I must tell of what went on outside office hours. Derby in the early 1920s was a quite charming market town full of history, old buildings of character and narrow streets - Sadler Gate, Full Street, etc. - and pubs. It is an old tale that Jimmie Doleman was in each of half-a-dozen or so at the same set time each night with cigar and buttoned-up jacket; but Jimmie was very sober, and a sidesman at All Saints, where, in due time, his funeral service was held. The digs Croxall found for me were in Hartington Street which turned out of Osmaston Road almost opposite Melbourne House, the residence of Deeley when locomotive superintendent. There were six or eight of us young men boarding in a house run by Mr and Mrs Farrow, some from the MR; Fletcher's, the sugar machinery firm; and two from Rolls-Royce, Russell and Robotham (later distinguished in tank production), who enlivened proceedings by mercilessly pulling Mrs F's leg at the evening meal. Farrow liked to promulgate on socialist brotherhood and occasionally we had 'candlelight' suppers - I presume to create brotherly atmosphere and deep thinking. It was all very entertaining but the food was pretty thin and the bath tepid at the best of times. My pal here was a young man serving an apprenticeship at MR Loco., G.W. Debenham. We cycled and walked around the lovely country of Derby, Notts. and Stafford: Debenham was a keen train timer and kept records of all the journeys to and from his home at St Albans. Not having to start as he did at 6 am I looked round Duffield and Belper for better digs, and a farmhouse near Ambergate seemed very attractive. The homes of the different strata in Derby were quite marked: the MR elite lived at Duffield and up the Wirksworth line at Keyworth and Melbourne. The lesser in Burton Road and so down the scale to Empress Road and Mill Hill area to the 'workers' at Alvaston and Pear Tree. Johnny Briggs our other tracer was perhaps an exception, for he lived at Duffield: every Saturday he gobbled a lunch at the Institute, caught the 12.45 train to York and spent the rest of the weekend in his beloved Minster, where he was a voluntary guide, to return by the 9.30 pm Sunday to Derby and a taxi to Duffield. Poor John, he kept sheets of squared-paper on which he had coloured the weeks and days up to retirement date: it is quite true that he failed to reach it by a few months, being found dead in his room one day in 1932. What they thought of him at York Minster is shown by the fact that he was given a funeral service in the Minster. Chambers sealed his drawers in the office until his executors appeared: but no will or executor was found and John's few hundred pounds went to the Government and he to the grave with his secrets unrevealed. Those were the days of large church congregations particularly if the vicar was a good preacher: Debenham and I used to find All Saints full on Sunday evenings to hear Revd Green; old Norman Hibbert, the local music professor, making the tracker action rattle away on the old organ in the West Gallery to the lusty singing of choir and congregation. His successor, Heath Gracie, got the last Compton pipe organ before World War II installed and we had a week's wonderful recitals from Susi Jeans and all the well-known people. It seems to have faded out in the last 20 years, alas! There was a fair amount of music making, the typical northern love of choral singing being in evidence: York (a garrison city) held a Military Sunday with service and massed bands in the Minster. To hear Tannhauser Overture played in such conditions remained a memory for life. By good luck I spent the weekend at Bishopthorpe Palace. His Grace's part was beyond the greenbaize door.

Attached to the Railway Institute described by Radford and which provided me with second-hand *Engineers* for a few shillings until my cupboards were full, was the Dining Club. For a small entrance fee one became a life member and received a little brass tab to put on your key ring. My number is 4595: the club was useful for lunches (at 1s. 3d.) for people living up the line and teas when on overtime. The Engineering Club held their annual dinner there where VIP guests like General Managers showed themselves to members. The returned soldiers got Symes's agreement to hold an annual locomotive drawing office plus photographic staff (always regarded as part of locomotive drawing office) dinner with programmes and homemade entertainment - serious as well as libellous - and the MR gave up a half-day in summer to play an inter-office cricket match: sides chosen to balance out some of the good amateur village green players like Chambers and Kirkman. Our side won one year by including a pupil who happened to be in the locomotive drawing office at the time - L.W.R. Robertson. I kept my end up while he hit fours and sixes. All very relaxed and light-hearted with Wooliscroft, Whitworth Scholar, umpiring (he 'umpired' to the MR pensioners' advantage in the later LMS negotiations). But the earthquake of amalgamation was just round the corner.

Chapter Five

G. Hughes

Towards the end of 1922 speculation was rife as to who would hold the top positions in the LMS group, formed under the Railways Act of 1921. The LNWR had already amalgamated with the Lancashire & Yorkshire Railway, with Hughes, ex-L&YR and aged 57, as CME, and with Captain H.P.M. Beames, ex-LNWR and aged 47, as deputy obviously a matter of age relationship. It was known that the MR Chairman was a powerful personality, but as Watson had been made General Manager of the combined LNWR and L&YR (still known as the LNWR), there seemed to be the chance of a real tug-of-war for the new LMS positions.

When the *Railway Gazette* came out with all the new names, there were some surprises. Hughes was the CME, but the appointment of Fowler, aged 52, as deputy obviously meant that on Hughes' retirement, which was due very soon, Fowler would become boss, and poor Beames would be pushed back again. Surprisingly, Anderson, a works man, was made motive power superintendent, leaving Fowler high and dry as a Midland man in the CME Department, whereas with Follows, a Midland man, as general superintendent, Anderson could expect some protection from the ex-LNWR barking dogs of the motive power department. It is quite possible that Anderson had visions of later going up to be general superintendent himself. To take his place in the CME Department, S.J. Symes was moved up from chief draughtsman to be works manager at Derby, and to succeed him as chief draughtsman at Derby H. Chambers was moved from the drawing office experimental section.

Hughes preferred to remain at Horwich, where he had a compact modern works, and a drawing office which appeared to have an up-to-date staff. Horwich, at the end of a branch off the Bolton to Preston main line, appeared to the outsider to be a railway village. The people at the works were sure of themselves; they had their own Mechanics' Institute, at which the senior draughtsmen taught mechanics and other subjects, all with a Mancunian pride. Their chief draughtsman, J.R. Billington, was appointed chief draughtsman of the LMS CME Department, an almost inevitable choice, with F. Grover of Crewe, who was more a general engineer, and H. Chambers of Derby, as assistants.

G. Hughes

SLS Collection

Things went on quietly, Horwich 4-6-0s being built in large numbers - 21 in 1923 and 41 later. Then came the same layout with a trailing bogie and tanks, making an extremely heavy Baltic tank. They all had long-travel valves, with two outside sets of Walschaerts gear, working the outside valves direct and the inside valves via rocking shafts. The details were far more workmanlike than those of the LNWR 'Claughtons', which had

81

LMS 4-6-0 No. 10474 - the last L&YR-type locomotive to be built at Horwich in 1925 and withdrawn 10 years later. It seen here as exhibited in the 1925 Stockton & Darlington Railway Centenary celebrations.   *SLS Collection*

LMS 4-6-4T No. 11111 built at Horwich in 1924.   *SLS Collection*

LMS 4-6-4T No. 11112.   *Ken Lea Collection*

remnants of Webb's designs, with lots of sliding bits and pieces. It always seemed curious that Horwich, with its posh dynamometer car (compared with that of Crewe, which only registered pull and speed), did not set about improving the 'Ironclads'; they had a bad name for coal consumption. Crewe went on with superheating its own designs and building its large new erecting shop, whilst Derby built Tilbury-type tank engines (Order 0/5871) with Belpaire boilers, Tilbury steam reversing gear and Westinghouse brake.

The colourful CME of the LT&SR was not the sort of man who would endure playing second fiddle, and he had left in MR days to go north, but his Beyer, Peacock-designed Baltics were his attempt to provide more power for the Tilbury section.

They were judged by Derby to be slow, heavy, and extravagant on coal, and in the period 1917-1919 all were relegated to working coal traffic from Wellingborough to Brent piloted by a variety of 2-4-0s or 0-6-0s. In 1920 they were all transferred to St Albans to work locals to St Pancras. Of the eight locomotives, five were sent back to the LT&S section shortly afterwards, leaving only three at St Albans until they were withdrawn between 1929 and 1934.

A somewhat amusing trial took place on the LT&S section in 1923 under the guidance of D.W. Sanford. In this trial a train fitted with roller bearings was tried against one with plain bearings, using 4-4-2Ts Nos. 2177 and 2179. Each ran trials with both the plain bearing and the roller bearing stock for coal consumption comparison purposes. The trains were allowed to roll down Laindon bank with the idea of measuring the relative resistance. The first trial figures came out completely unexpectedly in favour of plain bearings - I believe to Sanford's delight, as he liked upsetting the so-called 'obvious'. But the next weekend the roller bearing gnomes did their stuff and won the day.

At about the same time I had the job of drawing out an arrangement of Westinghouse air brake apparatus for a Compound, which was fitted out on 1034. Trials took place on the Midland main line between St Pancras and Leicester using the same two sets of LT&S stock used on the bearing trials and with the same result. Further trials were then abandoned and the Westinghouse brake was then removed from the Compound.

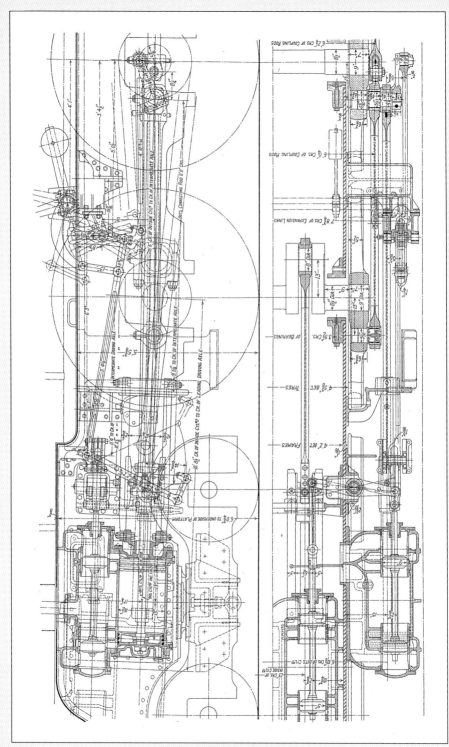

Valve motion of a Hughes 4-6-4 tank. Langridge developed this arrangement for use on the 'Coronation' Pacifics.

LMS 4-6-4T No. 2107, built by Midland Railway for London, Tilbury & Southend lines.

Ken Lea Collection

An extremely proud crew pose with LMS (LT&SR) 4-6-4T No. 2104 on a train for Southend.

Kidderminster Railway Museum Trust Collection

LMS 4-6-4T No. 2198 (October 1929 renumbering ex-2106) built by Midland Railway for London, Tilbury & Southend lines.   *SLS Collection*

LMS Tilbury type 4-4-2T No. 2118 at Plaistow, May 1935. The locomotive was built at Derby in 1923.   *SLS Collection*

North Staffordshire Railway four-cylinder 0-6-0T No. 23 as built in 1922.   *SLS Collection*

Stoke-on-Trent, the NSR or 'Knotty' headquarters, were not to be left behind in showing their paces. They had a little 4-cylinder 0-6-0 tank built to all the latest ideas, and their CME Hookham (Margot Fonteyn's uncle, balletomanes will recall) gave a paper to the Institution of Locomotive Engineers on its performance,* but it was not taken up by the powers that were. However, the NSR's works manager and chief draughtsman were to influence LMS locomotive design later; they were, of course, Messrs Ivatt and Coleman. Meantime there came reports of the success of their cast-iron packing rings made from a mixture produced in a local foundry. This was used in cylinder piston-rod glands in place of the usual metallic packing and its familiar protruding box, so I drew out new back cylinder covers to suit the change.

The first attempt to find standard boilers for various classes came from Horwich drawing office, in what was to become the familiar script of E.S. Cox. A Co-ordination of Design Committee set about standardizing usable items as renewals were required; these included washout plugs, taper pins and water gauges. The height of water level over the firebox caused a lot of discussion, but left-hand drive was decided upon at once. In effect this meant that two engines of the same class could be different in detail, so footplate staff and running shed people had a nightmare-ish time!

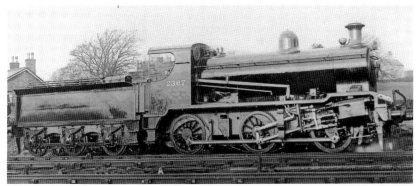

LMS four-cylinder 0-6-0 No. 2367 rebuilt in 1924 from NSR 0-6-0T No. 23.   *SLS Collection*

* 'Comparison between Superheated and Non-Superheated Tank Engines', J. A. Hookham, *Journal Inst. Loco E.*, No. 55, 1922.

Midland Railway Compound 4-4-0 No. 1034, Westinghouse fitted, at Knighton Junction, early in 1923. *SLS Collection*

NCC (Ireland) 'V' class 0-6-0 built at Derby in March 1923 as No. 73 but renumbered 15 before entering traffic. *SLS Collection*

Of new designs, Derby had some 4-4-0s and 0-6-0s to do for the Irish NCC, one of the Midland's old acquisitions, and a S&D 2-8-0 with a larger diameter boiler. Originally this 2-8-0 had been carefully designed at Derby about 1911; most closely concerned with it was James Clayton, who moved to the SECR in 1913. It seemed remarkable to me, in 1926, to find out that all the drawings had been completed before any work had been started in the shops. In these later years the shops were begging to get the next drawing from off the board, so little time was allowed between order and delivery. After the initial S&D to 0/4209 came a post-amalgamation batch to 0/6338; these having a boiler made up of 0-10-0 Lickey Banker flanged plates, but overall lengths as before to the 4-4-0 Compound boiler used on the first batch. Screw reversing gear and left-hand drive were fitted to this last lot, thus throwing out the steam reversing which, in spite of some fervent advocates, I never found reliable in any shape or form, be it Drummond, LT&SR or MR! I also replaced the original Lambert wet sanding by steam sanding. 0/6338 was put out to contract at Robert Stephenson's of Darlington and it was interesting to me to go through our drawings with their chief draughtsman who the previous year had turned out the 2-8-2 for the Kenya & Uganda Railway - one of the most handsome machines ever built. (The S&D 2-8-0 was illustrated in the *Railway Engineer*, October 1926.) For those who are interested in boilers I may mention that we dropped longitudinal stays in favour of gussets on the firebox backplate. Longitudinal stays, even of 1½ in. diameter, stretch considerably over that length of boiler.

One L&YR detail adopted as standard was the Horwich pop safety valve (which, if my memory serves me correctly, was Drawing 10203). Every railway liked to avoid paying patent rights, and 'got round' proprietary designs if they could. Examples are the GWR exhaust steam injector, the Silvertown mechanical lubricator, and MR superheater elements; the Horwich pop 'got round' the Ross design. By having a few holes in the restriction channel, it was also quieter in operation. Umpteen drawings of boilers had to be altered to show the new pad for this valve, and the holes to suit. Unfortunately the Horwich valve collected condensate in its column, with unpleasant results for bystanders, until someone wisely added a drain hole.

S&DJR large-boilered 2-8-0 No. 90 built Robert Stephenson 1924.   *J.M. Jarvis Collection*

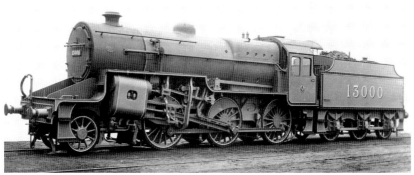

LMS Hughes 'Crab' 2-6-0 No. 13000, built at Horwich in 1926.   *SLS Collection*

The Horwich drawing office were evidently thinking about the future by getting ideas of a Pacific and a 2-8-2 on the drawing board. Compounding was also under consideration, and E.M. Gass, the assistant chief draughtsman, published some of Horwich's thoughts on the matter in his paper to the Institution of Locomotive Engineers.* What would have happened if Hughes had not resigned and LMS chief draughtsman Billington had not died suddenly, we shall never know. Billington's death had been a shock to the design staff. He was a brilliant designer very much *au fait* with what was going on in America and one who was not afraid of applying their ideas. The Horwich DO was probably at its best at that time and the works also being very modern one felt that this was a Swindon of the North - but much less hidebound than the GWR later became.

It must have been obvious that the CME's HQ office could not remain at the end of a branch line, but no steps seem to have been taken to think that one out before events compelled action. The Locomotive Committee responsible probably put off decisions like that, having their hands full with more pressing matters. However, before the departure of the L&Y chief, the 2-6-0 'Crab' was designed, very much obeying the rules of the various loading gauges - hence its steeply-inclined cylinders. The size of the cylinders and the pressure of 180 lb. seemed to me to hark back to R.W. Urie, as did the large axle boxes. They had a valve gear very much influenced by American practice – a long expansion link with small swing and bull rings in the piston valves. I suspect that there is strong circumstantial evidence that the 8 ft 0 in. + 8 ft 6 in. wheel spacing was copied from the old MR practice. Billington was, I imagine, a level-headed L&Y man whose remit was to design an all-route locomotive. You can say 'Let's take a chance and forget the Civil Engineer's loading gauge rules re clearance on curves and design wide up to the hilt' - as Coleman later did with Stanier's 2-6-0s, and as a consequence of which they had to be tried with fingers on all routes the Operating people wished to use them on - or you could obey the rules regarding maximum throwover on 7 chain radius curves and put your cylinders up in the air and space your wheels where you know they will be accepted by awkward people like old Worthington and his mates on the MR. It seems to me this is

* 'The Application of the Compound Principle to Locomotives', E.M. Gass, *Journal Inst. Loco. E.* No. 78, 1926.

what Billington opted for, otherwise he would not have put forward such a ghastly looking effort and one which would be criticized for its bad balance due to angled cylinders. As we know, in spite of having a flat-bottomed smokebox, with filling-in plates and awkward exhaust pipe branches, they earned their living very well.* Horwich had intended to incorporate vacuum brakes to conform to LNW/L&Y practice and to have a 4,000 gallon tender whose width would match up with that of the cab. However, their chief draughtsman dead and the imminent retirement of Hughes hanging overhead and the weight of MR personnel in key positions brought about the appointment of H. Chambers as LMS chief draughtsman at a very early age. The Horwich 2-6-0 suffered a major operation by the substitution of the so-called 'Standard' 3,500 gallon of the MR pattern for the L&Y wide tender and the scrapping of the vacuum brake for the 'Standard' MR steam brake - vacuum-controlled now of course, as the main train brake was now vacuum. Whether this was a decision by the Locomotive Committee or by the CME, I do not know for certain; the Derby drawing office were frozen out of anything outside their own Midland stock during the Hughes era. When you think of the two classes of the SECR, and later the SR, it seems strange that on the LMS no efforts were made to use the Horwich 2-6-0 parts as future standards. It may be mentioned - although this is another tale - that this obstinacy went right through to Stanier class '5' 4-6-0s and 'Jubilees', which had absurd little differences of detail which would never have arisen if rivalry between the design offices had been scotched at the beginning of the amalgamation.

LMS Hughes 'Crab' 2-6-0 No. 13030 on an express freight over Bushey troughs.

SLS Collection

---

* *Compilers' Note:* Langridge seems to have been a little confused with this statement as the Crab was, at least in theory, fitted with a modern drumhead smokebox. However, the aperture at the base for the blastpipe connections was so large that the better airtight properties possible with this type of smokebox may have been largely lost.

LMS Hughes 'Crab' 2-6-0 No. 13088 on a mixed freight.   *SLS Collection*

However, life went on, and we even worked overtime - 3 hours a night, 3 nights a week. This was apparently what the draughtsmen expected to happen during the winter. I joined the ranks of the married men, just escaping a basketful of confetti aimed at my fleeing figure as I made an early run down the back stairs (J. Rankin up to his merry tricks as usual!). Our little cottage is, I believe, buried under the Mickleover by-pass now. When I lived there, the first bus into Derby was 9.00 am, and the last one out of Derby 6.15 pm, so one had to walk 2 miles to the tram terminus, or cycle. I bought a two-stroke 'Vindec', with no clutch, but two speeds with belt drive. Sanford, who lived at Littleover, had a little Douglas with horizontally-opposed cylinders, which he considered far superior to my 'Vindictive', as he called it. I rather agreed with him when my carburettor refused to function, having collected oil at its base after standing. However, it did its job pretty well for a couple of years, by which time an enterprising builder put up a row of 'semis' at Ambergate. This became known as 'PT row', due to the number of railwaymen who bought them at £420 each - an attraction to newly-weds. Being fairly high up, we could see the Manchester to London expresses coming down from Matlock round the long curve into Ambergate - very attractive, with Reid's all-steel coaches, with their table lamps shining in the dusk.

One hundred yards from my Mickleover cottage was the farmer, Mr Bull, who had an interesting old car - a Humberette. The frame consisted of tubular members brazed into suitable sockets. It had a gate-change three-speed gearbox, and ignition control on the steering column. Once it was started - by hand (which took some doing), it would tick over merrily. I had it for a year or so; it would be a collector's piece now. A more suitable thing to house was a motor cycle and sidecar. This would also be a collector's piece; it was a Humber, with a belt drive to a three-speed gearbox in the rear wheel hub, and a single cylinder with side valves. It was most reliable, and would chug along at 25 mph, and even climb the slope beyond the 'halfpenny bridge' at Ambergate, which was about 1 in 6. Once I could not understand why power was failing. It turned out to be a lock-nut loosening on the valve tappet, allowing the head to fall, and thus giving practically no valve lift!

Chapter Six

H. Fowler as CME, LMS

By the end of 1925 the LMS had not solved the problems of fusing the companies together. The Chairman, Granet, was anxious to leave; the General Manager, Watson, went to South America, and was replaced by Burgess. Hughes had gone, and the 'Lord-in-waiting', as one writer described Sir Henry Fowler, had become CME, with Symes as assistant. Grover, the Crewe chief draughtsman, after a short spell on general engineering, became chief draughtsman, locomotives. Gass, of Horwich, took second place and someone decided to push on with the two large Compound designs. The decision was also taken to order three Garratts from Beyer, Peacock.

Work proceeded on the design of the 4-6-2 and 2-8-2 Compounds, and Derby was given the boiler to design. Campbell tackled its general design; it looked pretty awful, with an inset combustion chamber and several lap joints. If it had been built, goodness knows what it would have weighed; certainly the estimated 20 tons per axle would have been exceeded. I had the little jobs of drawing boiler seatings, stays and brake valves. Crewe designed the cylinders and actually cast some - Beames was anxious to get on with the slow-moving job. And then suddenly in the middle of October 1926 the whole job was stopped. Perhaps buried in the archives there is some record of what happened behind the scenes; I doubt if the truth has appeared yet in print, although various suggestions have been made. We had had the General Strike in May 1926; perhaps the thought of asking men to fire these monsters may have been one thing which weighed against building them.

Following Fowler's appointment as CME there were considerable changes in personnel. The NSR drawing office at Stoke was closed, and the men were split between Crewe and Derby. Some men from St Rollox and Horwich were also moved to Derby. The CME lost his general and electrical assistant; Cortez Leigh, an ex-LNWR man, took over as electrical engineer. Chambers continued as chief draughtsman at Derby, and he was able to take over the office - under the clock - formerly occupied by the electrical staff, to house his incoming men. J. Campbell moved across the landing as their leading draughtsman, his former drawing board in the corner being taken over by E.S. Cox, one of the arrivals from Horwich. J. Henderson remained as leading draughtsman of the existing part of the office.

Chambers was conscientious, and came round the office about once a week - more often than Symes, his predecessor. He was not a leader in design matters, and tended to agree with his older leading hands. Sanford, who had a brilliant brain, would doubtless add his comments in pungent manner, if called in. Henderson and Campbell were both Scots, but very different men. Henderson was an Aberdonian, and by this time, in the mid-twenties, he made little contribution to design; his main activity was checking drawings dimensionally, and conveying messages from the chief draughtsman to the men. Campbell was obstinately old-fashioned in matters of design, but took an interest in what his

Vacuum-fitted LMS Garratt 2-6-6-2T No. 4998 at Hasland shed, Chesterfield. This locomotive was built by Beyer, Peacock in 1927.   *SLS Collection*

LMS Beyer-Garratt 2-6-6-2T No. 4999 on a test train from Derby to St Pancras at Borrowash *c.*1936. This was to have been 'officially' photographed at Sharnbrook but the engine suffered a hot box and was taken off at Leicester. The test was never repeated. A very unusual picture of a Garrett on passenger stock.   *Kidderminster Railway Museum Trust Collection/Frank Carrier*

men were doing, and was slow but correct in his manner. He came from Dumfries, and in my time he lived at Fritchley, near Matlock, where there was a religious settlement.

Under these conditions how the job turned out depended very much on the individual draughtsman concerned. Most Midland men were slow to accept new ideas, but I suppose that that applied to almost any pre-amalgamation office. In general they were scared of wear in moving parts, which accounted for their addiction to short-travel valves and small slips of sliding parts. Their attitude was - 'If your locos do the job, why incur extra maintenance?' On the other hand, the few younger men in the office read and absorbed periodicals such as the *Railway Gazette* and *Revue Générale*, and knew what was happening elsewhere, especially about valve gears.

Apart from the usual odd jobs, the early days of the new regime provided me with some work in sending drawings of parts of MR designs to Beyer, Peacock for use in the Garratts. These included the pony truck and motion of the S&D 2-8-0, and axles and axleboxes of the '4' class. The line diagram prescribed the beloved 8 ft 0 in. + 8 ft 6 in. spacing of the wheels (shades of the old C.E. Worthington!), but even so a new bridge was required over the Soar near Kegworth before the engines could be accepted. To jump ahead a little - the first engine was delivered in July 1927 and was immediately inspected by Anderson, the motive power superintendent. He soon picked holes in it, and I had to design a timber false bottom for the bunker to improve the slope for coal. Sand boxes and other fiddling things had to be altered, and one gathered that J.E.A. was not particularly enamoured of them at all.

Immediately after the dropping of the design of the big Compounds came the order to proceed with a 2-6-4 tank design. Willie Armin laid out the diagram - an MR 0-6-4T with a leading pony truck, which provided a general purpose powerful tank engine with a wide route availability. The LNWR had their large 4-6-2 tanks, the L&Y various 2-4-2Ts and the 4-6-4Ts, the Northern lines had their heavy passenger tanks and the MR its 0-6-4T - a rather doubtful customer which was fond of coming off the rails when working the Tamworth mail train from Lincoln at speed. The MR had probably the tightest weight restriction of any of the component lines. Of course, the only wheel spacing acceptable to the CE of those days was 8 ft 0 in. + 8 ft 6 in. for the coupled wheels and this gave the tank engines a 'spread out' appearance. The MR standard boilers had 7 ft, 8 ft and 9 ft fireboxes and for the 2-6-4T the 8 ft, or 'G8AS' was specified, the MR 0-6-4T having had the G7. The G8 with a superheater had proved to be a good boiler on two classes of Johnson rebuilt 4-4-0s which had borne the brunt of express work, as route availability of the 4-4-0 compounds was limited to the London-Leeds-Carlisle road in MR days. Armin was given the detailed work on the frame, and carried on with the pipe and rod arrangement on the same drawing. E.S. Cox did the side tanks, cab and bunker, and the writer the motion. While there were plenty of older, better paid men to whom Chambers could have given the job, it was my chance to show how well Finlayson at Eastleigh had trained me. Incidentally E.S. Cox had just arrived and side tanks were hardly his line of business! Two thousand gallons of water and 3½ tons of coal pretty well settled the back-end shape of the engine. It is interesting to note that

LMS 2-6-4T No. 2300 at St Albans as built in red livery, with the exhaust injector between frames and 10 in. numerals.   *SLS Collection*

No. 2313 *The Prince* at Stoke on Trent in May 1930; lined black livery with 14 in. numerals, exhaust injector ahead of the cab step, with exhaust steam pipe running behind the reversing crank and below the tank, retaining pony truck and bogie brakes.   *SLS Collection/P.W. Robinson*

LMS 2-6-4T No. 2323 on a Manchester to Buxton express between Whaley Bridge and Dove Holes. The train consists of six ex-LNWR non-corridor coaches.

Kidderminster Railway Museum Trust Collection/Frank Carrier

LMS 2-6-4T No. 2420 at Greenock Princes Pier on 17th September, 1935, with larger tank vent fitted and no pony truck and bogie brakes.

SLS Collection/W.A.Camwell

whereas Urie's designer would not allow an opening in the cab side to follow the curved roof line, the LMS did so, no doubt following the precedent on the LT&SR tanks that no one had had his head knocked off by standing in the opening. Nevertheless the LSWR and GWR engines all made their driver and fireman stand inside the roof, thus protecting their heads from contact with arches of bridges built close to the loading gauge line.

A 26 in. stroke cylinder and a connecting rod about 8 ft 9 in. long helped to fix the pony truck position at the front. Many years previously American firms had supplied batches of 2-6-0s built to their practice whose drawings I discovered in the stores in my early MR days. Amongst this was a swing-link pony truck design which was copied almost word for word on the S&D 2-8-0 that Derby DO designed in 1910. This design duly appeared on the 2-6-4T, rather surprisingly, as H. Chambers was wont to discuss detail design with his former chief at Derby, James Clayton. The latter had, on the SECR 2-6-4T, succumbed to the GWR influence brought onto the SECR by Maunsell and had used their inclined plane control method on his pony truck. The trailing four wheel bogie was a standard article, so the weight distribution could be got out using the 0-6-4T as a pattern.

My job was the valve gear arrangement and great argument took place over this for the 2-6-4T. The archives of the ARLE would reveal the excited discussions and diagrams produced when the Association was endeavouring to produce some standard designs at the end of World War I. The aim was to design a set of two-cylinder engines as common user and in valve gear design there were two camps – and the odd superior person who knew it all and wasn't going to be shifted. There was the long-lap camp of the SECR (Clayton and the ex-GWR assistants), the short-lap camp of the MR (J.E. Anderson and D.W. Sanford, with slight backing from the other lines) and the GWR who just thought along their standard Stephenson gear lines. The ARLE-proposed 2-6-0 was a smaller loco with 8 ft- long firebox (MR Drawing S-1734), but they all had the MR pony truck, which came from the Schenectady 2-6-0s. Well, of course,

Midland Railway Schenectady-built 2-6-0 No. 2515 at the head of a goods train.
LCGB Ken Nunn Collection

no standard design was ever agreed on. The SECR was left holding the baby and the Government kept the Arsenal occupied in building SECR 2-6-0s which nobody wanted. How they went to Ireland and the Metropolitan Railway is another tale. By the time we came to design the valve gear for the 2-6-4T the LMS had started concentration of drawing office staff at Derby, and A.E. Owen from the Furness Railway was assistant chief draughtsman and virtually in charge of the design side. Owen was aghast to find that the good old short lap MR gear was specified, as were most of the younger men in the office. It was even more out of date seeing that a Walschaert's layout was inevitable - like the S&D 2-8-0 - which retains a constant lead as compared with Stephenson's gear. Chambers had said 'Follow the S&D 2-8-0 layout'. However, I had the *Railway Gazette* with the valve readings of the SECR 2-6-4T, and I proposed to Chambers that I should use the same 1½ in. steam lap as in the SECR design. After a great deal of battling and hard words, and no doubt a discussion with Clayton, Chambers accepted this, but insisted that there must be ⅟₁₆ in. exhaust clearance - 'We always found it necessary on MR locos'. The old MR men held up their hands in horror, predicting vast wear due to die block slip and big swing of the expansion link. I had done the Urie 4-8-0T and 4-6-2T valve gears a few years back. These had a longish travel but short lap and the radius rod was lifted from the front of the expansion link, which was a plain flat type with trunnions riveted on. The LMS favoured the box-type link as on the GWR and the S&D Walschaert's gears, although Horwich did not. This box link is a very tricky piece to make, depending on accurate jigging and a special grinding machine to get at the inside working faces. I had a look at the 'Crab' and Garratt gears in case some details from those could be worked into the tank layout, but the 'Crab' motion plate was too tall, and crocodile bars were 'taboo' as the 'Crabs' crossheads, which were of the GWR type, had been running hot. This was probably due to unsuitably tight working clearances, so the use of MR-type crosshead and bars on the tank was pretty well justified. However, the valve spindle slidebars of the 'Crab' looked a much better job than the S&Ds', so I used that pattern. It always amused me to reflect that this detail that I salvaged from the 'Crabs' persisted through successive types right down to the BR Standards. The 'Crab's' American long expansion link was also adopted, but not the piston valve design with its wide bull rings or the big lead of its setting. Instead the Schmidt standard ring was fitted, and with mechanical lubrication and consequent carbonization gave plenty of trouble until the valve with narrow rings was adopted (from a Doncaster drawing!) together with some degree of atomization. The connecting rod of the Garratts was just right. It was shown as 8 ft 9 in. between centres on the Beyer, Peacock drawing, but when I drew it on my scheme, with the same setting of cylinders and driving axle, the small end fouled the packing box. Beyer, Peacock had forgotten to draw the packing box in their scheme. The rods had therefore to be shortened to 8 ft 7 in., and it cost a few forgings which had already been made.

Rather than have a pocket in the side tank to accommodate the reversing shaft, Chambers agreed to my idea of an extended radius rod with slotted end, with the reversing shaft behind, thus allowing a flat-bottomed side tank. This arrangement was used on the Gresley locomotives, and I measured a

Gresley 2-6-0 at King's Cross with this arrangement to satisfy Chambers. I tried to get him to accept the Gresley reversing shaft with loose arms on squares, but he jibbed at that, so I had to have the cumbersome bearings with two plummer blocks. Nevertheless, I think that Chambers was very brave to accept an arrangement so foreign to Midland ideas.

The valve gear was tried out full-size on the valve motion model, which was on the wall in the drawing office stores just through the door behind my bench. The long throw of the return crank and the novel reversing arrangement required new pieces to be made. American practice, and experience with the 'Crab', advocated only a 45 degree swing of the expansion link, which involved a long tail to the link. Incidentally, the 'Royal Scot' draughtsman went back to a 60 degree swing of the link, and we had a lot of cases of the radius rod hitting the end of the slot in the expansion link. At high speed the rod evidently sprang and twisted the reversing shaft slightly.

As an aside I may mention here that when Coleman came to take over the office, already by then centralized at London Road, Derby, he had the Crewe valve gear model erected, which he thought - mistakenly, I believe - superior to the Derby one. It was therefore the Crewe model that I used years later for the 'Coronations'. I had a shock to see the old Derby motion model on the wall at Clapham Museum. It is not yet on display at York, but I am told that it will be shown in due course in an annexe to the museum. Surprisingly it is said to have some parts which have markings suggesting that they were made at Horwich, which is a mystery to me.*

Nobody was allocated to draw out the motion details, so I did practically the whole job; fortunately Finlayson had taught one to work fast. Campbell had designed cylinders for the proposed standard designs of the ARLE and this design was used on the 2-6-4T, with minor adjustments to suit the smaller diameter of cylinder and the frame location. Cylinders were very much of the usual type prevalent at that time in which the steam pipes ran down the inside of the smokebox and a Y-type exhaust casting sat on the faces of the cylinder flanges – this requiring some nice fitting to get the faces aligned and the cap both vertical and horizontal. The smokebox had a flat bottom; the steam and exhaust pipes protruded through the frame and the bottom of the smokebox, the gaps round the pipes being sealed with filling-in plates. And of course the bottom had to be covered by cement to fill the cracks and make the smokebox airtight. Very nice until the unfortunate fitter came to strip the smokebox at overhauls! This was a great improvement on the arrangement in MR designs and in the 'Crabs', in which the pipes had to be faced to bear on the underside of the saddle as well as against the frames. This was an almost impossible job, even worse than the old Adams (LSWR) 'Y' exhaust pipe. When new cylinders were required on the 2-6-4Ts, the steam pipe came straight through the side of the smokebox to the top of the steam chest. As it was a stiff pipe with no bends, expansion gave trouble at the joints.

---

* *Compilers' Note:* Apparently after it left Clapham it was placed in a leaky container in the yard at York until taken on by Derby Industrial Museum some time around the 1990s. They restored it and in the process found under the layers of black paint that it was originally painted green with orange lining, and that is the condition in which it has been placed on display. Made by Neilson & Co. in 1874, at the dawn of the Johnson era, it is believed to contain parts from Crewe, Stoke and possibly Horwich.

The pistons had another much-debated MR fitting - the shoe which rested on the piston rings and carried a spring on its back, which was supposed to keep the piston clear of the cylinder barrel. Perhaps it did, but the shoe scored a path in the cylinder and any outsider would have thrown out the idea long before it went, years later, after umpteen experimental types had been fitted. It should be remembered that many LSWR locomotives had cast steel 22 in. diameter heads running without tail rods or supports as standard practice. Another MR and LMS peculiarity was the non-adjustable solid spring links. Again they stuck to laminated springs throughout - exactly opposite to their later bedfellows the LNWR who were all for coil springs manufactured in their own shops, they used to say at 15s. a time in the 1920s!

There was a feeling for fitting exhaust steam injectors in the 1920s. Rather expensive and moody customers they were; the GWR got round the patent and made some themselves and kept them simple. The contract-made job was more or less automatic with pistons and valves and as it was at first placed between the frames and under the cab of all places on the 2-6-4T, it soon got an even worse name than it deserved. Of course, there were water scoops to pick up in either direction also cramming space down below. These delivered into the domes on the bunker tank and the water had a nasty habit of coming up at no little pressure through the vents and dousing the crew and floor of the cab – it's not easy to distribute 1,500 gallons of water into two side tanks and one bunker in a fraction of a minute at the best of times. Here the tank level indicator, even if trustworthy, was a long way behind the maximum actual water level when picking up from troughs.

Trouble also came from another place, the pop safety valves. The old Ramsbottom lever-loaded valves were considered too unreliable about that time and Ross's turned out a valve that went off like a gun and caused trouble on Maunsell's SECR engines. The LMS valve was a Horwich design which again got around a patent and could be made much more polite in its action.

The design had a nasty scare halfway to completion, for the SECR had the derailments at Bearsted and Dunton Green. However, it was said that the LMS engines were only for suburban work and so the design went forward. Nevertheless they could be mighty fast at times on the London lines. Perhaps the fastest were their successors on the Cheshire lines when these changed over from LNER to LMS control. Looking back they were built with loving care, for the skilled man was proud of his ability and respected by his superiors at that time, and the chap who can tighten 200 nuts an hour had not achieved his pre-eminence.

In any design, an engine diagram showing weights and wheel spacing is prepared and also an end view giving throw-overs on a curve regarded as standard by the Chief Engineer (CE) and usually 6 or 7 chains radius. This had to be agreed to by the CE, for he is the one Chief Officer at whose bidding trains may be stopped from running without question. The weight estimate was usually made in the DO by considering the differences between the new design and a 'pattern loco'. It was thus imperative that the true weights of the 'pattern loco' were known, otherwise the estimates for the new design may be sadly incorrect. The estimated weights for the 2-6-4T design were based on the book weight of the MR 0-6-4T built in Deeley's time. Unfortunately an actual weighing of this engine was not made at the time the 2-6-4T design was being schemed out and the latter came out at least 4 tons heavier than estimate. This was due to the fact that the diagram of the 0-6-4 was given light. Weight in working order is always a loose term: the CME knows that it can be adjusted if things turn out to be heavy by having hot water in the boiler - and not too much of it - a smattering of sand in the sandboxes and perhaps tanks not too full. Usually the weight table is guarded and no prying eyes of the Chief (Civil) Engineer's Department are allowed. One would hardly say that was unusual on any railway or even with contractors - an example of heavy overweight being the Garratt that the LMS bought a little earlier. [*Compilers' Note:* Such subterfuge still goes on today!]

Civil Engineers vary in their outlook: the old MR locomotive designer was particularly handicapped. In that office it was the practice to draw out, for their own information, a Bending Moment Diagram due to the proposed locomotive weights on the track and from this to derive an Equivalently Uniformly Distributed Load Curve for various bridge spans. This they compared with the 'Worthington 1911 Curve' which had been given them by the Civil Engineer of that name. Tender weights were also included, of course. In actual fact, this curve limited the development of locomotive size on the MR as Worthington objected to wheel spacings closer than 8 ft. 0 in. + 8 ft. 6 in. The catalogue of parts that had to be removed, in MR days, from the S&D 2-8-0 and the MR 0-10-0 Banker to enable them to be moved from the works at Derby to their areas of operation read quite fantastically. With the advent of E.F.C. Trench from the LNWR as Chief Engineer of the LMS things eased up considerably.

The engines were successful, even more so after the removal of such inaccessible things as the exhaust steam injector, and the fore and back water scoop, which filled not only the tank but often the cab also, due to the lack of air space and inadequate vents to prevent overflowing.*

---

* *Compilers' Note:* In the January 1978 *Journal*, A.F. Cook wrote:

> Previously our only knowledge of how Derby came to fit long-travel valves to these engines was E.S. Cox's remark 'I think the already designed Horwich 2-6-0 had some influence here' (*Locomotive Panorama* Vol. 1, E.S. Cox, Ian Allan 1965, page 58); this seemed a reasonable explanation. It is now clear that Mr Langridge, as the draughtsman responsible for the motion, selected the proportions of the valves, and persuaded his seniors to accept them.
> I confess to having probed this matter further in correspondence with Mr Langridge. His main source of inspiration was the study he had made of valve proportions and events on other railways, and the particular dimensions which he used in the 2-6-4T, apart from the addition of exhaust clearance, were those of the SECR 2-6-4T. As this latter type was an outcome of the migration from Swindon to Ashford in Maunsell's reign, it can be said that Derby received the 'word' from Swindon via Ashford six years before Stanier arrived. The reversing crank, although directly inspired by Gresley's design, had origins older than the Gresley locomotives, having been used on the Prussian State Railways at least by 1902. Considering that Mr Langridge's seniors appear not to have been fully convinced of the merits of long-lap, long-travel valves – as shown by the efforts to avoid long travel in some later designs by the use of double-exhaust valves – it was very fortunate for the LMS that the Royal Scots were given long-travel valves.

While I do not wish to flog the Ashford/Swindon relationship here, I must point out that Swindon published little beyond an engine diagram of their products, nor did their men join the recognized institutions. Before 1926 I can recall only Churchward's paper to the IMechE on boilers. When Maunsell recruited Pearson and one or two from Swindon, Clayton had already come from Derby. There, he had been an influential designer after being taken on the staff following the Paget 2-6-2.

The MR had always sent men to the big continental exhibitions and had amassed a vast amount of information from France and Italy, particularly when working out the final design of the Banker, No. 2290. It was one man's job (actually a tracer, Mitchell) to file all this in folders. Unfortunately when he left no-one was told to keep up the filing; when the room was wanted for Dynamometer Reports in Sanford's time most of it was scrapped! Curiously Sanford had little interest in history - he also seemed to be tone deaf, maintaining to me that there was no such thing as 'touch' in piano playing, but that is by the way.

The point I am leading up to is that Clayton, having seen all this information and having done the original design on Paget's engine, was as keen on 'long travel valves' as anyone. It was Anderson, MR, Sanford not having returned from the forces, who advocated short travel for the ARLE proposals; Clayton was on the other side. Of course Holcroft (*Locomotive Adventure*, Ian Allan, 1965) has told a different story; I may be unfair to him but I cannot help feeling that he focussed the laser beam on himself. Certainly he has written of his strong dislike of Clayton and, incidentally, of Bulleid.

From what I remember of the drawing etc. in the *Locomotive Magazine* (I gave my copies to the Hampshire Library at Winchester where there is a good Transport Section), the only feature on the 2-6-4T like Swindon practice is the tapered second barrel of the boiler; the rest is slightly MR (cab) or original. The valve motion is like nothing on earth, and the settings quite unlike the GWR's. I copied the SECR published settings as far as my Horwich expansion link and Gresley reversing arm allowed; there was no Swindon about it.

I agree there is 'little new under the sun'. Long ago I seem to remember Zeuner showing a diagram of a Von Heusinger (no self-respecting Austrian would use the word 'Walschaert') 'suppressing the lifting link', but it would not have been any good showing that to a practical locomotive man to support your scheme. Far better to give him a solid example like a Gresley loco which he could see for himself by popping across from St Pancras to King's Cross when he next went up to London.*

* *Compilers' Note*: In the April 1978 *Journal* C.P. Atkins, Librarian of the NRM, wrote:

It has possibly not hitherto been appreciated that the SE&CR 2-6-4T owed a great deal to a Derby 'antecedent' which never saw the light of day. With reference to tracings now deposited in the National Railway Museum, it is evident that during January 1914 Derby schemed a superheated 2-6-2T with 6 ft 3 in. driving wheels and outside cylinders with Walschaert's valve gear for the LT&S. The following month this was extended into a 2-6-4T, still retaining the G8AS boiler.

The original Ashford scheme for the class 'K' 2-6-4T is dated June 22nd 1914 (the 2-6-0 class 'N' followed on July 16th 1914) and it is very close to the locomotive as actually built. [*Continued foot of p.104*]

Some time around the end of the 1920s an ex-MR colleague at Eastleigh told me that James Clayton and the MR had parted bad friends as domineering J.E. Anderson had chosen S.J. Symes of the experimental section rather than J. Clayton of the design section to succeed him as chief draughtsman when he (Anderson) got promoted from the chief draughtsman's post on the MR. Evidently this blocked Clayton's chances and he was quick to get out when Maunsell's offer came along. I think the strained relations remained until Chambers succeeded Symes: Chambers had done the Banker cylinders under Clayton in 1913/14. There is no doubt that the Civil Engineer Worthington was the man who answered 'No' to most Locomotive Department proposals and, more annoying, would never say why: hence Clayton's clever Bridge Curve.

I saw a lot of Clayton at the pre-World War I Saturday afternoon meetings of the ILocoE in the intimate Caxton Hall room. He was a prime mover in working up the Institution, but refused to become President as he did not consider himself sufficiently high up in the profession.

After we had started on the 2-6-4T, Chambers applied for an assistant, on account of his increasing staff. It was said that T.F. Coleman was offered the post, but declined on the grounds that he was already a chief draughtsman, having reached that status on the NSR. He was by this time in charge of Horwich drawing office, which had lost all new design work. The post was therefore given to A.E. Owen from the Furness, who always talked lovingly of their Baltic tanks - not many people's choice. Nevertheless, he had the same ideas on valve gears as some of us youngsters, and I always thought that his backing persuaded Chambers to agree to 1½ in. valve lap on the 2-6-4T. I hope no-one will think that I had undue influence in the LMS 2-6-4T design; I happened to be the lucky person to be there at the time, as happened later with the 'Coronation', Ivatt's No. 10000, the BR valve gear and so on. My one disappointment was that Ron Jarvis got transferred to Brighton, instead of me, to redesign Bulleid's Pacifics! But that had compensations in my doing Harrison's 71000 and Sulzer diesels! However, I am getting ahead of myself.

When Owen arrived at Derby he was anxious to get his patent balanced regulator fitted on LMS locomotives. He had already had it fitted to some contractor-built locomotives for overseas. For a long time he pointed out in vain its superiority to the Crewe pattern, but at last Chambers agreed to a few '2P' engines being fitted. It did not, however, get a hold.

After the 2-6-4T, jobs which came my way included arranging exhaust steam injectors on the 'Claughtons', together with a steam brake on the locomotive and tender. That shook the bits and pieces of the equalizing gear! Then came the short-travel valve gear for the 2-6-2T. This was fitted with double-port exhaust valves, which were Sanford's idea for achieving the freedom of exhaust of long-travel valves, without the greater wear which was associated with long travel

[From foot of p.103] Comparing the Derby and Ashford 2-6-4Ts, the estimated weights are very similar, the fuel and water capacities identical and the wheelbase likewise, except that Ashford moved the trailing bogie pivot 6 ins further back. Between February and July 1914, of course, James Clayton moved from Derby to Ashford and doubtless took the idea with him. During the period 1903 to 1914 Derby schemed a whole range of large passenger tank locomotives with six and eight coupled wheels, but only the unfortunate Deeley 0-6-4Ts were ever actually built, although an altogether more appealing outside-cylinder 2-6-4T had been outlined as early as 1904, together with an otherwise similar elongated 4-6-4T version. It is interesting to note that in most of these proposals departures were freely made from the sacred Derby 8 ft + 8 ft 6 in. coupled wheel spacing.

valves in many people's minds. Prints of most of the 2-6-4T valve gear drawings were sent to North British as samples for the 'Scot', and many of the pieces forward of the valve spindle crosshead are the same on both designs; one figure which I recall as common to both was 4 ft 4 in. from the centre line of the cylinder to the valve spindle crosshead. The steam chest design and spacing of the ports was common to both classes and it was possible to take a piston valve assembly from an engine of one class and transfer it to one of the other class. For the inside motion of the 'Scot' Chambers sent Midland Compound drawings as patterns. This design was quite unsuitable for their Walschaert's valve gear arrangement and landed us with the dog's hind leg crosshead arm, which gave no end of trouble inside. The double-port valve was applied also to the '2P' 4-4-0 and to the Garratt. I drew out an alteration to the 'Scot' cylinders and to the cylinders and motion plate of the 'Rebuilt Claughton', so that the necessary valve liners for double-ported valves could be got in. Neither class was fitted with the valves, the opinion being that long travel was sufficient to give free exhaust. The 'Rebuilt Claughton' cylinders were cast with provision for the double-ported valves, but the second ports were never machined. In some ways it is a pity that we did not have a 'Scot' with double-port exhaust valves; a 9 in. diameter valve and a decent lead would have made a very interesting engine.

I see that the myth that North British built the 'Scots' from SR 'Lord Nelson' drawings has reappeared in extenso in a biography of Churchward of all places; it is untrue!* I was on the board in the locomotive drawing office, Derby, at that time and saw copies of my 2-6-4T (Fowler) motion being sent to North British as 'patterns'. If the reader can refer to copies of the *Railway Engineer* of that time the drawings therein will show that many details, e.g. piston valve assembly and guides, were interchangeable between the two classes. The 'Scot inside crosshead and four slide bars was pure MR Compound and the boiler a descendant of the MR Banker and S&D large 2-8-0 (which I drew out), with flat firebox plates and circular front tubeplate (not drumhead). Poor Herbert Chambers must have cut a few years off his short life travelling up to Glasgow to settle queries on the spot. He was of course the chief draughtsman LMS CME Dept at the time. This interpolation into my story is just to try and prevent repeated fiction becoming accepted fact.†

I was interested in Mr Newland's letter in the May 1971 *Journal*, for while he was at the North British Loco (NBL) at the time of the 'Royal Scot' design I happened to be at the receiving end for the LMS, checking over the NBL drawings for approval before production of the bits and pieces shown thereon took place.

* *Compilers' Note: G.J. Churchward, A Locomotive Biography* by Colonel H.C.B. Rogers, OBE, George Allen & Unwin, 1975, p. 190.
† This topic was clearly dear to Eric Langridge's heart and was visited over several years. It is hoped that the following summary of correspondence will give readers sufficient understanding of the level of influence which actually occurred to enable them to form their own opinion as to whether or not a myth has arisen. The first dissenting voice came from Mr D. Newlands who wrote from Canada in the May 1971 *Journal* as follows:

In regard to the 'Waterloo fairy tale', I have heard this discussed, and read about it at intervals over the years, the loudest arguments usually coming from those least in a position to know any facts. I have always understood that the Waterloo influence extended only to the 'Scot' boiler, so that Mr Langridge's provision of 'guide lines' for the design of the outside valve gear is hardly germane, and I believe the 'fairy tale' is rather more durable than he seems to think. [*Continued p.106*]

Meanwhile our chiefs, the late Messrs Black and Chambers, were spending nights in sleeping cars oscillating between Glasgow and Derby! I thought it was the late Mr Mackie, whom I came to know well later when the NBL was building diesels for the LMS, who drew out the 'Scot' boiler. Whoever it was, I have no doubt he had a drawing of the 'Nelson' boiler beside his board - I believe the NBL had flanged the plates for Eastleigh, together with many others including the LNWR G2 type and the MR Lickey Banker. If Mr Newlands could see the drawings which lie in front of me as I write - the *Railway Engineer* of December 1926 and January 1928 – he would see how carefully the NBL designer of the 'Scot' boiler avoided the notable features of the 'Nelson' boiler, e.g. the curved GWR style firebox sides and roof, the 2 ft GWR style steam space above the firebox and the direct roof staying at the front end, in favour of the LMS flat sides and top, the 1 ft 9 in. steam space and sling stays in the firebox roof. The one common feature would appear to be the ⅝ in. steel stays in the firebox sides. I hope this adds the final nail in the coffin containing the Waterloo tale: more well-known engineers than he have contradicted it, particularly E.S. Cox, although he was not, of course, at Derby as early as this. Perhaps I might add that the designer of the 'Nelson' boiler at Eastleigh (I believe it was E. Chard, who taught me a lot about design during the year or so I was in that drawing office) copied Swindon drawings which had been obtained by Maunsell's ex-GWR assistant, Pearson. Fortunately he and T.S. Finlayson stuck out about avoiding low superheat.*

[*From foot of p.105*] Perhaps I might be allowed to say my own little piece. I also was an employee of the North British Locomotive Company, and was in the drawing office when the 'Royal Scots' were being designed. During the lunch hour, I used to like to take a walk around and look at the various boards to see how matters were progressing, paying particular attention to the general arrangement of the locomotive, the boiler arrangement and the inside and outside motion arrangements. The boiler drawing was the responsibility of a draughtsman named Crosby or Crosbie, and even after 44 years I still clearly remember that he had the 'Lord Nelson' boiler drawings lying beside him. No-one with drawing office experience will need to be told that, while he did not necessarily copy them blindly, he would at least frequently have a look at them to see what somebody else 'had done before' when faced with problems similar to those on which he was engaged.

---

* *Compilers' Note*: This was followed in the October 1971 *Journal* by Mr Newlands who wrote again from Canada:

The only Mackie I knew at the NBL was the late Steve Mackie who, at the time the 'Scots' were in hand, would be about 18 or so. He probably made some of the boiler detail drawings, but development of the boiler arrangement was a job that would not have been given to an apprentice draughtsman. James Black, incidentally, was the Chief Designer at NBL, not the Chief Draughtsman, this latter post being held by the late William Brown.

Getting back to the 'Royal Scots' and the 'Waterloo fairy tale', Mr Langridge suggests E.S. Cox was not then at Derby. However, I gather from his book *Locomotive Panorama* Vol. I p.56 (Ian Allan 1965) that he was at Derby when the 'Scots' were being designed and, in *A Modern Locomotive History* (Journal of the ILocoE, vol. XXXVI, p.157, replying to H. Holcroft) he said, 'he himself had been closely associated with the design of (the 'Scot')…With the single exception of the firebox, no other part of the 'Scot' was modelled in any way from the 'Nelson'. He repeats this statement in essence in *Royal Scots of the LMS* (Ian Allan, 1970; contained articles by E.S. Cox, W.A. Tuplin, John Powell and P.G. Johnson, edited by Douglas Doherty (p.10)) but, in this book another eminent engineer, Dr W.A. Tuplin, makes a more comprehensive claim (pp.21, 22), while in *Locomotive Panorama* (p.59), E.S. Cox says, apropos the 'Nelson' drawings, 'the firebox was used almost intact' and 'the "Nelson" [*Continued p.107*]

[*From foot of p.106*] style of cab was followed'. My point is that the concept of the 'Nelson' did have some influence on the design of the 'Scot', and this is no fairy tale. Even if, as Mr Langridge says (and I agree) 'how carefully the NBL designer of the "Scot" boiler avoided the notable features of the "Nelson" boiler, e.g. the curved GW style firebox sides and roof etc.', he must have been looking attentively at the 'Nelson' drawing to see 'how we're not going to do it'. The changes were probably made in order to conform to LMS practice, as Derby did not go in for exotic fireboxes at that time, and the joint designers probably had an eye to the expediting of material procurement and subsequent manufacture, since time was of the essence with this contract. Brian Reed, in his *Loco Profile No. 8* (Profile Publications Ltd, 1970) account of the 'Royal Scots', calls these divergences 'retrograde', but were they? Curved firebox plates for instance: well I am all for curves in the right places such as the female form, but in a firebox, were they all that important? What about those Garratts with flat sided boxes on what we were always given to understand was a more or less ideal boiler? I imagine the 'Scot' boiler would be somewhat cheaper to build than the 'Nelson' one; it probably cost no more to maintain, and as to its ability to make steam, I never heard of a 'Scot' being shy of this, but apparently the 'Nelsons' frequently were until Bulleid cured them by modifying their drafting.

In the July/August 1988 *Journal*, Langridge re-visited this matter with the following broadside:

In *The History of the Southern Railway* by Michael Bonavia, Unwin Hyman 1987, the author finds room to bring up the old 'Nelson'/'Scot' heritage myth. He writes (p. 44) 'Maunsell agreed to lend the "Lord Nelson" drawings to the LMS and the North British Locomotive Company' - to help in the design of the 'Scots'. It is interesting to see what use they made of them. Fundamentally, one has four cylinders and the other three. Then in detail:

1.	Axleboxes	MR manganese bronze
2.	Bogie	MR type
3.	Wheels	MR 6 ft 9 in.
4.	Springs	MR type with solid links
5.	Guides	MR type
6.	Lubrication	MR type with atomisers
7.	Brake	MR steam type
8.	Outside Motion	Similar to LMS 2-6-4T
9.	Boiler	Parallel barrel with wagon top firebox as large as Derby S&D 2-8-0
10.	Tubeplate	MR type, outward flanged
11.	Firebox sheets	Parallel with Longstrand steel stays in water space (GWR style)

Bonavia continues - 'traditional MR features required alteration' - Actually areas of Longstrand stays collapsed and were replaced by traditional copper. I happened to design the details referred to under items 8 and 9. After nearly 20 years service they were rebuilt in the Fairburn/Ivatt era.
It is as well to get history correct and divorce it from hearsay and opinion. Anyone who knew the NBL Flemington Street offices would realise that they were not short of drawings for they had supplied most of the world with locomotives of one sort or another.

The *Journal* editor of the time, John D. Blyth, commented that this letter was accompanied with part general arrangement drawings of a 'Scot' and a 'Nelson' and it is hard to find any detail which is even similar, let alone identical! However, for a dissenting view readers are referred to *An Outline of GW Locomotive Practice* by H. Holcroft, Locomotive Publishing Co, 1957, pages 144-145, which includes the statement that the NBL 'Scot' boiler drawings were referred back to Waterloo for comment. More recently two books by J.E. Chacksfield, *Richard Maunsell, An Engineering Biography* of 1998 and *Sir Henry Fowler, A Versatile Life* of 2000, both published by Oakwood Press, each perpetuate the view that the 'Scot' was derived from the 'Nelson'. We hope the foregoing will allow readers to form their own opinion as to what level of influence existed between the two designs.

Sir Josiah Stamp had replaced Guy Granet in 1926: his title now was President of the LMS. It is a pity that no one has written a biography with more than a short chapter on his railway work. His address to the Derby Engineering Club, when he was their guest at an annual dinner shortly after taking up his appointment, sounded quite friendly; but you could feel the sharp brain working behind the keen gaze. After the General Strike episode, he had circularized the staff, thanking them for their work. The local secretary of our trade association, the Association of Shipbuilding and Engineering Draughtsmen, and I had fired an old MR '2F' up the Wirksworth branch, and found out what a large amount of coal it took to get up the hill. Percy Lucas and Cecil Paget had a less pleasant route to the Potteries on a '2000' class tank; their cab windows were protected against ready-to-hand missiles. Perhaps Stamp was out to create a new image all round, and this may account for the installation of those funny little station name boards.

By 1928, Stamp's analytical methods were being felt in the CME Dept. As regards locomotive costs, he had already got some facts from his method of individual costing of locomotives; he had started concentrating some departments at his new Euston House, and now it was the turn of the CME. Rumour had it that the HQ would be at Crewe, surely a sensible idea. Derby with its ancient cramped buildings, off the main line, would appear to have little attraction, and compared badly with Crewe's new shops, good offices and spaciousness. However, the Vice-President, Mechanical Engineering, R.W. Reid, had been the carriage & wagon engineer MR Derby, so perhaps he influenced the decision, which was that the HQ should stay put.

Soon we were told that the HQ locomotive drawing office would be situated at Derby; that was good as we should not have to move house. But more people would be coming from other drawing offices, and that was not so promising, as one would have to wait longer for men to die off before promotion came along. The new office was to be in the old stables, a ground floor building dating back, probably, to pre-Midland Railway days. Most drawing offices that I have visited have been situated on top floors, for the sake of good natural light - the MR one 'under the clock' had been built on the top of existing offices, and from its windows one could see locomotives going to and from No. 4 shed and trains leaving the platforms for the South and West. The stables had a few factory-like windows giving a view of dumped wagons! A window was taken out of the old office, our drawing desks lowered like coffins to the ground, and wheeled into the sepulchre; for although I was too young to realise it, it signified the end of steady MR ways and the start of the LMS maelstrom.

The far, northern, part of the stables building had been occupied by the Central Materials Inspection Bureau (CMIB) since the amalgamation. They had a few testing machines to deal with samples sent in, but most of the time their inspectors were out at contractors' shops. It is strange to think that in those days a footnote on all contracts stated that 'material was to be delivered by rail to the company's works'. Next to the CMIB came the three bays of the new locomotive drawing office, all open to the rafters, the floor covered with thick linoleum to keep out the damp, and heating provided by a newly-installed system of water-washed clean air blown over the draughtsman's head from strategically placed openings.

The far bay had a motion model on the wall and was occupied by Campbell and his men, the next by Henderson's squad, and the third by Tommy Hall, Dolman and company. Owen, as chief loco draughtsman, had a little office off this. Next, built on to the stables was an office block of fairly recent date. Sanford and Sutherland and one or two lads were here; Chambers, now chief draughtsman, his chief clerk, Whiteside, from Horwich; statistical and clerical men and a new genus - two lady tracers. Most men preferred to do their own tracing for, by the time they had fully figured up and marked which lines were full and which were dotted, they could have produced the finished job themselves. The rest of this building was occupied by Symes, personal assistant to Fowler, and his staff - clerical and technical inspectorate. On this upper floor access to the bridge to station and street was provided. 'Under the clock' only Fowler, on the first floor, and, below, H.G. Ivatt, now works manager, and their staffs remained. Accountants occupied the former drawing offices.

Before going further in time I must recall some memorable events of this period. There was the Stockton & Darlington Centenary (1925), when we saw engines and stock of the lines forming the four groups; Hughes' 4-6-0 and Reid's carriages from the LMS amongst others housed in the then-new Faverdale shops after processing 'live'. When one goes through Darlington today by train, one weeps to see the ruins of great firms like Robert Stephenson, and thinks of the loss of fine craftsmen. Then there were the Liverpool & Manchester Railway celebrations (1930); Edgar Larkin, then an assistant to the works manager, was officer in charge of things on rail, and with the help of one or two drawing office staff had a busy time there. I can remember seeing old *Lion* puffing round the large circular track laid in the park.

It must have been about this time that Fowler issued a note to the staff on the undesirability of their running cars, as by so doing they were undermining their own interests. Shades of King Canute! This did not apply to himself or to Symes, of course; they both garaged their cars in the works and had them looked after there, although I must add that Fowler could be seen cycling from his home at Spondon Hall into town, and was an ardent Boy Scout. Although Fowler had been President of the Inst. of Loco. Engineers, Symes was the only local member when I arrived in Derby. Centres had been started at Leeds and Manchester, and with the arrival of men from the old L&YR who were members, the membership grew. I remember one visit to Doncaster particularly, when Gresley, escorting one party round the shops, pointed out one old lathe still giving good service. Years later C.S. Cocks told me that Nigel Gresley would sit at a draughtman's board discussing something, quite oblivious of the passing of the 'knocking-off' time; he was one of the few designing CMEs, evidently. He enlivened the locomotive world more than any of his contemporaries, and deserves more appreciation than he usually gets.

Henry Fowler was seen at his best with learned societies. One bright afternoon he had arranged a visit of members of the Société des Ingeneurs Francais to Derby locomotive works, and people who had a smattering of French were asked to act as guides. Mine was mostly of the school variety and Sanford's that of 'Army Cockney' quality. I have a copy of the guidebook, in French, prepared for the occasion by Chambers's chief clerk, Whiteside, which

LMS dynamometer car No. 45050 after rebuilding in 1929. This was originally L&YR No. 293
built at Horwich.   *Kidderminster Railway Museum Trust Collection*

Interior of LMS dynamometer car No. 45050   *Kidderminster Railway Museum Trust Collection*

deserves a place in the museum. We enjoyed ourselves, Sanford particularly by taking his party into the town where the sales were on. Windows plastered with notices 'SALE' (meaning 'dirty' in French) tickled their sense of humour. After this, Whiteside was always known to Sanford and others as 'M'sieur Coté-Blanche'. He was the perfect chief clerk; clad in dark jacket, spats, with rolled umbrella, striding along with true Hunt's Bank pride, he was liked by all. His end was sad; he lived with his mother near Duffield, and, one night when out for a walk, fell into the river and was drowned. One result of the Frenchmen's visit was that I was invited to join their society as we took tea on the Midland Hotel lawn. I received their interesting 'Revue' for many years. By contrast, our own IMechE looked down on 'draughtsmen', as we were all called, whether you were a first class Hons man like Sanford, a Whitworth Scholar like Onions or an ordinary mortal like me, and would not elect me AMIMechE until 1929, 10 years after I had passed the qualifying exams. Apparently titles like 'personal assistant', whether it meant that you had influence on design or were little more than a doorkeeper, carried weight.

The L&Y dynamometer car had already been moved to Derby, where it came under the loving care of Sanford and Sutherland. I am not sure who accompanied it on the journey from Horwich, but F.A. Stubbs (of Horwich) was keen on telling everyone that he was completely *au fait* with all its workings. Perhaps that helped to secure him a position at Derby in charge of a clerical /technical section including Shimmin (ex-Maryport & Carlisle Railway) and Summersgill (ex-Horwich) which made returns on anything that came to hand to build up their paper castle. The car was used for testing a 'Scot's' coal consumption after various periods out of shops, in the endeavour to find an economically desirable time for change of piston rings, etc., and for other like tests. The routine maintenance of the car was carried out by its staff; this makes it all the more mysterious that the calibrating spring should have been adjudged to be 'incorrect' many years later. I had a few trips on board as an observer later on and the sheer beauty of the Eden valley on a bright frosty morning was enough to take one's breath away as the locomotive was 'warming up' on the way to Appleby.

Perhaps a note on the Horwich No. 1 car will be of interest. Both bogies were of the outside frame type; the drawgear and buffers at the 'dead' end were to the normal practice. At the 'live' end of the bogie, a flangeless wheel of known circumference was mounted between the running wheels, driving a roll of paper across the recording table at so many inches per mile. The wheel could be raised or lowered, to make contact with the rail, by a hand wheel inside the car. The drawbar at this end was coupled to a spring of known rate of deflection whose other end bore against a beam whose ends were coupled to the buffer spindles. On coupling up the drawhook to the locomotive, or tender, one got a base line for reading 'pull' from the pen on the roll. A pen from the chronometer marked the passing minutes: a heavy pendulum could record fore and aft forces. Readings were multiplied to give a line of drawbar horsepower (DBHP) on the roll by the ingenious rolling spheres on the rotating table of the Amsler gear. Other push-operated pens were available for recording passing points, stations etc. At that time testing was carried out on an agreed line: coal and water measured on and off tender. Later allowances were made for 'this and that' in order that the results from locomotive 'A' tested in the Highlands of Scotland should be comparable with those from locomotive 'Z' tested in the Sahara.

With the transfer of the office to the barn, more men were brought in from other centres. The former leading hands kept their posts; Henderson gained a senior man from Crewe in the person of Jack Francis. He was given a desk next to mine and we became great office friends, for Jack preferred the weary journey to and from Crewe, entailing a day of 12 to 15 hours, to getting digs in Derby. The LNWR must have let their drawing office staff run down for Jack was head and shoulders above the rest there. He was the only one to be transferred, whereas Horwich supplied Derby with good senior men and several bright younger ones. Horwich could beat Derby on that score - a tribute to Aspinall? It makes one wonder what would have happened if their chief, Billington, had not died suddenly; we might never have had taper boilers etc. Good draughtsmen are like good tools; no CME gets far without them and the CME was there (Beames) for the asking.

Jack had done the large diameter boiler for Beames' 'Claughton'; he was a first class designer, I think it was he who introduced me to a book on steam engines by Perry. It was the best I ever saw for boiler proportions, draughting and tube sizes, etc. I would put it alongside Altoona and Lawford Fry reports. Jack was also a first class classical pianist; Noel Eames affectionately nicknamed him 'The Sailor', from his tales of service abroad in World War I, in the engine room of merchantmen with ¼ in. plate between him and the ocean, and it stuck. He goes down to posterity pictured in Riddles' biography (they were fellow apprentices at Crewe). Music was the hobby of three other men from Horwich; they found houses in Duffield, a local councillor to back them, started an orchestra and gave concerts locally. I enjoyed playing with them for many years.

To counter the miserable conditions in the barn we still had the faithful John Smith. The store for shop copies was in the lean-to running the length of the barn. There, also, was housed the air-conditioning plant already mentioned, and John managed to supply the illegal cups of tea to keep the staff alive. It may be wondered what all those men did in the barn.

I got a wearying job calculating weights of 2-6-4T castings as it was thought that Crewe had rattled the patterns and produced overweight castings. Then a 2-6-4T got derailed and the centre of gravity had to be worked out for the inquiry. (At one time, after the SECR 'River' class derailment, the LMS design had been soft-pedalled.) A 'Scot' also came off the road and again a centre of gravity was required, this time for a Ministry of Transport inquiry next day, so one became expert at knowing what to take into account and what to ignore. Actually, it was easier with the 'Scot' as the North British had supplied a list of weights with the contract, whereas with the tank it was largely a matter of judgement; our shops would not supply detail weights as it upset their production lines. It took Fairburn to change that.

Fierce argument has always arisen over what line to take at amalgamations of locomotive departments. Should the 'best' examples of each class of locomotive be perpetuated, or should one start again with the 'best' bits of each design and collect them together to form a sort of hoped for Venus de Milo locomotive; or should one put into effect one's own special pet ideas? I think we must put the LMS's '9500' 0-8-0s in the second class, although whether the result was a beauty in appearance was largely a matter of individual taste!

Coal, being the basic fuel for power generation in the 1920s, required shifting in heavy trains by all railway companies; even the LSWR hauled trains of best Welsh coal from Salisbury (ex-GWR) to Portsmouth for the Navy, on which Drummond 4-cylinder 4-6-0s were used. The Midland double-headed their coal trains with 0-6-0s; the LNWR used 0-8-0s, as did the L&Y.

The Chief Officers of the LMS decided in 1927 that the standard heavy freight engine should be an eight-coupled locomotive with lightish axle load and a tractive power the same as that of the LNWR 'G2'. They ruled out the big L&Y 0-8-0, so apparently the 'G2' would be the chosen type. This was the last development of 0-8-0s on the LNWR, which down the years had hauled mineral trains slowly, reliably and without fuss. To the connoisseur of locomotive design they appeared crude and lumpy. They had cast-iron wheels, separate coupling rods with no knuckle joints, crank-axle with centre bearing on elaborate frame stretchers and a poor little rocking lever to turn the motion from the standard 'Joy' valve gear from outside to inside admission. The usual LNWR vacuum brake valves and 'Ting-Tong' pump were there and the important perforated pipe round the base of the tubeplate to throw out cinders - usually red-hot. However, the Midland people had what they hoped would be the winning dark horse - the so-called S&D 2-8-0. To me, then a young outsider brought up on the LSWR under Drummond and Urie influences, both the 'G2' and the S&D seemed to have good points; others on the LMS were, as we know, more partisan and never thought the decision to build a new design a fair one.*

Naturally, to decide whether to build a 'G2' or an S&D 2-8-0 required some road testing as well as records of maintenance costs. The Toton-Brent coal trains were chosen for haulage and economy figures. The route was the old MR one, Toton-Syston-Melton Mowbray-Kettering-Bedford-Brent. On the first test, incredibly to many, the 'G2' came out best. So the 2-8-0 was taken into the works, valves cleaned and adjusted and more trial runs were made. These were on service trains - no constant speed 'controlled' testing business but like against like train on alternate days. To some extent the results could be influenced by careful coasting downhill and luck with signal stops or braking - but probably the results were as good a comparison as one would get with latter day high-powered methods for the purpose required. The second test again favoured the 'G2' locomotive.

So very soon after this I was told to get out an engine diagram of an 0-8-0 using the LNWR 'G2' boiler on a chassis having MR type wheels, axles, spring gear and so on. As I was still only a grade II draughtsman, I suppose Herbert Chambers gave me the job in preference to others, more highly paid, as a reward for making a job of the 2-6-4T motion, which he had been able to take to the North British Locomotive Co. as a pattern for their outside 'Scot' motion. This also earned me a £15 per annum pay rise! I was then taking home £11 10s. 0d. per fortnight! Anyhow, the setting out of the 0-8-0 was a good opportunity

---

* *Compilers' Note*: It is curious no-one seems to have considered re-visiting the Hughes proposed 2-10-0 or 2-8-2; presumably out of sight, out of mind.

LMS '7F' class 0-8-0 (LNWR 'G2' class) No. 9411 on a Willesden-bound freight passing Kensington Addison Road, 26th August, 1933.

Kidderminster Railway Museum Trust Collection/H.C. Casserley

Motion of the preserved LNWR 'G2' class 0-8-0 LMS No. 9395 on the North Yorkshire Moors Railway at Grosmont, 7th July, 2009. *Simon Marshall*

to improve my experience and I was very grateful as there was then talk of bringing the best Crewe and Horwich draughtsmen to Derby which would probably push us small fry into the wilderness.

The first thing to do was to examine the 'G2' frame and cylinder layout to see how to do away with Joy's valve gear as instructed, and get in long lap valves. It would be nice to get outside cylinders and Walschaert gear in, but even with 19 in. diameter cylinders in place of the original G2's 20½ in., we were up against load gauge and weight distribution problems. I tried an inside Stephenson gear with expansion links after the GWR pattern in order to keep the eccentric throw down to 3 in., but the readings were poor and the GWR type of link (although I pointed out that Adams on the LSWR had used it as well) didn't appeal to Chambers' eye. So I tried inside Walschaert gear; Derby was familiar with this idea as the NCC (Ireland) was looked after, mechanically, by them and the NCC two-cylinder Compounds had had Walschaert's. I myself knew it from my earlier years at Eastleigh where the last Drummond 4-4-0s, '463' class, had been so fitted. This came out reasonably well, provided I could get agreement to lengthen the wheelbase one foot between the leading and driving axles. The 'G2' spacing was 5 ft 9 in. + 5 ft 9 in. + 5 ft 9in., and I wanted to go to 6 ft 9 in. at the leading end which would help lessen the incline of the cylinders and give a better length to the radius rod although even then the angularities were pretty fierce. I got away with that and then things became fairly plain sailing.

The LNWR calculated their tractive efforts on diameter of half-worn wheels, i.e. a nominal 4 ft 3 in. wheel was 4 ft 5½ in. when new. The wheel (a steel one) to be used on the new locomotive was to be a standard MR 4 ft 8½ in. on tread and the tractive effort to be based on this and a boiler pressure of 200 psi required a cylinder 19 in. diameter x 26 in. stroke to give approximately the same figure as that of the 'G2', viz. 28,241 lb., an excess, actually, of nearly 200 lb. on the calculated 'G2' figure. Thus we could use the standard 2-6-4T piston; the big-end loading indicated that a '4F' 0-6-0 bearing would fill the bill and the axle loading again compared favourably with the '4F', so that '4F' axles and spring gear appeared adequate for the 0-8-0. The outside coupling rods, being calculated against buckling by the force to slip the wheels, could also be to the '4F' section; the middle rod would have to be heavier as it must be strong enough to slip both intermediate and trailing wheels.

This rough sketch served as a basis for weight estimation and its distribution by taking a simple system of moments and loads. Thus a proposed engine diagram could be prepared for submission to the Civil Engineer. The weight differed little from that of the old 'G2'. What we had put on for extra length had been saved by the use of lighter coupling rods and cutting out the crank-axle centre bearing and stretcher. The extra wheelbase militated against curve negotiation and here until very recent times the position was very indistinct. Some CME Departments stipulated 'to negotiate a 7 chain curve'. Others a 5 chain and 4 chain 'when straining frames'. Some Civil Engineers resolutely denied allowing any gauge widening in yards. All the DO could do was to put the engine diagrammatically on a 7 chain curve and specify side play sufficient to negotiate the curve, after allowing for, say, thin tyres on driving wheels and thick outside. The old LNWR 0-8-0 had flangeless tyres on the middle wheels but later Civil Engineers appear to have barred this practice. Some thought I had pushed the boiler up too high, but that didn't worry me. I had been used to 9 ft 0 in. boiler centres on the old LSWR, and in the present case the LNWR tender with its horse-shoe tank and low level shovelling plate would be replaced by the standard 3,500 gallon LMS tender, having a much higher plate to avoid the fireman having to stoop. Larger wheel diameter, clearance of ashpan and the horizontal grate all influenced that decision. Later on I learned from an ex-Crewe colleague that the LNW 0-8-0s were called 'arse-burners', due to the fact that the engineman's platform had a little well in the middle to allow the fireman to stand low down when firing: no doubt his rear got somewhat warm!

The engine diagram having been accepted, the DO got on with detail drawings and material ordering. The locomotives were to be built at Crewe so the Derby DO knew they would be in for some criticism. Crewe shops had previously built the Horwich-designed 'Crabs' on a large jig for the frames and this step towards mass-production methods was to be used again.

Nothing unusual appeared in the frame design except that LNW adjustable links on the spring gear were dropped in favour of MR solid links and the LNW transverse spring at the trailing axle abandoned in favour of the conventional individual laminated springs. Vacuum brake gave way to steam brake, the Midland argument being that a brake which requires vacuum creating before being capable of operation was useless.

The valve gear arrangement which was handed over to me gave me a chance to propose (and get away with) a few ideas. The actual setting out of a Walschaert valve gear on paper calls for little ingenuity; your lap and lead lever proportions are settled. Your radius rod and eccentric rod are usually about the same length and only the problem of getting it all in the space available remains. With valve gear and connecting rod working over a leading coupled axle one is driven to use some type of shallow crosshead and slidebar arrangement. It seemed to me that the T-crosshead with three slidebars as used on the SR 'Lord Nelson' would work in very well. So I had a nearly horizontal motion plate instead of a vertical one to carry the wide top slidebar with the lower bars being attached to it at each end. This is bad for a deflection point of view when running backwards (and therefore a bad design for tank engines) but tolerable for main line locos. It is, of course, deflection and not stress that settles slidebar sizes. I could also meet the modern idea of building up sub-assemblies and so avoid a lot of lining up of slidebars on the half-finished locomotive by arranging this motion plate to carry expansion link brackets as well. The reversing shaft had to have its own supports on the engine frames and lifted the radius rod, which had extended side pieces, from the rear as on the 2-6-4T design. In order to simplify the valve spindle slide block arrangement, which again can mean a lot of lining up, I suggested the big diameter bush design. This means that it can all be turned up on a lathe or boring machine, centrality automatically being obtained. This scheme is also economical in length as the valve guide can be bored out to accommodate the end of the valve spindle and the fixing cotter sunk within the diameter of the big bush. This arrangement was, of course, a straight crib from LSW days and pre 'King Arthur' design. Chambers agreed to all this but made me put a packing gland on the end in case a weep of exhaust steam should find its way down the valve leg and bush. The tucking in of the eye of the valve guide within the combination lever which was embraced by the fork of the radius rod on the top of the two pins all came from LSWR experience – a neater and cleaner job I have not seen. I also put in decent pin diameters – 2 in. – against the MR 1⅜ in. on their S&D Walschaert gear, which size, I think, must have come from French or Italian drawings they had collected. The gear had 1½ in. lap and 1¾ in. steam port opening - 6½ in. maximum travel. At that time of day, Derby by-pass valves and air relief valves were fashionable and had to be fitted.

An interesting point about the wheels was that the balance weight crescents were to be cast in the wheels but to be open to the inside so that lead could be added to the amount required to obtain so-called 'balance'. The original 'Claughton' wheels had a large boss which had pockets for the same purpose - unfortunately the leverage of the mass was so small that its balancing effect was almost nil. In the case of the 0-8-0 I did not leave enough margin for error in the casting so Crewe had to rivet on some extra weights at the end of the crescent - and pointed out how ignorant Derby DO staff were about balancing! On the other hand, Crewe castings could have some ferocious blow-holes at times defying all calculated weights. Crewe had other queries about 0-8-0 details - the pockets for lead in the wheels were not to their old shape; the near horizontal motion plate was awkward to set up and so on - all of which could have been settled easily if Crewe had not been two hours' journey away. It was not 'the thing' to send mere draughtsmen out. W.G.F. Thorley has rubbed in the lack of communication and its evils in his *A Breath of Steam (Ian Allan 1975)*, where, incidentally, he shows a good drawing of the splitting of the valve spindle/crosshead joint on the 0-8-0, a thing I copied from Urie locomotives. Thorley also gives a shed fitter's view of Garratt maintenance.

The 'G2' boiler general sizes were adhered to, but the mountings were to new LMS style and the old double-beat, constantly leaking, regulator gave way to one with slide valves. The old type undoubtedly kept carbonization down with its whiff of steam going to the cylinders. The old tube size - 2 in. - was on the large size for their 14 ft 5⅞ in. length if you think of the 100/1 length/diameter ratio we normally regarded as a maximum, and we ran out one or two diagrammatic layouts with 144 tubes at 1⅞ in. diameter with 24 flue tubes at 5 in. diameter and others. But in the end we came to 124 tubes at 2 in. diameter, which gave 304 sq. in. free area, and 24 flue tubes at 5 in. diameter which, with 1⅜ in. superheater elements, gave 272 sq. in. free area. Slight alterations took place later. The basis of this 100 to 1 ratio was the fact that resistance to gas flow down a tube is related to its mean hydraulic depth (*see Appendix Eight*). D.W. Sanford restated this in terms of Area/Surface or A/S ratios and also suggested a Resistance Criterion factor for the comparison of boiler performance. Sanford had a remarkably clear, logical brain (he was a First Class Hons in Maths Cantab. man) and a gift for giving simple explanations of any abstruse problems. However, he constantly had to curb his impatience, like others who cannot tolerate lesser brains willingly. During the period after World War I, he was virtually the secretary of the ARLE when Sir Henry Fowler was in power

The first of the Fowler '7F' class 0-8-0s, No. 9500, built in 1929.   *Ken Lea Collection*

Fowler '7F' 0-8-0 No. 9531 on a coal train passing Toton up sidings, August 1931.
Kidderminster Railway Museum Trust Collection/W.L. Good

there. At some time in the Stanier era my colleague, Edleston, made a drawing of the firebox in which the sides were curved to the 40 ft radius of GWR practice instead of the straight side of the 'G2' type boiler originally used. I cannot say whether this was actually done on some spare boilers or not.

The engine came out within estimated weights. It looked very much lighter and less 'beefy' than the G2, and it wasn't long before complaints were made that it was 'weaker' than the old LNWR engines. Several people worked out the tractive effort figure but no-one could doubt that, on paper, the new engine had 200 lb. in hand on the old one. Some said that the larger wheel diameter was the cause, others that it was the regulator, but to quieten the motive power people, the CME agreed to increase the cylinder to 19½ in. diameter on later engines. The internal feelings between the different divisions rather prevented anyone saying they were tip-top locomotives, and the work for which they were required was underestimated. Very shortly much more powerful engines were to appear in the shape of the Stanier 2-8-0s, which naturally pushed the smaller engines to second line jobs.

The testing people in due course made their trials and reports on them and at least one thing I remember in their favour was the nice flat economical coal rate over a wide range of power. The bearings that were sufficient for MR days were not equal to the rough and tumble of LMS handling. Quality of materials went down with economic pressure from commercially-minded managers and oil became poor. All this can be false economy from an engineering point of view; cheapness does not really pay. However, I sometimes wonder if critics of bearing sizes ever had a go at designing themselves! With our gauge one has to arrange things so that the frame and projection of horn guides pass between tyres, i.e. about 4 ft 5½ in.; so, if you dish the wheels in you may get, say, 4 ft 8 in. over extremes of bearings. I have looked up some crank axles I came across in my day and they run like this - a diagram would make it clearer I confess:

Loco	Length bearing	Web	Journal big end	Web	Eccentric seat	Total	Distance between wheel bosses
MR '4F'	8¼"	4"	4½"	4"	7¼"	2' 4"	4' 8"
MR '990'	9"	4½"	5"	4½"	5"	2' 4"	4' 8"
LSW 'D15'	9"	5⅛"	4½"	5⅛"	3¾"	2' 3½"	4' 7"
LSW 'M7'	7½"	4⅜"	4"	4½"	7"	2' 3⅜"	4' 6¾"

Of these engines the '990' had Deeley valve gear and the 'D15' Walschaert with one eccentric required each side. Other railways' locomotives having Stephenson's (or double eccentric) valve gear would be in the same boat, so criticizing the old MR for small bearings just does not hold water! Looking back I cannot help wondering what sort of a machine No. 9500 would have looked like if another draughtsman had been given the job of scheming it out.*†

*   *Compilers' Note:* The class eventually totalled 175, numbered 9500 to 9674, all constructed at Crewe between 1929 and 1932. Withdrawal began in March 1949 and heavy inroads were made into the class in this year and in the two years following, so that at the end of 1951 only 53 remained. The last to be withdrawn, No. 49508 in January 1962, was one from the first batch, so their span of life ranged between 17 and 33 years. [*Continued p.120.*]

[*From foot of p.119*] Following publication of this article on the 0-8-0, Mr D.H. Stuart wrote in the March 1971 *SLS Journal* that in the interests of accuracy:

1. At this period cast-iron wheels were used on the 'G2' on leading, intermediate and trailing wheels only. All driving pairs were steel castings, though of the same pattern.
2. All the LNW engines when new had in-line coupling rods with knuckles. When they were in for repairs, separate rods were often used depending on what was available. This enabled the wheels from Webb compound coal engines to be used without renewing crank pins.
3. The stretcher for the centre bearing could hardly be called elaborate. It was a simple girder fixed to the motion plate and rear frame stretcher.
4. As the 'G2' had direct motion, there was no rocking lever in the valve spindle connection.
5. The ash ejector was a very efficient piece of apparatus in keeping the smokebox clean. It is not correct to state that it threw out red hot cinders.

Eric Langridge responded:

I would say I wrote of what I saw with my own eyes at Crewe in 1928 and from drawings Mr Grover, LNW chief draughtsman, supplied to me. In reply to the separate points made by Mr Stuart:

1. It seems unlikely that the same pattern would be used for iron and steel castings as the pattern-maker uses different shrinkage allowances to suit the materials.
2. 'Swapping' wheels from 4-cylinder compounds 20 years or more old with new engines seems a doubtfully wise practice. Quite apart from strength considerations, finding sets of wheels and axles with dimensions to match up with others on the loco must have been a weary job. Separate rods required a crank pin journal twice the length of that for straight through rods on the driving and intermediate axles. Still, as R.A. Riddles has said, LNWR engines always got there.
3. The stretcher had to be lined up carefully so that the bearing it housed was line-in-line with the other two. What load or forces it carried was anybody's guess.
4. In order to get inside admission the LNW mounted a little rocking lever with centre bearing brackets on the top slide bar!
5. Regarding the ash ejector, Mr Riddles seemed to think otherwise, and so did Mr Jack Francis.

† *Compilers' Note*: The pattern maker's shrinkage allowance for cast-iron is ⅛ inch per foot while that for steel is ³⁄₁₆ inch per foot, a difference of ⅟₁₆ inch per foot. This would equate to about an extra ⅜ inch around the periphery of the pattern of the un-tyred wheel - a perfectly simple modification, the remaining dimensions almost certainly being within acceptable tolerances for the subsequent machining operations. The preserved 'G2' No. 49395 is fitted with a direct motion valve gear without rocking levers. In an article in the October 1961 *Journal* Dr W.A. Tuplin pointed out that the valve gear of the LNWR 'Princes' was modified from 1920 onwards to delete a similar rocking lever and substitute a direct motion. It is therefore suggested that a similar modification would have been made on the 0-8-0s in time, so Langridge may easily have inspected an earlier version and assumed it represented the entire type.

In the May 1971 *Journal* Mr D. Newlands wrote from Canada saying that:

… it seemed strange that an engine designed for service on this railway should not have been provided with bearings that would have been 'equal to the [*continued lower p.121*]

Routine alterations kept many men busy; Horwich-style limits and fits had to be added to many details; flanged plates (even deep ones for splashers) in place of plate and angle; washout plug alterations and so on. Drawings for contractor-built locomotives and railcars had to be sent out. Water tube boilers were 'in the air'; little ones like that proposed by Williams, a larger one on a proposed 2-4-0 tank drawn out by Tommy Hall.

Campbell's squad had the standard No. 2 Passenger with 6 ft 9 in. wheels, in place of the old MR size of 7 ft 0½ in., cylinders and piston valve liners modified to accommodate double-exhaust valves and one, No. 601, with Owen's balanced regulator (this was shown in Shield's paper, *ILocoE Journal* No. 93, 1929). They followed on with an 0-6-2T design on the lines of the LT&SR. However, this got stopped (a sign of the times?), and a 2-6-2 put in its place. After Campbell had got moving on the frame, for some reason I have forgotten, Chambers put me on to look into the valve motion. He had fixed on a single slide bar and position of motion plate: the approved diagram had of course the 8 ft 0 in. + 8 ft 6 in. coupled

---

[*from p.120*] rough and tumble of LMS handling'. The designing, indeed, appears to have been largely of the nature of 'what we did before', inevitable, no doubt, in any drawing office with a continuing tradition and admirable in that it avoids unnecessary proliferation of spares etc. It was unfortunate perhaps that so much of the tradition inherited by the LMS was of Derby origin, so that, until the coming of Stanier, this railway suffered from an excess of 'Midland Magic'. The use of the '4F' bearing on the 0-8-0 was a case in point, as one of the principal weaknesses of the '4F' Standard Goods was apparently its inadequate axleboxes.

This was followed in the August 1971 *Journal* by Mr A.J. Barber of New York, who pointed out that:

The writer consistently maintains that the engine was designed bearing in mind the G2. If this were so, figures, appearance and history do not support the idea. In fact the writer consistently shows that whenever LNWR features were considered they were dropped, e.g. 'LNW adjustable links of the spring gear were dropped in favour of MR solid links' and 'the (boiler) mountings were to new LMS style and the old double beat, constantly leaking, regulator gave way to one with slide valves'. Freight engines usually had a long life, but 17 years must be close to, if not an all time low. Kicked from pillar to post the 'G3' could not even find a home on the L&Y when the WDs returned from their soldiering!

W.G.F. Thorley in his book mentioned above refers to these engines as a 'mixed blessing' and describes numerous defects, coupled with a heavy incidence of heated engine axleboxes and a host of minor defects such as leaking injector steam and delivery pipes, which made the class a heavy drain on shed maintenance resources. Admittedly the BR '9F' 2-10-0s ran for an even shorter time than 17 years, but that was hardly through any fundamental fault in the design, while it must be remembered that some of these 0-8-0s lasted 33 years. With regard to adequacy or otherwise of '4F' axleboxes it should be realised that the bearing surface may also be increased by increasing the journal diameter, at least at the design stage, thereby reducing bearing pressures, an option apparently not considered. In conclusion it seems lamentable that more than a quarter of a century after the Langridge-derided GWR had produced the prototype '28XX' 2-8-0, apart from long travel valves Derby DO still seemed unable to grasp fully the essentials of what Churchward had achieved.

The first LMS built '2P' 4-4-0 No. 563 at Derby station, May 1928.   *R.J. Essery Collection*

LMS 2-6-2T No. 15553 as originally numbered when built at Derby in 1932.
SLS Collection/Real Photographs

wheelbase. The wheel diameter, 5 ft 3 in., would allow us to use the Garratt pattern with a little alteration to the balance weight; the coupling rods could be '4F' section as the slipping load, which we used for calculating this, was pretty well the same, but a larger hole would be required for the big end pin. The position of the motion plate prevented me using the 2-6-4T arrangement of reversing shaft, so I put up to Chambers a scheme, used later by Gresley on his 'P2' 2-8-2 and 'V4' 2-6-2, of passing the reversing shaft arms between the outside supporting plates and the link proper, and lifting the radius rod in front of the die block. He jibbed at that, so there was nothing for it but to use the conventional suspension link with reversing shaft above. The built-up single-die link was the only example of its sort on the LMS. The arrangement of reversing shaft with its centre line on that of the expansion link is more correct for 'both ways running', as on a tank engine, and convenient when clearance is tight under the boiler: but on a tender engine the lifting link behind the expansion link can be arranged to give negligible slip in normal running positions, e.g. as on Urie locomotives. The tight clearance on outside-cylinder locomotives rules out a screwed-on retaining nut on the leading coupling rod pin, and Derby still favoured the continental-style split brasses threaded in after mounting the rod over the solid collar of the pin. These were then held tight by glut and cotter.* After the prejudice against the bolt through the pin had been overcome (although we had some fractures later), the circular end became possible with thin retaining collar. Cylinders, by this time, were machine moulded: I had an interesting week or so with Millington, the works metallurgist, making sketches of the new core boxes for the previous spaces covered by patterns. Millington became well known amongst amateur violin makers for his instruments; that was his absorbing hobby.

While I was running out the balance weights at the correct angle for the 2-6-2T, I also examined Beyer, Peacock's calculations for the Garratts which they had supplied with the contract. They balanced 17½ per cent reciprocating weight in the outer coupled wheels, 30 per cent in the drivers, 19 per cent in the inner coupled wheels. In all cases the weight was placed dead opposite the crank, a practice common in contract shops. If the weights had been placed at the correct angle, they would have been at four degrees for the inner and outer, and six degrees for the drivers. We balanced the 2-6-2T's wheels on the machine in the wheel shop, but I doubt whether Beyer, Peacock had this refinement at that time. In any case I don't think anyone should lose a lot of sleep over that matter.

A welcome break came when the ILocoE made their first visit to Germany in 1928. We lesser lights had to pay our way to their frontier, but then we all enjoyed the hospitality of the Reichsbahn and the firms we visited. My programme mentions the belt system at Schwerte, the welding-up of tubes and fire hole rings etc. At Cassel there was Schmidt's high pressure boiler locomotive (*Fury* prototype) in Henschel's shops, the huge 2-10-0s in the state running sheds, where one member spotted a hair line crack in a motion rod. Then an excursion to Minden, where another nearly got left behind in the forest on the return journey when the coach was stopped for him 'to pay a call'. Our

---

* *Compilers' Note*: A cotter is a tapered pin or wedge, and the glut is the block against which the cotter bears, machined with a taper matching the cotter such as to give an even loading.

LMS 2-6-2T No. 58 (originally No. 15557) at Derby shed, 3rd March, 1947.

Online Transport Archive/ J.M. Jarvis

LMS 2-6-2T Nos. 15520-15539 were condenser-fitted when built in 1931. No. 15524 was renumbered 25 in 1934 and is seen here at St Albans on 25th May, 1935.

SLS Collection/W.A. Camwell

chief host, Dr Wagner, the Reichsbahn's CME (with his complete command of English) and Sanford got on very well together, having the same sort of brain. At Cassel our hosts dined us late, and some were a little unsteady walking up the station platform to join the night sleeper to Berlin. I heard a well-known voice ahead say, 'Don't worry M'sieur Chambres, I am quite all right'. However, someone on the journey accidentally pulled a lever beside his (top) bunk and the train came to a sudden stop in the middle of nowhere; it was the emergency brake that he had pulled! Much argument and shouting before we got away. In Berlin we saw the locomotive with AEG pulverised fuel firing, and locomotive testing at the Grunewald plant. There we learned that the Schmidt high pressure had given a coal consumption of 1.94 lb. per DBHP. Unofficially two of us managed to hear 'Fidelio', conducted by Klemperer at the Berlin Opera, and to measure the deflection of the old Cologne railway suspension bridge under load; something more than 8 inches in relation to the road bridge alongside!

Visits abroad are common today: this one gained by absence of red carpet, keen interest on the job by all, and through being a small party. Although there were supposed to be some CMEs with us they failed to appear, and Clayton and Kelway-Bamber did the honours very well. Dr Wagner gave papers to the ILocoE as late as 1935 on high speed locomotives, before being engulfed in Hitler's Germany. Back home in the office, life seemed very dull; was this premonition of something in the wind? One or two 'transferees' left; one, Crossley, I remember as the man who drew out the full-size ellipse of the 'Crab' valve travel, when he was at Horwich. It was the first time that I was struck by the advantage of big leads in increasing the valve openings at short cut-offs. It was not until Coleman's time that we were able to put that into practice, for, of course, it was dead against GWR ideas. Crossley turned over to teaching at a technical college, where pay was very much better then, and the job held good prospects.

An advertisement appeared in the press for a draughtsman at Lentz valve gears, which I answered. Poppet valves were beginning to draw attention due to Gresley (Lentz)* and Beames (Caprotti)† fitting up their locomotives with different versions of these gears. Caprotti was run by Beardmore's in England, but Lentz appeared to have no regular makers here. So I went up to Lentz's office in Westminster, where I was interviewed by Lindars, whom I guessed to be of Austrian origin, and Poultney, who was a writer of articles in the *Engineer* in Pendred's time. They were quite keen on having me, but I should have to work in the Paris office of Dabeg, an associate company (feed water heaters, I remembered). Lindars was very charming, but had very steely eyes; Poultney did the talking. Years later I noticed Lindars' name as conductor at a Hallé concert in Manchester, so perhaps he was an aspiring Richter.

Anyhow, going home to think it over, it seemed a bit risky, particularly as Stamp had launched his 'rehousing-of-staff' scheme, really to do with people

---

* 'Poppet Valves on Locomotives', O.V.S. Bulleid, *Journal Inst Loco E*, No. 90, 1929.
† 'A New Locomotive Distributing Gear using Poppet Valves', A. Caprotti, *Journal Inst Loco E*, No. 68, 1924.

who had been moved from one centre to another, and had granted me a loan (90 per cent at 4 per cent) for a house on the northern outskirts of Derby. Living at Ambergate in 1928 was very pleasant with a fine fast train service, a view of trains coming round the curves and diving into the Toadmoor tunnel (shortly to be opened up), but hardly, for educating young children, an ideal spot. So I turned the job down, mentioned it to a colleague, who took it: the LMS lost a good man and Lentz gained one!

Strangely, things began to get interesting again. As a result of severe collision damage two LNWR 'Claughtons' required a new front end including a new set of cylinders. It seemed a pity to spend the insurance money from the fund allocated by the accountant on a straight replacement of something which was getting out-of-date when, at a little more expense, a better, more modern set of units could be produced. The decision as to what should be done took some time to settle, due to the fluidity of top level affairs on the LMS at that time. I was told to get out a scheme for a rotary Lentz gear for a proposed 'Claughton' rebuild. It was to have three cylinders on an existing frame. I cannot remember having any drawing from the firm, I just followed Gresley's 'Shire's' arrangement as given in the paper by Bulleid in the *ILocoE Journal*. Another new set of cylinder patterns would be required in addition to the cost of gear and valves to be bought from the Lentz patentees. After a month it came back: 'Please get out a scheme for a four-cylinder arrangement'. Meantime Jack Francis, sometimes in overcoat and often fortified with hot Bovril from my stock of cubes, was designing a three-cylinder arrangement on the lines of the 'Scot' but using the LNWR chassis and his (Jack's) large diameter boiler. In between he would demonstrate on his board how easy it was to play Chopin's 'Winter Wind' study if only you practised passing your thumb under your little finger. Crewe drawing office under Beames had previously designed alternative boiler layouts for the 'Claughtons', slightly larger in the barrel than those of Bowen-Cooke's era. Of these designs Jack's 'Scheme Three' had been built and Derby was willing to accept this design which already had a good reputation for free steaming. It had, too, been 'Midlandised' to the extent of using MR-type fittings under the 'Co-ordination of Design' Committee's recommendations.

Several 'Claughtons' had been transferred to the Midland Division for working between Leeds and London, much to the disgust of MR crews, who, used to right-hand drive, found sighting signals across the boiler awkward. The fireman had to fire round the driver's legs or become left-handed. The brake valves were mounted high on the Belpaire firebox away out of reach and the brakes were vacuum operated. So, if in a hurry on the shed, you couldn't just 'bash' the steam brake on; you had to create vacuum first before you could destroy it to apply the brake, and you might bump the next loco by then! The piston valves were double ported on the steam side

Colonel Hewitt Pearson
Montague Beames

with Schmidt wide rings and had ball valves in the heads which dropped off to connect the two ends of the cylinder when coasting. Unfortunately carbon on the seats prevented proper shutting; hence steam leaks and high coal consumption. When 'castrated' (Sanford's expression) and fitted with narrow rings the economy was as good as those fitted with Caprotti valves. The rocking lever and pieces between the outside and inside valves was like Webb's 'Black Prince' - far too flimsy for the 'Claughtons'. And, of course, with no double heading, one fireman had to shift 60 or more lb. of coal per mile; for you still require the same horsepower on the job, whether it comes from one or two engines.

The 'Scot' had turned out to be a good all rounder: you could thrash it if occasion demanded and yet it did not fall to pieces and could be made to give economical figures, which pleased both Crewe and Derby. This led Fowler's Personal Assistant Symes and the Motive Power Department to favour a three-cylinder arrangement for the rebuilds, all high pressure. At this stage some more detailed investigations into the three-cylinder proposals were made in the Derby drawing office. The 'Royal Scot' had divided drive, outside cylinders driving on the middle axle and the inside one on the leading driving axle, whereas in the four-cylinder 'Claughton' all cylinders drove onto the leading axle. I remember one or two cases of violent slipping resulting in the trailing wheels shifting on their axles - but so they did on the MR Compounds on the Western Division in their early days! No doubt these were due to one of the wheels gripping the rail after a slip and the mass of revolving and reciprocating parts to be decelerated proving too much for this axle away at the trailing end. Extra sand boxes to trailing coupled wheels became common. Otherwise the 'Claughton' layout of drive is very attractive, giving nearly perfect balancing. However, practice on multi-cylinder engines at that time favoured divided drive and the DO schemes proceeded on this basis.

In view of this, one can hardly blame those responsible at the time for deciding to stay conventional and rebuild these two engines with three cylinders and Walschaert's valve gear. At the same time a great chance to 'break through' was lost and awkward situations arose in later designs in this country due, in the main, to hanging on to piston valves and rod-driven valve gear. This decision to rebuild the two locomotives as three-cylinder simples came, no doubt, after much argument between Symes, Beames and Anderson.

Jack got on with his motion. Due to the retention of the old bogie and coupled wheelbase, the dimension from the outside cylinder centre line to the driving axle became 16 ft 3½ in., as compared with the 16 ft of the 'Scot', necessitating a very long connecting rod. For this Jack designed a particularly beautiful rod with 11 ft 6 in. centres for this outside motion with straight taper channelling; the extra metal required at the point of maximum bending moment being obtained by a slight bellying of the outside profile. It also had a solid bushed big end and the design resembled Swindon outside rods.

The Derby 'Scots' had coupling and connecting rods made of ordinary 38 ton steel: the North British 'Scots' had these made of Vibrac (*see Appendix Ten*). This latter was a high tensile alloy steel. As the stresses in these rods is, in the main, a bending stress due to centrifugal force, the strength of the rods is closely related to the section modulus, and there is not much point in using an

LMS rebuilt 'Claughton' 4-6-0 No. 5927 *Sir Francis Dent* with large boiler and Caprotti valve gear at Earlestown, 18th July, 1935.   *Midland Railway Trust/R.G. Jarvis Collection*

LMS rebuilt Claughton 4-6-0 No. 5910 *J.A. Bright* with large boiler and Walschaerts valve gear at Crewe works, 27th August, 1933.   *Midland Railway Trust/R.G. Jarvis Collection*

expensive steel, particularly valuable for its tensile quality. Also, there had been some suspicious hair line marks on some of the North British rods.

Thus the Derby 'Scots' as built could be distinguished from their earlier sisters by the thick flanges of their rods. In addition, they had the brackets carrying the valve spindle slide blocks bolted on to the outside slidebar brackets instead of being cast on as were the North British examples. The reason for this was to provide clearance for the long valve spindle liner with double exhaust ports, should this be fitted in the future. (Of course, we know that it was not.) In later years Stanier had some Swindon style rectangular rods fitted, and yet later, Ivatt had fluted manganese molybdenum rods made: so that what with swapping of details it became almost impossible to say which had which.

Early in 1929, design of the new and altered parts for the 'Claughton' rebuilds started in the Derby DO. Not many men were engaged on this particular job but they comprised one or two representatives from Crewe, Horwich, Stoke and Barrow-in-Furness. An early instruction was that the cost of the rebuild should be kept down and this led to some anomalies because sometimes the answer to a query to HQ would be 'Throw it out' and at others 'Keep it in'. An example of the latter was a frame stretcher in front of the firebox, a typical lumpy Crewe steel casting, that survived all rebuilds to the bitter end. The old LNWR-type 6 ft 3 in. bogie was also retained: this was of the Webb double radial type, the centre traversing in curved slides with no rotating pivot. All platforms, steps, splashers and cab were discarded, thus doing away with the characteristic LNWR features. I was given the job of making a drawing of the frame, shewing holes to be filled up and those to be drilled new in the existing 1¹⁄₁₆ thick plates; it looked like an old fashioned fly paper when I had finished it. However, the works did not approve of this and decided to provide new plates. Axlebox guides, some cross stretchers and spring and brake gear fixings were re-used. Then came the ordering up of steel castings; a loose extension on the pattern of the 'Scot' motion girder, and slight machining modifications on others. The LNWR had a great love of coiled bearing springs under the coupled wheels. They were cheap, home-made and easy to replace, but they must have given the engine crews a lively ride as no dampers were fitted. The dragbox was modified to couple up to a standard LMS (MR-type) 3,500 gallon tender. We decided to dispense with the 'Scot' inside 4-bar crosshead, with its troublesome anchor link to crosshead arm, and to use identical 2-bar crossheads on inside as well as on outside gear. I did the new motion plate drawing and Jack the crosshead and bars. The old leading wheels were moved to the central position, and had their two-throw crank axle replaced by a plain one: the old centre wheels with a new one-crank axle were moved to become the leaders. These had to have their coupling rod pins replaced so that they would clear the passing crosshead, but the old crank pins with the eccentric bearings for connecting rod and coupling rod in what had been the leading wheels (now the middle ones) were retained. Jack had thus to draw out a new front half-rod, its driving (middle) bush having a large hole to suit the pin, giving it a throw of 12 inches. The connecting rod worked on the outer, smaller, bearing, giving the big end a throw of 13 inches. Actually, new crank pins were made for the rebuild as the old method of fixing the return crank on the LNWR engine was by means of a square spigot, whereas LMS designers preferred a four-stud attachment.

The wheels had to have their balance weights altered and so looked a bit of a botched-up job, but cheapness was the order of the day. Obviously the whole set had to be rebalanced throughout to suit the new reciprocating masses. We used the old steel boxes with pressed-in brasses (as used later on Stanier locomotives), rather than the then standard LMS bronze type. Through ignorance of its shortcomings we used the old LNWR reversing screw and bracket, which was later found to have the habit of working loose. This trouble persisted through the subsequent rebuilds. The cab followed the style of the 'Scot' with boxes over the trailing wheels. Due to the 'Scheme Three' boiler having a different type of front tubeplate fixing to the main frame, the 'Scot' pattern inside cylinder had to be altered on the top to suit. The distance over the frame fixing flanges had also to be machined to 4 ft 2in. instead of the 'Scot's' 4 ft 1¾ in. as did the other stretchers of the 'Scot' pattern. In the future, this retention of old LNWR thickness and the 4 ft 2 in. frame spacing was to prove a nuisance for interchangeability and showed that it would have been better to start off with a clean sheet. Perhaps one should not say that all LNWR character had been wiped out, for the large diameter wheel bosses on the coupled wheels plainly indicated that they came from Crewe. However the symmetry of these was spoiled by the plates added at the wheel rim, these being required to provide for the altered balance of the three-cylinder arrangement.

The 'Scheme Three' boiler was slightly larger in many dimensions than the old 'Claughton' boiler with a higher working pressure. The main points were the increased firebox volume and heating surface for the same grate area and the large diameter of the small tubes, thus making a low resistance boiler. The square-based front tubeplate required a flat-bottomed smokebox and this necessitated filling-in plates around the blastpipe connecting pipes, as is usual with this design. Adverse criticism is often levelled at this form of smokebox although it was standard practice for many years, for example, on Adams' outside cylinder 4-4-0s and 4-4-2 tank engines. The MR arrangement of loose filling-in plates with asbestos packing glands was a poor substitute for cement used for filling up crevices by the old engineers. The boiler was supported at the rear end by the usual 'expansion angles' riveted to the firebox sides. These rested on ⅛ inch steel liners placed on top of the frames and a short length of angle fixed to the engine main frames. Unfortunately no spigot was provided in the liner to counteract any side thrust from the firebox, the only resistance to this being half a dozen small diameter bolts fixing a clip over the expansion angle lip. The liner, having no proper slot to resist sideways thrust, wore badly, the thin end often working out and getting trapped in between the wheel spokes. Until one could reposition the expansion angle - a major operation - this trouble just had to be lived with.

The brake on the old 'Claughton' was vacuum-powered, the usual LNWR practice for passenger engines. The brake percentage was also low, owing to the opinion that the train should slow up the engine rather than vice versa; the merit being that the couplings stayed taught. The vacuum brake cylinder gives a very gentle increase of pressure throughout the brake gear compared with the 'bang' from the steam brake cylinder of the MR and subsequently LMS practice. Consequently the full rods and compensating gear of the old 'Claughton' design, which was retained in the rebuilds, suffered severe wear.

The next surprise for me was to be put in a little office on my own. Although there was financial gloom in 1929 - Stamp cut all wages and salaries by 2½ per cent - the technical press had details of various ideas being tried out: there were Cossart poppet valves, Willoteaux piston valves; Gresley with his limited cut-off and floating big end bush - taken from America, I thought, until I read in Ricardo's biography that he had used it on heavily-loaded big ends in internal combustion engines with success. Chambers's idea was to modify the valve gear on a No. 2 Passenger by using an extra eccentric to accelerate the movements. He had, of course, visions of a patent, hence the privacy. But after a couple of months, he agreed that there was nothing in it: perhaps he had chosen the wrong man to work it out; Bulleid had to go outside the SR drawing offices to find his collaborator.

Back in the barn I found that Jack had got transferred back to his beloved Crewe, so I had a few more jobs to do on the rebuild. Steam brake cylinders replaced (very unwisely) the LNWR vacuum ones on the equalized gear; the fashionable equipment of the day was fitted - air valves, by-pass valves, vacuum pump and all the operating bits and pieces, Midland style instead of LNWR style, which were more within reach anyhow. A bridge loading curve, another device of James Clayton to try and understand the workings of the civil engineer's mind, just about finished my records concerning the drawing office work on Nos. 5971 and 5902.

Next, 20 'Scots' were put up for tender. With the first lot North British had been asked to supply an extra boiler and a set of motion. Owing to the 'running hot' cases having been in the Atlas-built locomotives, these spares were specified by the LMS to be built at Queen's Park, so they naturally thought they would get the next 20. But no! The building order was given to Derby (boiler making had already been concentrated at Crewe). Ivatt, in later years, liked to chuckle how, by careful (?) accounting, they had managed to land that order - and the order for rebuilding the 'Claughtons'. The set-up then was:

Vice-President, Euston, R.W. Reid (Reid died in March 1929)
CME, Derby, Sir Henry Fowler
Deputy CME, Crewe, H.P.M. Beames
Personal assistant to CME, S.J. Symes
Works manager, Crewe, F.A. Lemon
Works manager, Derby, H. G. Ivatt
Assistant works manager (Derby), R.A. Riddles

Just to add to the mixture, A.H. Nash was the 'first assistant' to the Derby works manager. He was Swindon-trained, and came on to the LMS through having been locomotive superintendent of the Midland & Great Northern Joint Railway (M&GN), which department of a joint railway came under the old Midland chief mechanical engineer. He was a friendly, energetic man (like 99 per cent ex-Great Western Railway men I was to meet later on - so different from many enthusiasts). Of the others mentioned above: R.W. Reid I never spoke to; Sir Henry Fowler might have been Bishop-Cardinal; Beames, a judge; S.J. Symes, the ordinary man; F.A. Lemon, the autocrat; H.G. Ivatt the patrician; R.A. Riddles, the go-getter.

LMS 4-6-0 No. 5500 *Patriot*, formerly 5971 *Croxteth*. The first two of the 'Baby Scots' ('Patriots') had certain parts of the 'Claughtons' they were alleged to have been rebuilt from, e.g. the wheels.   *Ken Lea Collection*

LMS 4-6-0 No. 5501 *St Dunstans* at Crewe North shed in 1938. It was formerly No. 5902 *Sir Frank Ree* - the original name transferred to No. 5530.   *SLS Collection/L.W. Perkins*

LMS 'Patriot' class 4-6-0 No. 5521 *Rhyl* at Bushbury shed, Wolverhampton on 7th May 1938. It was No. 5933 until 1934 and named in 1938.   *SLS Collection/L.W. Perkins*

The event in 1929 which was to lead to sharp changes was the sudden death of R.W. Reid. (Strange too that a similar event was to occur 25 years later.) Reid was well liked on and off the railway in Derby. His death in March meant that there was now no mechanical engineer at top level, and a vacant Vice-Presidency. However, life went on; Derby shops turned out their first 'Scot' in June 1930, and the two 'Claughton' rebuilds, No. 5971 *Croxteth* and No. 5902 *Sir Frank Ree* in November 1930. These were the last big engines to be built under the Fowler regime, for on 31st December, 1930 he ceased to be CME. The weight in working order was given as 'Approximately 80 tons'. Beames' large-boilered four-cylinder 'Claughton' had been quoted as 79 tons 1 cwt, so the new engines had as good an availability as the old. By comparison the 'Scot' weight was given as 85 tons. Jack Francis' boiler seemed as happy feeding three cylinders as it had been with four: the Western Division liked it, with its surprisingly large route availability, and the Loco. Committee decided to be less stingy and 'rebuild' more 'Claughtons'. Thus Crewe works came into the picture and a succession of orders followed each other, so that as soon as one batch of 10 was completed another was on the way - a works manager's dream! A few modifications were incorporated on these, some in order to use LMS standard ideas and others to reduce cost. This time they were going to have 'Scot' wheels, axles, boxes, spring and brake gear, but 1⅛ in. frames instead of the 'Scot's' 1¼ in.: a fiddling difference, saving weight at the expense of inter-changeability. The inside motion was as per the first rebuilds. The coupled wheelbase became 7 ft 4 in. + 8 ft, the same as the 'Scots'. The bogie centre was pitched 9 ft (instead of 9 ft 1 in.) in front of the first coupled axle, but the old 6 ft 3 in. LNWR bogie was re-used on the first 10; subsequent ones had the LMS 6 ft 6 in. bogie. So we had the manganese axleboxes and hard laminated springs, the poor balance of the three-cylinder engine compared with the smooth ride of the four-cylinder one, completely balanced, with no hammer blow, as standard for the future.* Willie Armin had another frame to draw out; I altered the cylinder drawings so that a long liner to suit Sanford's double-ported valve could be fitted if required, and the motion plate and valve spindle guide support so as to get the liner in and out. I followed on with a pipe and rod arrangement drawing, besides other odd jobs. These engines had now lost all LNWR features except the whistle and, like the first two, were popularly nick-named 'Baby Scots'. The CME Department disliked such frivolity and preferred '5X'. Of course the 'Scheme Three' boiler was fitted to all the locomotives and its mounting on the frame stretcher at the vertical front tubeplate prevented interchangeability with the 'Scot' details. In 1934 the actual engine numbers which the 'Rebuilt Claughtons' had inherited from the their predecessors were dropped and the whole class renumbered 5500 to 5551 and they became known as the 'Patriot' class, the name given to No. 5500 in place of *Croxteth*.

The experimental high pressure compound 4-6-0 No. 6399 *Fury* had been delivered; all I had to do there was a cylinder by-pass valve for 900 lb. pressure,

---

* *Compilers' Note*: It is known that a three-cylinder engine can have perfect dynamic balance: EAL was probably referring here to the balance of forces between opposed inside and outside cylinders of the four-cylinder engine; see note on Bulleid Pacific balance, Volume Two, page 131).

The LMS's ill-fated experimental three-cylinder high pressure compound 4-6-0 No. 6399 *Fury* in Derby paint shop *c.*1934. Built by the North British Locomotive Co. in 1930 and rebuilt in 1935 as No. 6170 *British Legion*.   *Kidderminster Railway Museum Trust Collection/Frank Carrier*

'Royal Scot' class 4-6-0 No. 46164 *The Artists Rifleman* at Crewe works, February 1950. Built at Derby as LMS No. 6164 but with a Stanier 4,000 gallon tender.   *SLS Collection/L.W. Perkins*

and so on. Also at this time of Fowler's supersession there was a 0-8-4T proposal on the boards. It was to have had 20 in. or 20¾ in. by 26 in. cylinders and 200 lb. pressure. A proposed 0-4-4T got as far as an outline drawing, S4613. Some details were drawn out before the job was put aside, only to be taken up seriously again just before Stanier's arrival.

Sir Josiah Stamp's predilections can be gauged from the appointment he made as Reid's successor. All locomotive men associated the name of Reid with their craft; the only bearer of it whom I was privileged to meet was manager at Springburn when, on one side of the erecting shop, huge steam locomotives were being assembled for abroad, and on the other diesel-electric locomotive No. 800, was slowly taking shape, and eating its head off in wages.

Stamp's choice was, of course, Sir Harold Hartley; Oxford Don, late Chemical Warfare Chief, FRS. The appointer of Kenneth Clark as Keeper of the Ashmolean Museum - a truly catholic set of interests - but not an engineer. Naturally, a Don would have to have to do with that blessed word 'Research'; exactly whichever definition of it Josiah had, visually it took the form of a new building a few yards south of the old (and new) C&W block, continuing the building line, and within a yard or two of the, even then, busy and noisy London Road, with 4-wheeled trams rattling along badly-jointed rails. In charge, for signing PT and pass forms, orders for pencils, rubbers, etc. was an MA; a rather nebulous gentleman I found him to be, when I was sitting on the Test Committee 20 years later, deciphering what they wanted housing in the Amsler dynamometer car. His name was T.M. Herbert, officially interested in air currents, I believe. The office part of the building consisted of little 12 ft square rooms: I remember there one DSc in charge of a metallurgy section, who soon got fed-up and went to Swansea; and later the famous T. Henry Turner, a great talker, guaranteed to finish with a eulogy of all things LNER. Several younger members were recruited from the locomotive drawing offices; naturally, mostly from Sanford's and other experimental sections, and mostly Degree men, often at a loose end. There was a workshop in which were a few pieces of apparatus, and, the most useful thing to me, a draughtsman, a trained lady Librarian, who produced précis of magazines, etc, and ran a library, much of it from its old home in the loft 'under the clock'. Sir Henry Fowler had by now become a rather nebulous figure so far as the CME Department was concerned, his old colleagues and protégés also not having much use for him. The Motive Power Department (MPD) were quite happy with 'Scots' and 'Baby Scots/Patriots', 2-6-4 tanks and 'G2s', and, reminiscent in some ways of the old LNWR Webb/Whale situation, thought that his post and salary could well come to one of their members. So it did not seem illogical for him to be 'shunted', to use a phrase of one of them, into a convenient post in the new Research Department, concerned with metallurgy. However the MPD were 'beaten to it' this time by an 'organizer', E.J.H. Lemon, and would have to bide their time. Thus Lemon, with two departments, became my next CME.

'2P' class 4-4-0s Nos. 636-665 were built in the Lemon regime. No. 641 is piloting Compound 4-4-0 No. 906 on a St Pancras-Glasgow express at Dumfries, 14th August, 1939.   *SLS Collection*

No. 653 was another '2P' class 4-4-0 built in the Lemon regime but fitted with Dabeg feed water heater, at Crewe North shed *c.*1934. *Kidderminster Railway Museum Trust Collection/Frank Carrier*

Chapter Seven

E.J.H. Lemon

From his very first actions as CME, Lemon appeared to be a much tougher man than either Fowler, his predecessor, or the late Vice-President, R.W. Reid, in reorganizing the CME Department.

Most of the smaller repair workshops had been got rid of; the big shops could go on building 'Baby Scots' and 2-6-4 tanks without his bothering, so that he could turn his attention to office reorganization. The new wing of the C&W offices at London Road, Derby, built by his predecessor to house the central drawing office (upstairs) and accounts office (ground level) could be turned into HQ drawing offices for both departments under one chief by removing the C&W accounts to the barn, where they would be within visual distance of the CME accounts, and by moving the locomotive drawing office to the former C&W accounts office in London Road. Price, the C&W chief draughtsman, would soon be going, and young Chambers could then take on both offices (at reduced total salaries); in due time, no doubt, the personnel could be merged and reduced (Coleman's remark about 'Carriages being boxes on wheels', made many years later, comes to mind). No consultation with staff being necessary in those days, the change was put into effect.

The snags to us poor draughtsmen were complete divorce from any locomotive shop and shed (you would be better off in a contract shop), and ½ mile to the Institute dining rooms, library and station. There was, of course, a path under a road bridge and across the main line to the west to the station, then 'open', but this was soon declared 'out of bounds'. People slipping out early to catch the lunchtime bus had their names taken and passed to the boss by a zealous door porter; so although the 'loos', etc. were wonderful for a smoke (smoking being prohibited then in the building), the change helped to destroy further the old happy family feeling. Those with benches on the south side were lucky, 'worth ten years extra on your lifespan', so said Jimmy Dolman; those on the north had to contend with the traffic noise beforementioned.

The C&W staff were completely cleared out of the ground floor of the old building too. By knocking down inside walls, a spacious office (with private loo, etc.) was made for the deputy CME, now to be housed here at Derby; his chief clerk next door on one side, his chief draughtsman (later called chief technical assistant) on the other. That was on the sunny south side, of course; across the corridor on the north side were the clerical people with Whiteside (M'sieur Coté-Blanche, previously mentioned). The furniture for the deputy's office came from Sir Henry's room 'under the clock'; it

(Sir) Ernest John Hutchings Lemon

137

'2P' class 4-4-0 No. 654 and an unidentified 'Prince of Wales' class 4-6-0 back down to the station from Crewe North shed, 7th April, 1934.

Kidderminster Railway Museum Trust Collection /Frank Carrier

BR '3F' class 0-6-0T No. 47679 at Rowsley shed on 27th February, 1949. Originally LMS No. 16762 and renumbered 7679 under the 1934 scheme. Nos. 16750-16764 were built in the Lemon regime.

SLS Collection/L.W. Perkins

comprised a beautiful long table with desk built on to it at one end. It may have been used by Johnson. There was also a huge armchair and bookcase, containing some unique records which I took the chance of examining during one of the periods that I was 'acting something or other'. Unfortunately, C.S. Cocks, when he came in BR days, showed no interest in them, and they were vandalized or destroyed.

The photographer and staff remained in the locomotive works area as before (they worked for all departments, of course, being 'on call' at all times to go and photograph accidents, etc.) Likewise, John Smith and the shop copies stayed there, necessitating a long walk by road when the boards to which they were fixed had to be brought across for 'marking up' or alteration. This probably led to the use of drawings rolled on sticks, but still 'true to scale' in the old Midland manner. It is strange, in looking back, that, in my Eastleigh days about 1915, I can remember no one using a drawing except for something on a new thing like a Urie job: every one knew how to repair the older stuff; fits were judged by the amount of shake. I suppose it was the day of the craftsman and very much cheaper in the use of time and paper.

In this way Beames became resident at Derby and, perhaps strangely, became very much liked. When he retired in 1944, he asked that the binoculars that we proposed presenting to him should be of British make. Of his loyalty to him throughout, Stanier made public tribute (it can be read in the *IMechE Journal*). It is sad therefore to read in a recent autobiography that 'had Beames become CME, the changes would have been far greater than those by Thompson after Gresley'. This seems to me to be an inapposite remark, for surely that is exactly what Stanier did. It is a twist of historical fact, very unfair to Beames. Symes vacated his office block, some going with him to Euston, where he became Lemon's locomotive assistant (I think Purves was the C&W assistant); others dispersed to the works and to the Research Dept. Amongst those who went to Euston were two figures to gain promotion, E.R. Brown and E.S. Cox, both undoubtedly useful men with their language and memoranda-making capabilities.

I cannot remember that we saw Symes again in the locomotive drawing office; he was probably occupied with higher policy matters. Alternatives to steam power were lifting their voices. Tommy Hornbuckle, Wh.Sc., a close associate of Symes in MR days, became very involved with diesel-mechanical proposals of various makers; he will appear again in my picture later. Also there was Maurice Henstock, who had stuck to his evening classes better than I and gained the much prized BSc(Eng) London degree; this was before the days of the so-called 'Red-Brick Universities'. Maurice married into the railway, and after many patient years as assistant to the notable T.F.B. Simpson, works superintendent, Derby, broke through and finished up as stores superintendent, LMS.

The actual locomotive drawing office itself had three private offices, only one of which was occupied, by A.E. Owen, as chief locomotive draughtsman. Adjoining an 8 ft 0 in. glazed wall was erected to enclose Sanford, Sutherland, Stubbs and his little squad. Outside were the lady and gentlemen tracers, then Henderson's men, next Doleman's. On the other side were Sanford's ever changing squad, as they were mostly pupils, etc. passing on their way to better things, Tommy Hall's, and then Campbell's men. The centre line of benches were occupied by Richardson ('No. 4 Goods Scab!' was one of his famous calls when no one could find the drawing), the office boy and people working for either gang. Richardson was the general factotum, doing a bit of clerking on drawing registers, etc., as I have mentioned earlier.

We had moved in in August 1931; very soon the 'works managers' of the four remaining large works became 'works superintendents', and were given charge of all matters concerning non-standard, pre-amalgamation locomotives allocated to their area. Only Standard LMS locomotives drawings would be dealt with by Derby HQ locomotive drawing office. So we said 'Goodbye' to Doleman and company, who were to be housed in the old works manager's office 'under the clock'. Ivatt, now as works superintendent, moved up into Sir Henry's old office at bridge level.

The area of our office left vacant was divided off, and made private for a Costs Committee. This was chaired by Riddles, who had S.H. Whitelegg (Horwich), and Williamson (St Rollox) assisting; they were all assistant works managers at that time. Percy Lucas was their draughtsman, so altogether it was a highly-paid affair. I can remember them getting no further than dealing with pipe clips, of which I happen to have still their request for 20 or so prints of Derby drawings. One consequence of the absence of Whitelegg from Horwich was that it allowed Bond to return to the LMS as an assistant to Shallcross (works manager there) from his employers, the Vulcan Foundry; he was very fortunate with the state of employment as it was then. Bond records that it was necessary to 'put Whitelegg in his place' when the latter returned to his job at Horwich; strange for S.H.W. seemed a mild character - not like his brother R.H.W. who had been locomotive superintendent of the LT&SR, and GSWR - the rat race was on! S.H.W. left money for a scholarship to be awarded by the ILocoE, which is carried on by the IMechE today.

Very quickly Beames showed his interest in design; a note came round that he would see all new tracings and initial them - which he did, and in a more thorough way than later on was the case with Stanier. Then one just put on some chalk to kill the greasy nature of the cloth, so that Stanier could sign it on his walk round the office. (The joke about this was that often a 'gold tracing' was taken off the original bearing his signature, altered by erasing the unwanted parts, given a new number, printed and issued to the shops - so is history falsified.)

My first visit to Crewe came about as a sequel to Beames' interest in poppet valves. Chambers took me across; on arrival at Crewe station we were met by the Crewe 'hearse' - an old glass-sided car, so that the locals could see and forewarn the porter who was coming - and put down at the main office door just beyond the bridge. We went into the drawing office, Chambers introduced me to T.G. Lightburn, who had been getting out some schemes for 'experiments' with poppet valves, and went on his own business. No one could enter those offices for the first time without thinking of Webb and the other great figures of the past who had passed that way. Lightburn's sketches were not very exhilarating but, as instructed, I 'listened and learned' and brought them back home with me. I was left to find my own way back to the station over the spindly bridge, normally used only by the VIPs.

In LNWR days Beames had produced one of the 'Prince of Wales' 4-6-0s in which the inside Joy valve gear was replaced by outside Walschaert's, driving the piston valves which were, as before, above the inside cylinder barrels, by means of a horizontal rocking lever passing through the frames. The rather criss-cross appearance of the valve rods earned it the nickname 'Tishy'* and it received extra publicity as it was built by Beardmore's - one of its post-World World War I adventures into locomotive building - and was exhibited at the White City in 1924. Well, Lightburn's schemes reminded one of 'Tishy'; they had inside cylinders with the Caprotti valves (working vertically, of course) in a projection of the casting sticking outside the main frames, giving the impression the cylinders had erupted: the cylinder clearance volume must have been colossal. It was soon agreed that Caprotti fitted in better with outside cylinders, if these were of any size. I went into this scheme very thoroughly; it must be remembered that the result was to have the same tractive power and weight (for route availability) as the 'Prince of Wales' class which it was to replace, so that to compare it with the later Stanier efforts, which were much heavier, is quite wrong. The boiler pressure was to go up to 200 lb., so that wanted stressing out; the leading and middle coupled axles were moved forward 9½ in. Alternative sizes of cylinder were suggested, depending on whether or not new wheels would be allowed - 19 in. x 28 in. or 19¾ in. x 26 in.

Next I reproduce a note in Jock Henderson's hand:

> Mr. Langridge; Rebuild of Prince of Wales Class Engs., Same boiler with rearranged tubes, see if Press. can be raised. Outside Cyls. Walschaert Gear long travel. See if any pattern we have of cyls. will work in.

After doing that, the only thing I have record of is a request to compare Belpaire with round-top boilers. This might have been Lemon's non-locomotive man's request in order to save money - he was that way inclined; or it may be that an accountant's costing had shown up comparative costs, for my book has six or more pages of weight and water content of boilers of similar design, but for the firebox shape.

Then I went on to get out various schemes for a 2-8-0 freight with a 'G9BS' boiler (large S&D type) or its round-top alternative, all with outside cylinders and Caprotti gear. I have a print R.S.1552, dated 9th December, 1931, and the job went on well into the new year, with its change of CME.

Beames was evidently keen on improving the commercial efficiency of locomotives (he had already built the 'Crabs' on a jig and belt system), and a lot of rods flashing about in the dust seemed as antiquated to him then, as it does to us now; hence the nice enclosed poppet gear and its better valve events. Beames was a great advocate of poppet valves. He had already, in 1928, fitted 'Claughton' No. 5908, with poppet valves using the Caprotti arrangement - bevel gears on the middle coupled-axle and propeller and cross-shafts to gearboxes and cams mounted on the cylinder casting. Reversing, and various degrees of expansion, were obtained by moving a sleeve along a scroll, thus altering the relative position of the operating cams and obtaining an almost infinite number of cut-off positions. The results he published showed a saving

---

* *Compilers' Note:* The 'Tishy' nickname given to the 4-6-0 'Prince of Wales' engines fitted with outside valve gear came from a contemporary race horse which kept falling over its own legs.

LNWR 'Prince of Wales' class 4-6-0 No. 56 (later LMS No. 5726) on a passenger train at an unknown location. This locomotive is one of the five modified with outside valve gear and known as 'Tishies'.   *Kidderminster Railway Museum Trust Collection/V.R. Webster*

LMS 2-6-0 No. 13234, one of the batch Nos. 13225-13249 built in the Lemon regime at Willesden shed, 25th August, 1935.   *SLS Collection/W.A. Camwell*

of over 20 per cent in favour of the Caprotti engine. This modification included a complete new cylinder casting to new patterns. He had therefore favoured the rebuilding of the two accident-damaged 'Claughtons' as large-boilered Caprotti four-cylinder locomotives. He was before his time, however, and we had to wait until the arrival of Ivatt to get out of the groove. O'Brien (L&YR) had got sacked following a paper he gave to the ILocoE in 1924, wherein he showed that electrification would pay on the railway, main line as well as suburban; Beames just got pushed back and his department starved of money. The first cost of Caprotti was admittedly high, but any excuse can be better than none, if you want to supersede someone. Other senior officers were due for replacement, V.P. Follows, motive power superintendent, and J.E. Anderson; so it may be that Stamp was looking for fresh young blood (non-Midland) in the top posts. Certainly it was rumoured that D.C. Urie hankered after the CME's post. In the event, E.J.H. Lemon got the Vice-President's seat, and Urie the motive power superintendent's job. It is interesting to read from K.J. Cook's autobiography* how Stanier, feeling that his way up was blocked on the GWR, accepted the LMS CME's post, knowing that he would have no control over motive power matters, as he would have had at Swindon.

Although what follows extends into 1932, the date of Stanier's arrival on the LMS, it really belongs to the Lemon era, so I will recount it here. *Fury* had been withdrawn after the burst tube accident and one or two test runs; I was told to get out a schedule of alterations to make her into a standard parallel 'Scot'. Nothing was done; the boiler was disposed of, and the chassis left to rust in the yard for a year or two, when Crewe drawing office under Coleman got out the drawings for rebuilding her with taper boiler.

The drawings for the 0-4-4T were slowly taking shape, but early in 1932 there was talk of altering the wheel diameter from 5 ft 7 in. to 5 ft 3 in., replacing the exhaust injector by a live steam one. The new tractive effort, and the weight which would be saved, were worked out, but whose idea it was I do not know, and the locomotive came out finally with 5 ft 7 in. wheels, as originally proposed.

Various 0-8-0 suggestions were made, and the following got out in January 1932 shews what was in the wind. Obviously Beames was still in charge.

Proposed 'Altered G2' 0-8-0 compared with other classes - January 1932

	2-8-0	*2-6-4T*	*0-8-0 'G2'*	*Altered 'G2' Outside Cylinders*
Cylinder centres	6'8"	6'8"	-	6'8¼"
Between frames	4'2⅓"	4'1½'	4'2" & 4'0"	4'2"
Frame thickness	1"	1⅛"	1"	1"
Journals	8" x 8"	8" x 9"	8" & 8½" x 9"	8"x9"
Centres of bearings	3'7⅓"	3'7"	3'10"	3'7⅓"
Bearing to frame	3⅓"	3¼"	2"	3⅓"
Between wheel bosses	4'4"	4'4"	4'7"	4'4"
Cylinder to frame	1'11"	1'2⅓"	_	1'2⅓"

* *Swindon Steam 1921-1951*, Kenneth J. Cook (Ian Allan, 1974).

Weights

						Total
2-8-0 S&D (o/6338)	9-0-0	14-2-0	15-2-0	16-0-0	14-7-0	68-11-0
'G1' (7″ & 7½″ x 9″)	-	15-0-0	17-10-0	15-5-0	12-10-0	60-5-0
'G2' (8″ & 8½″ x 9″)	-	15-10-0	18-0-0	15-15-0	12-15-0	62-0-0
Altered 'G2', outside (proposal)	-	-	-	-	-	64-2-0

Alterations required to 'G2' boiler:

Flange and width of smokebox tubeplate.

Dome and regulator shortened 6¾″.

Expansion angle raised one pitch of stays.

Estimated Changes in Weight in the Altered 'G2'

'G2' 0-8-0	Altered 'G2'	Weight 'on' or 'off'	
		cwt	*qtr*
4'3½″ wheels with cast-iron centres	4'8½″ wheels, steel centres	+2	1
7'4″ leading wheel to buffer	7'10″ as above	+1	1
Inside cyls 20½″x24″ and piston valves	Outside cyls, s'box saddle frame stretchers	+37	0
Joy motion inside	Walschaert motion outside	–	–
Centre bearing on crank axle	Straight axle, no	-6	0
Frame 2'2¼″ deep (min.) and cast-iron splashers and sandboxes	Frame 2'8″ deep (min.) no splashers	-15 +11	0 0
Cast-iron dragbox, vacuum cylinder	Plate dragbox, steam cylinder	-10	0
Transverse spring I&T wheels	Underhung springs D&T wheels	-2	0
Frame stretcher & boiler support casting	Plate stretcher	-2	0

18 cwt
to the bad

'G3' class 0-8-0 No. 9613 with Dabeg feed water heater.　　　　　*Ken Lea Collection*

Chapter Eight

W.A. Stanier

The news of Stanier's appointment came as a bombshell to the Derby locomotive drawing office staff. How many men would he bring, and so on, were the questions? Presumably he would be at Euston, or rather Drummond Street, as was Symes, nicely separated from the motive power superintendent, in Euston House, by the railway station.

Few people knew much about GWR detail practice; they had kept themselves to themselves and not taken any interest in ILocoE affairs. I can remember nothing much after Churchward's paper to the IMechE about 1905; the few Swindon men who had gone to the SECR had not given much away. Rumour had it that some inspectors were coming; actually they included Read, Dymond and Maurice Burrows. Burrows was a very charming fellow who died young, just after being appointed CME of the North Eastern Region at York in BR days. It was also rumoured that there was some argument as to who should become Stanier's technical assistant. Apparently it rested between Cox and Dymond; Cox was appointed, no doubt because he had got on well with previous heads, and had no addictions one way or the other on design matters.

No doubt Stanier found his first job was the visit to America of a 'Scot' and coaches from May to November 1933. All he could do in the short time available was to alter the spring gear and bogie. J-brackets - requiring the welding on of a few pieces to the main frames - 6 in. longer springs, and screwed tension links took the place of solid links. From my experience such links are never adjusted after installation, freeze up and become unmoveable. Threads invite growth of flaws, and J-brackets make it difficult to get a spring into place. As regards the bogie, Chambers came out to me and said, 'He wants a bogie bolster fitting; I think we have one on our old 0-4-4 tank'. I pointed out that there was a spring-loaded anti-roll (supposedly) device and that what Stanier had in mind was a solid weight transfer bolster. It is sad, but I doubt if Chambers had ever seen the GWR arrangement or he would have surely realised that the old MR bolster was out of the question. Anyhow, he said, 'You know best; draw out something like that'. It was an easy job to draw out a bogie stretcher omitting the weight-carrying centre and with two extending hands to support the spittoons which slid thereon and received the semi-spherical undersides of brackets fixed to, and lipped under the frame. That is dated in my book 'Jan. 15, 1932. Details from *Engineering* 1923'. I hope I saved him some unpleasant remarks from William Stanier; perhaps the latter thought 'They aren't so daft after all'.

(Sir) William Arthur Stanier
SLS Collection

Frank Carrier and I were colleagues in the Derby DO for 30 years until his early death in 1952. It was general knowledge in the DO that the locomotive to go to the USA would be one of the later batch of 'Scots'. Neither Frank nor I did any of the drawings concerned in titivating up the locomotive with searchlight, bell, longer springs and so on. How much of the preserved No. 6100 ever went to the USA and back must be doubtful as she was rebuilt in 1950 with taper boiler, new cylinders, pistons, reversing gear etc, apart from swapping wheels, etc. Changing identities was a custom on the LMS - *Silver Jubilee* is another example.*

Mr Cameron's remark about the 'Scot' motion girder rang a bell in my memory box and made me dig out my Midland Railway (by that time LMS) draughtsman's time book - a useful *aide-de-memoir* compulsorily in use at Derby LDO. Sure enough it reads '11/3/30, Alteration to Outside Slidebar Bracket, Royal Scot, to make possible removal of 9in. Double Exhaust Liner, Drg. R.S. 1187'. Unfortunately my book ended in May 1930 and my memory has to fill the rest of the story, which is that the bolted-on girder was altered to match up. I think, but without the drawing I cannot be dead certain, that we widened the walls at the expansion link, which was such a fiddling job. The 'Scot' order was Derby O/7580; the 'Rebuilt Claughton', the official title for doing 5971 and 5902, was Derby O/7560 and my book records '24/8/29 (to the end of the year) Claughton Motion Details'. A few other odd jobs intervened at times, of course. The crucial entry is '25/1/30, Drg. of Slidebar Bracket 30-11640, Rebuilt Claughton and Scot'. This confirms Mr Cameron's detective work. In short, I did the motion for the two engines which had slightly different wheel spacing from the 'Scots', and made the slidebar and motion girders interchangeable for 'Scots' and 'Claughton'. As Mr Cameron says, the original 'Scots' girders would never have got changed, so 10 to 1 the clue as to the identity of No. 6152 is right: I confess I had forgotten all about it! Just one other comment; the photograph of No. 6100 in *Railway Engineer* shows coil springs on leading and intermediate axles.†

LMS 4-6-0 'No. 6100 *Royal Scot*', alias No. 6152 *The King's Dragoon Guardsman*, after return from the USA tour.   *J.M. Jarvis Collection*

*   *Compilers' Note*: In the February 1975 *SLS Journal* K.R.M. Cameron wrote: 'I feel I should try and throw some light on the alleged mystery about the actual identity of the "Scot" which went to America in 1933. For the sake of clarity - I hope - I will refer to the two locomotives concerned as "6100" and "6152" as in their original forms, and "6100" and "6152" as they were dealt with in 1933. The exchange between the two engines did take place, but I have no information whether or not they reverted to their original identities subsequent to the return of "6100" to the UK, nor do I know if and how the locomotive accountant reconciled the mileage records of the two engines.

    Early in 1933 engine "6152" entered Crewe Works' B Belt in the centre bay of the erecting shop south (10 shop) for service repairs, while engine "6100" went to the new work side, i.e. the north bay of 10 shop at Crewe. Within hours the leading fitter on the stripping of "6152" expressed the view that the sheds must have been swapping motion details (a practice which at that time was forbidden) because he had noticed that a union link from the motion of "6152" was clearly stamped "6100". The type marks were unmistakably in the neat, almost engraved, style used by North British Locomotive Co., and further investigation showed that every motion detail - something like 50 items - on "6152" was similarly stamped "6100"! A quiet look at the motion details of "6100" in the adjoining bay showed not very surprisingly that they were stamped "6152"!

    Apart from motion details, however, two other features of construction betrayed the exchange. The North British-built "Scots" had spiral springs on the leading coupled axle, whereas the Derby-built batch had laminated springs throughout, yet here was "6152" with spiral springs and "6100" with all laminated. This evidence later disappeared as all the "Scots" eventually got new springing gear with laminated silico-manganese springs and adjustable spring links. The remaining evidence, however, could be seen by the practised eye even from a moderate distance, and the "Scot" preserved as No. 6100 should be readily identified to this day as either the "6100" which went to the USA, or the original No. 6100 if in fact the exchange was ever reversed. On the "Scots" the outside expansion links were carried on trunnion bearings mounted on a six-bolt flange in the centre of a massive cast steel motion girder bolted between the slidebar bracket and the reversing shaft bracket, and on the original North British engines, Nos. 6100 to 6149, this trunnion flange lay flush with the web of the motion girder. On the Derby-built engines, Nos. 6150 to 6159, and on all the "Jubilees" and "Baby Scots", the motion girder at the trunnion bearing was strengthened by having a distinct raised boss on the casting, and which is generally clearly visible on photographs of these engines. Without seeing any numbers, therefore, one could instantly identify an original "Scot" from a Derby one. To the best of my knowledge these motion girders were never removed from the locomotives even at general repairs, unless accident repairs called for renewal, in which case it is likely that the later pattern would be utilized.

    I can also clear up the point about whether or not the builder's plate remained on the engine when it went to America. It did not, as "6100" was given a completely new smokebox wrapper plate when being prepared for the trip to the States, and no maker's plate was fixed to it.

    As a final point of interest regarding this eventful story, the tender which went with "6100" to America was a new one, and one of the earliest to be fitted with roller bearings. It was not completed and painted until four days before it was due to be loaded on board ship, and therefore never got a trial run in traffic. It did get a "trial" run however, loaded with coal and water, by being pushed one Sunday afternoon by two of the foremen (I was one of them) the full 600 ft length of 10 shop, to demonstrate its ease of movement. The "trial" was watched by an important group of VIPs, including H.P.M. Beames, F.A. Lemon and others. Despite the lack of running I believe that the tender bearings ran without a hitch throughout the whole 11,000 mile tour.

    I hope the foregoing historical note will clarify this mystery once and for all.'

†   Photographs of the preserved No. 6100 do not show this distinct raised boss on the motion girder at the trunnion bearing, indicating that the locomotives have almost certainly swapped back to their original identities, and that therefore in all probability no parts of the preserved 6100 ever went to America other than the bell and the nameplates!

LMS 0-4-4T No. 6408 with stovepipe chimney in the St Albans bay at Watford Junction, 4th
September, 1937.   *Online Transport Archive/ J.M. Jarvis*

Frank Carrier, Langridge's friend and colleague at work. He was very artistic and an excellent
photographer, many of his photographs being used in this work.

Kidderminster Railway Museum Trust Collection

My work on this 'Scot' was followed quickly with a request to do the same for the 'Rebuilt Claughton'. Next came the removal of the bogie brakes on the 'Scots'; it is rather funny that there was a fear that the bogie brakes might pick up and cause derailment, when you think of the multiple-units being braked, and pushed, nowadays. To make up for the loss of power, we increased the power of the coupled wheel brakes, necessitating some stressing-out and doubts about the high pressure of blocks on wheels. Maybe that was the start of thoughts of 'double blocks'.

When Stanier made his first visit to Derby locomotive drawing office, he came round with Beames, hobbling as usual with his stick, and Chambers. Some drawings of the 0-4-4T were still on the boards. Of course Chambers was on tenterhooks and Stanier on the defensive. The only remark made within my hearing was, 'Can't you get a long travel gear on it?', which, as it was a slide valve job, did not strike me as very deep thinking. Stanier had a pleasant manner, a soft West Country 'burr', very different from the northern sharp vowels, deep-set eyes slightly close together, a keen look that could be determined if required. Later I came to the conclusion that he was no designer as such, but then, how many CMEs were?

Another of the 'left overs' was a 2-6-0 tender engine for the NCC. This was a straightforward job; all we had to do was to widen the dimension between frames of the Fowler 2-6-4 tank and design the boiler expansion angles supports so that the parallel 'G8aS' boiler did not fall through. Otherwise it was like the 2-6-4 minus tanks, and without the rear part of the frame and bogie. A dragbox to mate up with the tender took its place. The gauge of the NCC was 5 ft 3 in.

Hornbuckle, mentioned in previous articles, was busy at Euston getting involved in diesel-mechanical shunters which outside makers were anxious that the railway should try out; it gave both parties experience for future development. This was 1932 and in the next few years some seven types of diesel-mechanical locomotives built by outside contractors were bought and tried out in service by the LMS. One rather different was a proposal by Haslam-Newton; in this they would supply the equipment for an engine which the railway would build. The idea would be worked out jointly by designers from both parties.

Haslam-Newton were a Derby firm, normally thought of as electrical engineers; in this case they appeared to be backing an idea of their designer, Smith, in a non-electrical proposal. (Later they made a torque-control, carbon block resistance unit, used for some time on diesel-electric shunters before more refined methods ousted it.)

The job came down to Derby locomotive drawing office, and Chambers nominated Frank Carrier to collaborate. The interest here was that the LMS were forced to come down to their younger drawing office men to do the locomotive part of the design. He spent some months working with Smith in Haslam's office, and came back with a great respect for him. They made a very good pair, Carrier keeping the brilliant Smith from running off the rails completely. Frank was an ideal choice for he was fine, quick, draughtsman with a sharp brain and a knowledgeable railwayman. In the days when we lived at Ambergate he would go off on his big Dunelt two-stroke, visiting the various running sheds etc. I believe he was *persona grata* at the old Grantham London & North Eastern Railway (LNER) shed and travelled the stretch between there

LMS NCC 2-6-0 No. 90 *Duke of Abercorn.*   *SLS Collection*

LMS NCC 2-6-0 No. 98 *King Edward VIII* at Belfast York Road, 22nd April, 1951.
                                                          SLS Collection/T.J. Edgington

LMS diesel 0-6-0 No. 7054 built by Hunslet inside Derby shed, May 1936. In the background is 0-4-4T No. 1375. *Kidderminster Railway Museum Trust Collection/W. Potter*

LMS diesel-mechanical 0-6-0 No. 7056, built by Hudswell, Clarke & Co. in 1934, stands with its coupling rods removed outside Crewe works, August 1939. Behind it is one of the Armstrong Whitworth diesel-electric shunters of 1935/36.

Kidderminster Railway Museum Trust Collection/W. Potter

and Peterborough very many times with many crews. In the office he must have been a thorn in Campbell's side; he was too quick for that gentleman and small radii on finished drawings Frank could put in freehand. It was sad that he should die at an early age; his last sketches were to do with J.F. Harrison's proposals for his BR class '8' 3-cylinder 4-6-2.

No. 1831 was the result of the collaboration. The power unit was a Paxman diesel, the transmission hydraulic to a jackshaft, thence by connecting rod to the three coupled axles. My own humble part came in joining up the controls and making the thing look like a locomotive. The frame was basically 1831's, rebuilt from an MR Johnson 0-6-0T, and the locomotive drawings were finalized in the railway drawing office. I had the pipe and rod and others the frame, etc., but Haslam's did all concerning their gear. The crux of the transmission lay in the fluid flywheels; a disc with slots could be moved across the face of a corresponding face of a moving disc coupled to the output shaft allowing more or less fluid to pass, under pressure from the diesel-driven pump, and so creating a torque. Coolers were on the roof, and much auxiliary equipment was obviously required. The fluid transmission was the Achilles heel; development such as we see today might have given it a better chance of survival. But at that time lack of interest at top level and lack of money killed it.

The moves at top level that I mentioned as being imminent in the last chapter took place in 1932: Vice-President Follows was succeeded by E.J.H. Lemon; motive power superintendent Anderson by D.C. Urie. Symes was hardly wanted at CME HQ once he had effected the introduction of Stanier to the senior members of the staff, and he moved across to become stores superintendent. A change of policy, this, for a technical man to hold this post. Riddles came up to take his place as Assistant CME, Ivatt moved up to the mechanical engineer's post, Scotland; Bellamy became works manager, Derby Loco.; Bond the same at Crewe with J. Rankin as assistant. With Beames continuing as deputy CME and still located at London Road, Derby and Chambers in nominal charge of both C&W and CME drawing offices, a new post was soon to be created, i.e. chief locomotive draughtsman, for which Sanford was nominated.

LMS 0-6-0 diesel No. 1831 as built.   *SLS Collection*

In due course, actually 29th April, 1932, line diagrams of Stanier's proposed locomotives arrived in the locomotive drawing office; Stanier's trademarks, which he could not get rid of even if he had wished, were taper boiler and low superheat. The Swindon boiler had a coned barrel with its lower side horizontal. Developed out flat the circumferential edges became a wavy line necessitating a former jig to guide the planing tool; drilling the undersized rivet holes followed this edge. After rolling to shape, the ends had to be pressed to become true circles so that one barrel would slide over the next (similarly with the throat plate). The large radiused firebox sides and top also produced wavy edges, and required pressing in order to make 'square' joints. While the firebox stay holes could be drilled 'square', those for the transverse stays had to be drilled out after assembly and tapped with long continuous threaded taps, and washers with inclined faces were required under the nuts, altogether an expensive job. I will mention the internal details later.

The Crewe boiler shop was praised generally by Stanier for its work, although he was critical of some of its tools in his early days on the LMS. Very reasonably he had no time for their 3-roller tube expanders and brought in a 6-roller type to avoid the tendency of the former to make triangular holes. He also disliked the 1⅛ in. rivets used in the 'Royal Scot' boilers: the pressure used on the hydraulic riveter in closing these distorted the edges of the lap joint plates. All the boilers during his time on the LMS had ⅞ in. rivets in ¹⁵⁄₁₆ in. holes. On the other hand, Fell, the boiler shop foreman, surprised Stanier by saying that Crewe could drill the wrapper plates for the 4-6-2 outer firebox in one piece on the flat and before rolling to shape, whereas Swindon had always made them in three pieces with a joint strap on the water line, even on their 4-6-0 boilers. The craftsmanship in the pattern and boiler shops at Crewe was obviously of a high order. The 'limits and fits' for stays and rivets worked to in the boiler shop were to the best machine shop practice.

Jack Francis, who had been brought back to Derby earlier, was given a copy of E9, the 4-6-2, and I, one for a 'Rebuilt Claughton' with taper boiler. As we were again next to each other in the drawing office, we discussed things together naturally; it has been stated that Stanier brought a box of Swindon drawings with him, but, if so, only their top-feed and regulator came our way. For the rest Sanford gave us a copy of the *Railway Engineer* dated July 1919 which became well thumbed, containing an article and details of GWR boilers, which we assumed to be current; and a copy of the general arrangement of Gresley's 4-6-2 from a *Railway Gazette*, useful for the wide firebox design.

The frame for the 4-6-2 was given to Willie Armin, the outside motion to Percy Lucas; I cannot remember who did the rest. I suspect that Frank Carrier being next to Percy did most of the motion; it looks as if they had a copy of the GWR motion, otherwise they would not have driven the expansion link by a projection on its side, very near the loading gauge line. Of course, there were four separate gears, but a divided drive to the coupled wheels rather spoiled the perfection presumably aimed at. I doubt if Euston had thought much about the strength of frame passing under the firebox front; Armin had a job to get enough plate there. The so-called 'breathing plate' at the rear had a persistent way of shearing off its fixing bolts, giving rise to thumps under the footplate which made some crews refuse to take the locomotive out. The pony truck design came from the Fowler-rejected Compound; it was a thing of many plates, gussets, spittoons and fussy control gear - and heavy.

It seems that Stanier opted for the GWR style of staggered cylinders and equal length connecting rods. Each cylinder, having its own valve gear, would then produce the identical indicator diagrams, outward and inward strokes, although the inward ones would differ from the outward due to the effect of the angularity of the connecting rods. So far as torque is concerned, it would then be like a 4-cylinder vertical steam engine. At that time Cox could have shown him the Horwich class '8' layout, for he was an L&Y man, but evidently with its scientific imperfections it was outside the pale. A few years later, when Coleman took the same scheme as drawn out by myself, it was accepted; great men can change their minds like the rest of us.*

---

* *Compilers' Note*: In the March/April 1990 *SLS Journal*, Joseph Cliffe wrote: Four sets of valve gears for 4-cylinder simples with 90° cranks are very rare and I do not readily recall other examples. The two other cases in England, the 'Lord Nelsons' and the North Staffordshire Railway No. 23, both had 135° cranks to give eight beats per revolution. I believe the reason for the choice of four sets of valve gear on the Pacifics was connected with the 1931 test results on the GWR 'Kings', which were fresh in Stanier's mind in 1932. These showed indicator card variations of as much as 18% between inside and outside cylinders, apparently due to the cranked rocker gear in front of the outside cylinders. This is as much as or more than the alleged defects in the Gresley Pacifics. Sam Ell at Swindon subsequently designed a modified conjugated gear for the 'Kings' but it was never fitted.

In the May/June 1990 *SLS Journal*, H.A.V. Bulleid wrote:

I think readers will be interested to hear Stanier's version of why he put four sets of valve gear on the first Pacifics. The following is a transcript from the 1962 tape recording I made with him while preparing *Master Builders of Steam* (Ian Allan, 1963 & 1983):

HAVB: Why exactly did you go to four sets?
WAS: I went for four sets of valve gear on the 'Princess Royal' because I hadn't been able to work out in the Drawing Office a satisfactory two-valve-lever operation. It wasn't until I had Coleman as Chief Draughtsman that I had what I wanted in that direction.
HAVB: So you did make an attempt to get a two-gear arrangement?
WAS: You're right, yes. The difficulty was this; you see the Drawing Office cylinder arrangement didn't make the application of a cross-over lever easy, and it meant, in need of getting the engine out quickly, it was simpler to put four valve gears on.

This was followed in the November/December 1990 *Journal* by Joseph Cliffe, who wrote:

Sam Ell's paper to the Swindon Engineering Society giving details of his modified 4-cylinder valve gear was published in February 1933, a full year after Stanier joined the LMS, but well before the 'Princess Royal' appeared. Nevertheless, it is probable that Stanier was fully aware of it. Ell's gear was patented and it seems unlikely that the LMS would have paid royalties to use it, even assuming Stanier was interested. There may be more than one reason why Stanier did not want to repeat the shortcomings of the 'King' arrangement, and as is made clear in the letter from Anthony Bulleid, he accepted four sets of gear as it was not possible to devise a satisfactory alternative in the time available.

It is evident that a more careful analysis than before was done on 'King' class No. 6005 in 1931 under Ell's supervision. Churchward was not very interested in IHP as such and concentrated on drawbar improvements. Previously Swindon had taken indicator cards mainly to check cylinder compressions, especially after superheating was adopted. There was some concern that the low clearance volumes used with saturated steam might give too much compression with superheated steam. Hence Churchward's belief that there should be no superheat in the exhaust. There may have been some truth in the higher compressions but Swindon were reluctant to increase clearance volumes in the belief that

It would be interesting to know what were the shortcomings of the 'Kings'. By the time the clearance was reduced to 5 per cent, I would think that the port cross section was so small that the steam had a job in getting out at all.* It is difficult to see how suspending the combination lever could appreciably alter its horizontal movement (I note Ron Jarvis did this, out of necessity, in the 'Merchant Navy' rebuilds) and the rear sliding block method of supporting the radius rod, as compared with the suspension method, limits the possibilities of variation of its stroke. I started that style of suspension, which I had copied from Gresley, on the Fowler 2-6-4T, but that was a 'both ways' engine. Unfortunately Chambers took my gear to the North British Locomotive Co. as a pattern for the outside gear on the 'Royal Scots' and they meticulously copied it; if left to themselves, they would no doubt have designed a suspension gear like that of the 'King Arthurs' [and the 'Lord Nelsons'!] - a much more suitable arrangement for a 'one-way' engine.

Looking back it is interesting to note that Drummond on the LSWR went through the cylinder spacing trouble. He started with Stephenson gear for his '330' class 4-cylinder engine and upside-down Walschaert's for the outside and staggered cylinders. Then he put the Walschaert's the right way up with piston valves on top (the '330s' had flat valves underneath) and finally the '443' 'Paddleboxes' had the cylinders in line with the outside Walschaert's gear and rockers to the inside valves. In my apprentice days I worked on some of these in Eastleigh works and so took some of my ideas to the Midland later.

The boilers on Nos. 6200 and 6201 had tubes 20 ft 9 in. long - reminiscent of Vincent Raven and the old NER, where his Pacifics had tubes 21 ft between tubeplates - and 16 flue tubes, each carrying two individual flow-and-return superheater elements, i.e. the steam made one pass down and back to the header. This design was detailed by Jack Francis from a Euston engine diagram.† We were told to shorten the tube length to 19 ft 3 in.; we were told to

---

[*from foot of p.154*] this would increase steam consumption. Not until 1936 with the 'Granges' was clearance volume increased with appreciable improvement in their performance.

The 'Kings' had an unusually low clearance volume of 5.5% and the 6005 indicator cards showed high compression in the outside cylinders, and some trials with reduced leads were made, without much effect. Double chimneys later made some improvement. The Churchward bent rocker was an attempt to correct for the angularity of the connecting rod but was only partially successful. Ell's gear gave a complete equalization, obtained by suspending the combination lever on a swinging link instead of direct on the valve spindle. An additional modifying link made the connection to the valve spindle. Although giving equalized distribution, Ell's gear did not give exactly synchronised exhaust beats, which was considered very important by Swindon for good steaming. Ell suggested this could be obtained with his gear by using unequal exhaust laps, entailing non-standard valve heads. This may well have been the reason his gear was not used; another was almost certainly the tendency for Collett to block any ideas he did not fully understand, of which this would be one.

---

* *Compilers' Note*: The late L.D. Porta advocated a clearance volume of 5-6 per cent, refer to his paper *Fundamentals of the Porta Compound System for Steam Locomotives* re-published in *Advanced Steam Locomotive Development, Three Technical Papers*, L.D. Porta, Camden Miniature Steam Services, 2006.

† By way of comparison it is worth recording that the GWR 4-6-2 No. 111 *The Great Bear* had tubes 22 ft 7 in. between tubeplates.

The frame and cylinders of a 'Princess Royal' class 4-6-2 under construction at Crewe works. *J.M. Jarvis Collection*

The frame and cylinders of a 'Princess Royal' class 4-6-2 with bogie and rear driving wheels outside the erecting shop at Crewe works. *J.M. Jarvis Collection*

make the small tubes parallel, no reduced ends, to screw the large flue tubes into the firebox tubeplate - no copper ends as on LMS hitherto - and to provide just two rows of these. As to weights, Euston were a bit short of experienced designers. If they based them on former Horwich sketches they would be 'chancing their arm' on an unknown quantity, so presumably they used the 'King' weights with a pony truck behind. As the job grew, Chambers could see that the locomotive would come out very heavy, but got no help from Euston; the boys there had done their job and departed into the wings, i.e., riding on footplates and inspecting, etc. I am afraid that the worry on a naturally worrying sort like Chambers led to his illness and early death.

Weights became public knowledge at the time of the Bridge Stress Commitee in the 1920s (when Sanford was delighted to find Loco. 'K' - a L&YR 0-8-0 which, due to upside-down balancing, made the river bridge at Newark really bounce; the MR '2000' tanks came a good second); but as the 'Kings' came after that time and being GWR products, one would have thought their figures trustworthy. However, truth will out, and a recent letter in the *Model Engineer* states that 'the writer had seen weights of 'Kings' at 96 tons instead of the official figure of 89'. So perhaps there is an excuse for No. 6200 coming out at 111 tons instead of the diagram weight of 103 tons 15 cwt. If the civil engineer made any objections, he must have been over-ruled (a good job it was not old Worthington of the MR).

So far as the press and the general public were concerned, No. 6200 was reviewed in August 1933 and the 2-6-0 in February 1934. Dates on cards may lead one up the garden path as any former works manager could say; which side of the dividing fence it was on 'the day' was what went down on the accountant's books, finished or not.* No. 6200 left Crewe shops one afternoon in 1933 for official inspection at Euston. Unfortunately she ran a hot crosshead and was put into Rugby shed for the night - the same sort of thing had happened to the original 'Crabs' with bronze slippers and crocodile bars a few years previously for no apparent reason - remetalled and, no doubt, with clearances not as shown on the new Swindon limits and fits in force as shown on a Swindon drawing. No one at Derby except the VIPs had seen her; as I have said we should have seen more if we had been at a contract shop! She had been 'designed by W. A. Stanier'; by the time the 'Coronation' came out, it was 'designed by the Drawing Offices at Crewe and Derby' - a nice compliment. An immediate result of the overweight was holes and thinning down of castings for No. 6201, and a general re-examining for future; but the third engine was held up pending some

* *Compilers' Note*: * In the January 1978 *Journa*l, A.F. Cook wrote: Several writers over the years have said that 2-6-0 No. 13245 was the first Stanier engine, for example E.S. Cox (*Locomotive Panorama Vol. 1*, Ian Allan 1965, page 109). In fact No. 6200 was the first locomotive to Stanier's design; the engine history card now in the National Railway Museum, York, shows its completion date as 27th June, 1933, whereas No. 13245 was not completed until 21st October, 1933. I am indebted to Mr C.P. Atkins, Librarian at the NRM, for giving me this information. These dates also correct an impression given by O.S. Nock in *William Stanier* (Ian Allan, 1964) where, on page 85, it is said that the Pacific 'preceded the Mogul by about eight months'. Whilst the dates of the drawings, or the dates of the commencement of construction, may have been eight months apart, the completions were only four months apart.

The firebox and boiler of a new 'Princess Royal' class 4-6-2.   *J.M. Jarvis Collection*

The fittings on the boiler backplate of a 'Princess Royal' 4-6-2.   *J.M. Jarvis Collection*

mysterious rumours. For Riddles in charge of No. 6200 it was 'right man in the right place'.

I must go back to my receipt in May 1932 of the proposed 'Rebuilt Claughton' diagram from Euston. It seemed strange that they had stuck to the 3-cylinder engine (instead of four) and just replaced a good parallel, cheap, boiler by an expensive taper one of unknown performance: 225 psi working pressure as compared with 200 psi before, a straight taper barrel 5 ft 2 in. to 5 ft 9 in. diameter, the Swindon figure of 2 ft between inside and outside firebox roof plates and with vertical firebox front and back plates. Apart altogether from the tube arrangement and low superheat it is difficult to see the merits of the taper boiler proposal: it had less firebox volume and heating surface and was much more costly to build. However, even as occurred after nationalization 15 years later, criticism from lower down the ranks was not exactly welcome and bad marks were no doubt chalked up against those concerned. It almost seemed as if Crewe were sensing trouble, for they went on building parallel boilers before there were engines to take them!

I must also introduce Coleman into my picture. He was now chief draughtsman, Horwich, having refused to come to Derby as I have recounted already. Stanier had a 2-6-0 on the list of designs; as Derby locomotive drawing office were busy, the design could go elsewhere; Martin at Crewe was not a very impressive man and they had lost their leading draughtsmen, so he gave it to Horwich. They could increase their staff, an easy matter with the slump on and good ex-contract men 'walking the streets'. So Coleman took on G.R. Nicholson (Yorkshire Engine Co. trained and later working in South America), L. Barraclough (ex-North British Locomotive Co., whom he had left at the end of the LNER 'Sandringham' order) and two others, and thus was off to a good start. The connection between my 'Rebuilt Claughton' and the 2-6-0 was that their boiler was to have the same diameter but a one foot shorter barrel and a 9 in. shorter firebox. I was not told of this at first, so drew out a straight taper barrel but on hearing of it a month or two later, it seemed obvious that money could be saved by having a cylindrical front barrel, long for the 'Rebuilt Claughton', shorter for the 2-6-0 and the same tapered barrel for both. For this purpose copies of the Derby design were sent up there. Crewe were making all boilers, so it would simplify their work. This had been done in bygone days at Swindon, of course, and the idea was accepted.

Another change to the original diagrams came in the backplate: it was now agreed that this should have a 6 in. rearward slope, similar to the MR Compound boilers, thus increasing the firebox length to 10 ft for the 4-6-0 and of course increasing the grate area. The barrel remained at 14 ft 6 in., giving the 160 small tubes at 2 in. diameter and the 14 flues at $5\frac{1}{8}$ in diameter, 14 ft 3 in. long with four elements, a free area/grate area ratio of 3.9/29.5 or 13.2 per cent. We at Derby, not being told otherwise, put the safety valve seating on the firebox top; unless it is built on before the firebox is assembled it cannot be put on. Someone (Stanier?) must have said they wanted the safety valves elsewhere for no seating was on the firebox of the 2-6-0 boiler. Again, you cannot fit two square-based standard Horwich-type 'pop' safety valves on the manhole with two top feed clacks, so obviously you consider fitting two direct spring-loaded

LMS 4-6-2 No. 6200 *The Princess Royal* as built with Fowler tender, entering Crewe station in 1933 at the head of an express from the West of England made up of GWR stock
.
Kidderminster Railway Museum Trust Collection/W. Potter

LMS 2-6-0 No. 13245 as first turned out with a GWR-type safety valve bonnet.
R.J. Essery Collection

Swindon type safety valves with two-stud fixing, also used by Drummond on his domes, which will go in nicely.

Coleman, tucked away at the end of a branch line, disinclined to have anything to do with Derby, making the most of Stanier's visits to Horwich, having the right confident approach to him, with his fast-working contract-shop men, soon made a show. They put the cylinders horizontal, not bothering about gauge clearance on curves; mounted a flowerpot safety valve casing and made the chimney height a little lower than the cab (Coleman had a good eye for a picture). The only drawback was that the engine had to be tried over all routes before being accepted by the civil engineer. She was also considerably heavier than the old 'Crab'; nevertheless she was out running as soon as the two 4-6-2s, long before the taper 'Rebuilt Claughtons'. Maybe Coleman thought the flowerpot the best-shaped casing for the line of his engine, he may have been trying to impress the new boss or it may have been one of his jokes; of course, it was soon replaced by the non-standard rounded casing above the top feed, much taller than those fitted to any other Stanier locomotive. What Coleman thought of this replacement is not recorded.

In my opinion, Stanier knew that the safety valves on the 2-6-0 were going on the dome but may not have realised that 'pop' valves would not fit in. I doubt if anyone mentioned the casing shape to him until it was *fait accompli*. Coleman was in a hurry to make an impression and get his locomotive out first, having no love for Derby, and would not worry Stanier with a lot of queries; and his new contract men were also keen to show that they could deliver the goods quickly.*

---

* *Compilers' Note*: In June 1981 *Journal*, K.R.M. Cameron wrote:

I remember the building of these locos very well, being one of the Crewe erecting shop Foremen during the building. The advent of a new type of locomotive of Stanier design was quite an event, and it did not entirely surprise us when the first 2-6-0 boiler arrived from the boiler shop with Swindon type safety valves on the taper barrel, which of course was of the 'broken back' type, i.e. the front wing parallel and the second one steeply tapered. At this stage I may add that I have never kept detailed notes of boiler numbers, dates etc, and must rely on that most unreliable of statistical records, my memory!

The first change in practice we noticed was in the lagging of the boiler. The LNW type was to my mind a very inferior and cheap looking blanket. The boiler for 13245 was to be lagged with a sort of asbestos mud (we called it 'monkey dung' at St Rollox) thrown at the boiler, to which it was supposed to adhere when it dried. It did when you started, but as we worked round the boiler whole sections dropped off and we had to start again! The experts said that we should not have painted the boiler - red oxide - before applying the mud, but it was too late to undo the coat of paint. We were then told that the boiler should be pre-heated before application, and this was duly done but with no greater success. I can recollect Mr Riddles himself hurling handfuls of the stuff at the boiler but to no avail. We finally abandoned the practice and provided sheets of chicken wire netting between which we sandwiched multiple sheets of crinkled aluminium foil - 'Alfoil' it was called - and this practice became the accepted one. The outer clothing plates followed the parallel/taper shape of the barrel, and to complete the Swindon picture the GW coned safety valve casing topped the top feed casting.

Eventually 13245 was turned out in this fashion, and by this time 13246 to 13250 were in advanced state of erection similarly equipped. I believe that I am right - always assuming that my memory isn't playing tricks with me - in saying [*continued foot of p.163*]

LMS 2-6-0 No. 2950 (formerly No. 13250) at Crewe South shed on 19th April, 1936. The first 10 engines of this class had boiler cladding in two sections, parallel and taper and like Churchward's short-cone boilers and with safety valves on 'dome'. All other Stanier engines had uniform taper for the cladding.   *SLS Collection/W.A. Camwell*

LMS 2-6-0 No. 2969 at Crewe South shed, 19th October, 1935. Note the uniform taper of boiler cladding compared with No. 2950 and the safety valves on the firebox.

SLS Collection/W.A. Camwell

Chambers was very worried lest the new taper boiler for the 'Rebuilt Claughton' should come out heavy and so prejudice the locomotive's route availability, so I had to calculate the weight of every plate, etc., and the water content of both parallel and taper boilers. If the same man did both, any bad judgements he made should cancel each other out. My result was that the taper would be 6 cwt lighter, due to less water being carried. Thereupon, someone advocated that, if the old style MR sloping back firebox plate were used, we could have a bit more grate area. This was agreed and I finished it off on those lines. As an alternative again, it was decided to use high tensile (34 ton/sq. in.) plates in place of the then usual 26 ton/sq. in., thus reducing thickness and weight. It also proved possible to adjust press block procedure so plates for the 2-6-0 boiler could still be of mild steel. Thus the outline of the taper boiler was finally settled. The bottom of the barrel lay horizontal as in GWR practice. The staying of the plates was normal, longitudinals being favoured rather than gussets. Screwed-in flue tubes took the place of LMS copper-ended expanded ones. No reduced ends were allowed on the firebox end of small tubes and a wide bridge piece between tubes in the firebox tubeplate was specified. A 'gold' was taken off my tracing, altered number given (13234), (retaining Stanier's signature!), dimensions altered and sent to North British for their order for 50 locomotives.

The purist must smile at the way a locomotive designer will work out heating surfaces, etc., to the third place of decimals, but cheerfully accept a 10 per cent alteration in, say, free area ratios without turning a hair.

The LMS (Derby) bogie, post-1925, had 6 ft 6in. wheelbase from the 'Compound' and 3 ft 3½ in. diameter wheels from the Johnson 'No. 3' passenger engine, with some trepidation at the time. It, and I think the Crewe one, transferred weight via the bogie centre. As previously mentioned, shortly after Stanier's arrival Chambers said 'Stanier wants a bolster bogie on the 'Scot'; have a look at the MR 0-4-4 Tank job'. I suggested Stanier wanted a weight transferring bolster rather than a spring loaded anti-rolling(?) device, so Chambers said, 'Get on with it'. You have to alter the centre arrangement to just a side control and make a new cast-steel bogie frame stretcher, with facings to take the 'spittoon' arrangement if it is a plate frame bogie or take brackets on the

---

[*from foot of p.161*] that 13245 was the only locomotive to go into traffic with the Swindon safety valve casing, because it seemed like the conjuror's 'now you see it, now you don't' before we got instructions to take off the Swindon casing and fit the elongated 'bowler hat' type. At the same time the stools and boiler lagging bands were modified so as to give the continuous taper from smokebox to throat plate, although the boiler itself could not be altered. The Swindon safety valves had to remain, but at some point quite soon we got the order to fit Horwich 'pop' valves to the top of the firebox. Since a number of boilers were already complete it was not possible to rivet on the appropriate safety valve pads, but in order to fit the 'pop' valve heavy steel seatings were made and fitted to the top of the firebox, being scraped and bedded down to a steam-tight surface, then fixed with steam-tight thread countersunk screws, the square heads then being cut off to give a flush finish, after which the whole pad was seal welded to the firebox wrapper plate. The Swindon safety valves were removed and the holes in the top feed casting were plugged and welded up. The later top feed castings were then further modified as they did not need to be as high as the earlier 'bowler hats'. It is at this point that I cannot say definitely at which locomotive in the series this became the standard practice, but I have the feeling that it was before we reached the tenth locomotive.

main frame if it is a bar frame bogie. The point is you have to have one or the other; you can't switch them about as for example on Drummond LSWR locomotives. So if we stick to numbers - names fuddle me - 5500 to 5551 were built in the Fowler/Lemon era, while the Stanier 4-6-0s started at 5552 and thus:

ED 173	4-6-0 passenger engine, parallel boiler	6' 3" bogie
ED 176	4-6-0 with 3 cyls and tapered boiler (Stanier)	6' 6" bogie
ED 272	4-6-0 passenger engine	
	3 cyl. type with 2A boiler	
	(Parallel boiler conversion, Ivatt)	6' 3" bogie

The above are taken from the diagram book. The Crewe 6 ft 3 in. bogies seem to have wandered about the 5502 to 5551 series until scrapping came, but never to Stanier's engines.*

Other points of interest about the Stanier 4-6-0 locomotives were as follows: LMS-type mechanical lubricator to cylinders, GWR-type sight feed lubricator to the regulator in smokebox ('head' of oil supply was too small to be effective). The very long regulator rod 2¼ in. diameter about 22 ft long (!) running in a steam-tight tube from the firebox to the regulator in the smokebox header casting was supported in the middle by a bearing in the steam collecting trumpet; all wheels of steam valves on the GWR-type steam fountain had wire-wound insulating handles; signal gear operating four ashpan doors; the smokebox had GWR-type door and fixings, and spark deflector plates inside. The boiler fittings all went Western and internally the steam collector 'trumpets'

---

* *Compilers' Note:* In June 1976 *Journal*, Revd G. Neale observed that: 'The diagram ED 176, the original "Jubilee" design, shows a 6 ft 3 in. wheelbase bogie with 3 ft 3 in. diameter wheels. These dimensions were LNWR standards and used for instance on the "Claughtons" and the "Patriots". The later diagram ED 176 K shows the LMS standard 6 ft 6 in. wheelbase with 3 ft 3½ in. wheels'. J.F. Clay replied in the same issue that officially the LNWR type radial bogie was retained on the first 12 'Patriots', the two original rebuilds and Nos. 5502 to 5511 of the batch sanctioned by Stanier in 1932. Nos. 5512 to 5541 were classed as 'rebuilds' but there are doubts about how much, if anything, from the replaced 'Claughtons' survived. Nos. 5542 to 5551 were unashamedly described as new engines. Nos. 5512 to 5551 are credited with having 'standard' bogies and it is perhaps significant that Nos. 5500 to 5511 were excluded from the rebuilding with Class 2A boilers by H.G. Ivatt from 1946 onwards. The official drawing of both original and rebuilt 'Patriots' shows bogies with a wheelbase of 6 ft 3 in. and 3 ft 3 in. diameter wheels. A bogie of similar dimensions is shown on the drawing of the first 'Jubilee' and the official description stipulates 'standard' bogies.
  In the July 1976 *Journal* J.F. Clay quoted R.J. Essery in *Model Railways*, January 1975, that 'The first five "Jubilees" should have been "Patriots" - they have "Patriot" bogies with 6' 3" wheelbase. The rest of the class have 6' 6" wheelbase and their tenders, the last five Fowler coal rail riveted type to be built, were numbered 4559 to 4563, with No. 4558 behind the last "Patriot" to be built, locomotive No. 5551'. Mr Clay also quoted an item from the July 1952 *Railway Observer*: '"Jubilee" No. 5613 *Kenya* is running with the bogie off a "Claughton" class engine'. Further research revealed that dates of shopping from the engine record cards for No. 45613 were:

Heavy General	21-06-51 to 11-08-51
Light Intermediate	15-06-53 to 02-07-53
Heavy General	15-12-54 to 19-01-55

[*Continued on p.165.*]

[*From foot of p.164*] The figures for overall length given on the engine record cards do not shed any light on the question of which engines had the shorter bogie. Possibly one of the original five bogies was fitted to No. 45613 and its 'Patriot' origin may have led to the description 'Claughton' class. The later 'Patriot' bogies were not correctly described as being of the LNWR radial truck pattern.

In the January 1979 *Journal* Mr J. Cliffe wrote that Mr Langridge,

… mentions that the last 40 'Baby Scots' 5512 to 5551 had LMS type bogies with 6' 6" centres; this fact does not seem to have been previously recorded. Official engine diagrams show 6' 3" centre bogies for the whole class, including the 1946 diagram for the taper boiler conversions which of course did not apply to the first 12. The subject of early 'Jubilee/Patriot' bogie design still seems to be clouded in mystery following earlier correspondence. The first 53 Crewe-built 'Jubilees' 5552 to 5556 and 5607 to 5654 do appear to have had 6' 3" bogies and this is confirmed in two books by J.W. Rowledge and from photographs which show 'Claughton' type wheel centres on these engines. In a paper to the ILocoE in 1948 J.C. Loach, an LMS man, states that also these 53 engines had Webb type radial guides instead of centre pivots. It might appear that, due to their Crewe origin, these engines used up scrapped 'Claughton' parts. However a plate type cross stay was used instead of the LNWR round bar at the front.

An early 'Jubilee' drawing dated 6/32 shows an engine with 6' 3" bogie, stovepipe chimney and a 'Patriot' style cab and, perhaps with some significance, is described as 'Taper Boiler Claughton'. Later in 1932 a decision was made to transfer construction to Crewe instead of Derby. Was there, therefore, a switch to 6' 6" bogies, intended for Derby- built 'Jubilees', to 'Patriots'?

In the July 1979 *Journal* Langridge replied: LMS engine diagram numbers should be taken with a pinch of salt; some have suffixes up to the letter 'N' and to get the history of a class one would have to consult each issue from 'A' onwards. Some public libraries - notably Westminster in Charing Cross Road, London - contain a range of *Engineers* and *Railway Engineers* when drawings of locomotive details like bogies were often printed. The 'Crewe' bogie was a 4-wheeled radial truck with rectangular section wheel spokes and centre pin fixed in cross stretchers. The Derby one was the Adams type 6' 6" bogie as on the 'Compound' with oval spokes. Later it had wheels with Stanier triangular section rims as well. My old friend and colleague J.C. Loach may have slipped up in his 1948 remarks; we all make mistakes.

Which locomotive had which bogie is largely a matter of academic interest as 'swaps' took place down the years. I remember seeing a rectangular spoked wheel with LNWR stampings under a 'Patriot' one day. One chief draughtsman used to keep two or three men on bringing drawings up to date with latest practice, but I have no doubt that, for example, some 'Compounds' finished their lives with their original crossheads although there must have been a dozen issues of altered drawings, trying to keep up with the changing fashions of whitemetalling etc. Perhaps that is why one man always spent his first hour in the office ticking off the things he wished to hear in his copy of *Radio Times* before getting down to the boring job of drawing alterations.

The three drawings of the first 3-cylinder 4-6-0 were all titled 'Rebuilt 3-Cyl. Claughton' - someone other than the CME Dept. must have started the now popular names. Naturally when we got on to the taper boiler version it became 'Taper Boiler Claughton'.

Mr Cliffe then commented:

I have subsequently seen the 1945 frame arrangements drawing D45-16950 for the rebuilt 'Patriots', which still shows a 6' 3" bogie, albeit with centre pivot. Nevertheless there seems to be no question that the first 12 engines had LNWR bogies. Presumably Loach was in a position to check his 1948 statement on 'Jubilees' also. Whatever bogie was fitted to the 53 Crewe-built 'Jubilees', it was of a different design to the contract-built engines, since photographs clearly show a different cross-stay.

in the top firebox corners took the place of the old dome collection. Production methods of screwed stays were improved to give more precise fitting and tubes were expanded by the new roller expanders giving a better and truer round hole than the old LMS tools. Fusible plugs are details which are always debated by engineers: the coarse threaded type now became standard. The Caledonian Railway hooter - which at first failed to hoot due to condensation in the barrel - was supposed to have been chosen by a committee of divisional mechanical engineers: whether it had a true Caledonian pitch was hotly contested! Top feed clacks with internal removable trays on a manhole were 'Swindon' but pop valves mounted on the firebox were 'Horwich'.

The wheels had triangular section rims and bolted-on balance weights. The axleboxes went over to steel castings with pressed-in brasses (the LNWR had previously done this), and also had lubrication introduced through the back of the brass onto the axlebox horizontal centre lines. Improved sliding underkeeps and pads were fitted where possible.

The back steam chest cover was extended with two feet to carry the valve spindle crosshead slides (instead of having them on the motion plate as previously); this got the nickname of the 'clog'. This perhaps was Barraclough's idea, for it was typical contract-shop design. The Horwich version had a circular extension, but the Derby one I did for the '5X' class had vertical walls which I thought simplified pattern making and moulding.

Horwich used the bent-lever rectangular-sectioned combination lever as on the 'Crabs', but I put a more good-looking straight-fluted lever on the '5X' and Coleman preferred that for all future builds. So far as the valve gear was concerned, the same travels were used as before on the 'Patriot', but redesigned details included reversing screw having a direct pull on the rod (no one-to-one lever); spring balance instead of weights on the reversing shaft; crossheads with bronze slippers (fitted originally and abandoned later on the Horwich 'Crabs'); felt oil-retaining pads let into bearing bushes; small end needle lubrication instead of trimming on connecting rods; piston heads with screw fixing on rods which also 'bottomed' solid in the crossheads having no 'draw'. The inside cylinder had a curved top flange to mate up with the circular smokebox, which also had a saddle support at the tubeplate. The outside cylinder steam pipes ran in one piece from smokebox header through glands in the wrapper plate; one would have thought troubles from expansion of these stiff pipes would have occurred.

Steam brake was fitted on engine and tender; a vacuum pump was fitted on the left-hand side, but the usual Gresham & Craven combined ejector and driver's fitting was anathema to Stanier, and Chambers asked me to get out a driver's valve to be mounted on the firebox backplate with connections to a combined ejector fitting mounted in front of the cab. I did this by using a disc valve controlling the vacuum and a steam plug controlled by a little vacuum cylinder, on the lines of the old Adams' (LSWR) locomotives. This was approved, but judge of my disappointment, when Chambers took it to Gresham & Craven for them to manufacture. Of course, Chambers was very close to the Gresham's, so I suppose that it was understandable.

Meanwhile I found it possible to use a larger element fixing flange on existing header castings; in this way 'bifurcated' elements came about, and were fitted in a few cases. Schemes were proposed for three and four rows of flue tubes, with 1 in. and 1¼ in. elements, but nothing materialized and production of the low-superheat boiler went ahead. A contract for 50 complete locomotives was also placed with North British. The leading bogie was the standard LMS 6 ft 6 in. wheelbase type but with side bolsters. This arrangement had already been produced for the 'Scots', replacing their original centre bearing, and applied to these 50 '5Xs' ordered from North British. The Crewe-built 1934 programme locomotives had the 6 ft 3 in. bogie.

In between the stop-go of the 'Rebuilt Claughtons', the third 4-6-2, No. 6202, came out of the mists; it was to be turbine on the lines of the W. Sweden/Ljungstrom pattern. Chambers, it appears, was told to pack his bag and join Stanier together with Guy and Struthers of Metropolitan-Vickers for a journey to Sweden; not a pleasant crossing for Chambers with all his present worries with Stanier's locomotives. Francis had returned to his beloved Crewe drawing office, so the job of modifying his design fell to me. Soon after Chambers' return I was told to get out a tubeplate for this third boiler, to give a higher superheat as Guy said he must have hot, dry, steam, otherwise his turbine would be inefficient and its blades damaged by drops of water. For calculation of superheat one could go to Rowlands's method (see Loco. Engrs *Journal*) or Lawford Fry and the Altoona reports. Sanford and his mathematical boys had evolved an extension of Fry's formula in which a proposed layout could be compared with known results. This became used by later people who did not always acknowledge its originator. By sloping the firebox throat plate over the rear-coupled wheel and trimming a little off the corner of the main frame thereabouts and making the slope of the plate as steep as the plate in the press in the boiler shop would allow, I could increase the firebox volume and shorten the rather long tubes of Francis' design. This tubeplate had 32 large tubes, the maximum I could get in using the existing header casting (No. 6200 had 16), and 112 small, giving a free area ratio of 51 per cent, i.e. what was considered normal, not high, superheat. However it meant that you could use the same header drilling as on the low superheat '6200' and giving the steam a double pass through the element instead of a single one helped to push the temperature up. Collecting steam in the top firebox corners, Swindon fashion, was then the vogue: the regulator in the smokebox became simply a shut-off cock with this engine, the regulating being done by valves mounted on the platform by the turbine casting and operated from the cab. So the boiler was still domeless except for the top feed connections. In order to keep the areas right the 32 elements were 1⅜ in. diameter instead of the former 1¼ in. ones. This scheme is dated February 1933. There were thus then three low and one higher superheat boilers for three engines. However, Metro-Vicks (Guy and Struthers) were not ready with their equipment, so this boiler became a spare for the first two engines and was soon fitted to one to try out the effect of higher superheat.

Normally a steel boiler lasts the life of the assembly, a new copper box being dropped in through the foundation ring hole, or by removing the backplate in the case of larger boilers, after perhaps 10 years or so. With the earlier Stanier engines a lot of money was spent getting rid of imported GWR ideas that did not work on the LMS. One fairly disturbing job was to mount an extra dome on the boiler barrel to house a regulator without disturbing other plates. This

LMS three-cylinder 2-6-4T No. 2508 at Harpenden, June 1935.   *SLS Collection/J.H.L. Adams*

Derby works erecting shop *c.*1935. To the left is Stanier 2-6-4T No. 2448 under construction.
                                                    Kidderminster Railway Museum Trust Collection

would account for Nos. 6200 and 6201 appearing thus with a straight throat plate. The boiler for the next lot of 4-6-2s (Nos. 6203 to 6212) was the same design as on the turbine. One of the batch was drilled for 40 flues and this was exchanged for the original one on the turbine.

On the other side of the drawing office, Campbell's section were designing a three-cylinder version of the Fowler 2-6-4 tank engine. All three drove on on to the middle coupled axle; the outside motion with the valve spindle, slides on the 'clog', the long crocodile slide bars, the motion plate hidden by the coupling rod, and the taper boiler, made this a very handsome locomotive. This boiler, slightly longer in the barrel, with the same grate area, was proposed as a replacement of the parallel 'G' boilers with 7, 8 and 9 ft-long fireboxes. It had 14 large, 140 small (1¾ in.) tubes, and with ratio of free area/grate of about 12 per cent would not appear to be a free steamer. Nevertheless, it was a very strong locomotive compared with its forerunner on the Tilbury, the 4-4-2 with a 6 ft 9 in. firebox, and was well-liked according to Thorley, writing in his book. Whether he refers to the engines as originally built or to those of later date with the higher superheat and 6 in. longer firebox (an expensive alteration to frame and stretchers) I do not remember. Then Campbell's squad put the taper boiler on the 2-cylinder 2-6-4 tank with few other modifications - the shortened wheelbase was not yet acceptable.

Across at Horwich, Coleman appeared to grow in favour. To follow his 2-6-0 engine and tender on which he had been complimented by Stanier, he was given the 2-cylinder 4-6-0 which became the 'Black Five'. For some years before this a modernized version of the LNWR 'Prince of Wales' 4-6-0 had been under investigation by H.P.M. Beames and his drawing office at Crewe. Apart from the fact that the 'Prince's' construction was too light, so that it fell apart too soon, it was a fine revenue earner. The 'Prince of Wales' boiler was almost identical with the 'G2', used on the 'Baby Austin' '7F' 0-8-0s. But by now time had pretty well run out for the old regime and with Stanier's appointment in 1932, preparation of proposed engine diagrams and bridge stress diagrams ceased in the provinces, at any rate for a few years.

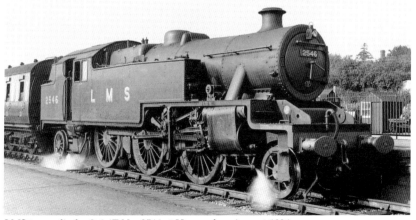

LMS two-cylinder 2-6-4T No. 2546 at Harpenden, August 1936.

Online Transport Archive/J.M. Jarvis

The engine put forward by the new office, although called at first a rebuilt 'Prince of Wales', was in fact a much more powerful job. It had over 25,400 lb. tractive effort compared with the 'Prince of Wales' 22,000 lb. and it was longer and heavier. In a short time all reference to the old 'Prince of Wales' was dropped and it became a 'Class Five Mixed Traffic Engine'. It would appear that Chambers, although chief draughtsman, LMS, was not consulted on the design, for I see there is a curious note from Henderson dated 30th October, 1933 which says, 'Look into the effect of altering the wheelbase of the proposed 2-cyl. 4-6-0 from 7' 0" + 8' 0" to 8' 0" + 8' 6". JH'. This must surely be a harkening back by a Midland mind to the wheel spacing of all their six-coupled engines, No. 4 goods etc, although it is true the Horwich 'Crab' and the taper 2-6-0 had this spacing. This must be one of the most curious proposals ever made and no more seems to be recorded concerning that suggestion! I estimated the extra weight as follows:

		cwt	qr	lb.
Boiler barrel lengthened	1 ft 6 in.	24	0	0
Coupling rods lengthened	1 ft 6 in.		3	0
Connecting lengthened	1 ft 6 in.		3	0
Frame lengthened	1 ft 6 in.	6	0	0
Platform lengthened	1 ft 6 in.	1	0	15
Pipe and Rod lengthened	1 ft 6 in.		3	0
Total		33	1	15

The Horwich proposal for the coupled wheelbase was 7 ft 0 in. + 8 ft 0 in. Their boiler had the barrel the same as the taper '5X', firebox the same as the 2-6-0. The bogie was the same as the taper '5X'; the Stanier wheel rim section, type of axlebox and so on were all incorporated. The cylinder patterns were those of the taper 2-6-0. They had different centres and offsets from those of the taper '5X'and the spacing of the frames was likewise different, thus upsetting the free interchangeability of many details. It is remarkable that these differences were allowed to creep in at the start of new designs, a thing unthinkable under Whale of the LNWR or Drummond of the LSWR. No doubt it was a relic of the rivalry between the three DO chiefs with no over-riding personality. The mark of Horwich is evident to the outside view in the shape of the ribs on the hind steam chest cover - curved instead of straight - and in the shape of the combination lever, which had a 'dog's hind leg' twist in end view instead of a straight set as on the '5X' three-cylinder engines.

As we know, Coleman's scheme was chosen, and before all the drawings had been completed an order for 50 had been placed with Vulcan Foundry. They may have actually done some of the design themselves; much of the design bears their stamp, and it is interesting to note that Charles Finlayson, brother of J.J. at Eastleigh and uncle of T.S. (then at Gorton and lastly, at Derby), was chief draughtsman at Vulcan. The Vulcan Foundry-built engines Nos. 5020-69 started appearing first, Crewe producing Nos. 5000-19 shortly afterwards. There seems to be a likeness between the class '5' and the LSWR 'H15' in details. In general there was nothing new about these engines for Urie had introduced his two-cylinder, outside gear pattern 4-6-0 back in 1913 (incidentally his chief

LMS class '5' 4-6-0 5020, the first of the series 5020-5069 built by Vulcan Foundry and in fact the first of the class to appear. *Ken Lea Collection*

draughtsman was contract-shop trained) and the SR had perpetuated it in the 'King Arthur' design, which had quite similar dimensions to the class '5'. Thus, even with moderate superheat, there was no reason why the 'Black Staniers' should not have got a good reputation from the first. The class grew steadily, aided by the massive order that Armstrong Whitworth obtained for 255 engines at one fell swoop.

The first order of engines had all the features that Stanier introduced in his early years with the LMS, such as top feed trays, smokebox regulator, trickle sanding etc. Other Swindon practices that came and went were the pressed-in oiling rings between eye and jaws of the motion rods, e.g. on the combination lever ends. Here the trouble was, of course, that rattle and wear soon killed any press-in feature; the rings just became loose. (These were also tried on Maunsell

LMS class '5' 4-6-0 No. 5009, one of the series 5000-5019 as built, at Wick shed on 11th June, 1936 and fitted with tablet catcher for single line working. *SLS Collection/W.A. Camwell*

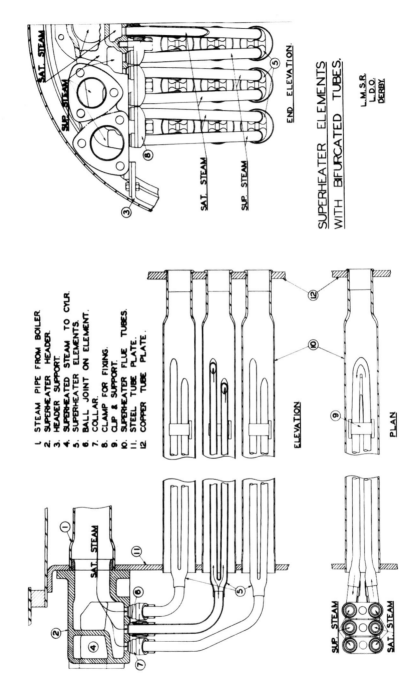

J.M. Jarvis Collection

Stanier flues and superheater elements.

SECR engines under the influence of Swindon-trained inspectors.) Also in the early Stanier years the impression (or even instruction) put around that the engine be 'notched up' to 10 per cent cut-off did not help towards sweet or comfortable running. The amount of slack or 'knock' that was tolerated between coupled axlebox face and guide face was incredible, particularly in the war years and in the north country. This again tended towards rapid wear. A bad reaction to this was in the spring gear where buckles were shifted on springs due to constant knock in boxes. As the class '5s' used the same flanged plates for the firebox as those for the taper '5X', when the design of the latter was changed to a recessed front firebox tubeplate, the class '5s' were built with the same feature. Similarly they gained a dome regulator and three-row superheater arrangement, and the grate area went up from 27.8 sq. ft to 28.65 sq. ft. Spring gear also changed: in the original design they had compression links with double adjusting nuts and rounded knife-edge washers bearing on end-shoes on the springs, and this gave way to J-brackets and screwed links in tension.

Many years ago I was told by a MR man that the GWR had the worst maintained carriage brakes because their vacuum pump was so powerful that it would deal with any leak bar a hose-bag off its nozzle. Perhaps the LNWR 'ting-tong' one was equally good. Anyhow, pumps became the fashion after Grouping, everyone thinking they got vacuum for nothing that way. However, like Drummond's feed-pumps, they proved to be expensive to maintain and so the C&W were told to improve their maintenance and the pump, like Drummond's, was eliminated. It was said on the LMS, whose pumps were a crib of the GW's, that you could not keep the gland packing tight, that the suction valves knocked themselves to bits and that piston rods broke at the end attachment to the crosshead due to sloppy crossheads. In the matter of isolating valves it must be remembered that the LMS locomotives, as distinct from the LNWR, were steam-braked and the arrangements on the GWR and LNWR vacuum-braked locomotives would not apply.

In the February 1976 *Journal* Revd H.G. Neale wrote:

> While at Crewe I played a minor part in connection with the drawings for the bogie vacuum brake on the LNWR 19 inch goods engines. Regarding the GW-type vacuum pumps fitted to LMS engines, I was told by a Loco Inspector of a case in which a Stanier engine with this pump was hauling a fast train with a horsebox on the tail end. The horsebox left the track and the vacuum pipe was ruptured, but the loss of vacuum was so slight that the train ran on much further than it should have done before the driver noticed anything amiss. A subsequent experimental run showed that the pump was so efficient that at high speed it could almost cope with an open vacuum hose at the rear of a train. For this reason, among several, the pump was then normally isolated by means of a valve already included in the pipe layout. The LMS engines were provided with both large and small ejectors in any case. But the reason for the hasty removal of all vacuum pumps (except the LNWR type) was the near disaster which, within the space of a few days, befell two 'Black Fives' on fast trains. In both cases the left-hand piston rod fractured in the neck just forward of the crosshead cone, wrecking the lh cylinder and dropping some dangerously large pieces of material close to the line.
>
> The cause was ascribed to the presence of the vacuum pump drive, taken by means of an arm from the left hand crosshead. At that time the 'Black Fives' handled the fastest trains on the Midland Division and were subject to rapid wear of both crosshead slipper

and piston head. They were doing work which should have been undertaken by the then recalcitrant 'Jubilees', which had larger wheels and shorter stroke. Within a week there was a small mountain of discarded vacuum pumps at Derby works, and no doubt at the other main works too. As far as I know there were no similar fractures on other classes of engines. This type of pump and drive had already been in use for seven or eight years without disaster on the 'Royal Scots' which were, I think, the first engines to be so fitted.

In the same issue of the *Journal*, H. Phillips of Hugh Phillips Engineering Ltd, wrote:

As I have become quite involved in braking matters of late, following Gresham & Craven Ltd agreeing to my supplying their products to the British preservation movement, I asked their now retired Managing Director, Mr G.C. Marsh, to whom I am indebted for the following, for his recollections.

A Committee reported on 'The Unification of Brakes on British Railways' in 1922, following tests of the various systems then in use. Especial mention was made of the steam consumption of the systems and the lowest was recorded by the GWR locos having crosshead-driven pumps and ejectors - the latter only needing to be used at low speeds or when stationary. Following this report both the LMS and the SR embarked on pump fitting programmes, but they were removed after a relatively short period due to maintenance and operational difficulties. The latter arose on trains which were double-headed. On such trains the extractive capacity of the pump on the train engine adversely affected the brake application made by the driver on the pilot engine, particularly at high speed. One of several incidents occurred at Carlisle where a train over-ran signals, the pilot engine driver made a full brake application against his own and the train engine's pumps plus the small ejector on the pilot engine. It was customary on the LMS to run the small ejector continually but, correctly in this case, in accordance with regulations, the train engine driver had shut down his small ejector. The LMS was the only railway which did not isolate the ejector upon a brake application being made; when pumps were fitted no further precautions were taken. This problem did not arise on the GWR where during a brake application the pump was isolated from the train pipe and connected to the 'top side' of the vacuum brake cylinders on engine and tender. It is therefore suggested that the removal of pumps was more as a result of operating difficulties than of maintenance, especially in the light of the long term success on the GWR.*

Coleman was obviously on the way up, and a lack of discipline on the part of Martin at Crewe enabled Stanier to transfer him (and his ex-contract shop men) to Crewe, and let Martin finish his time out 'off the map' at Horwich.

The next scoop for Coleman was rebuilding of *Fury* with a new design of inside and outside cylinders, and a new design of taper boiler. The boiler, done by Nicholson, one of Coleman's 'importees', more nearly resembled a Swindon product than any so far designed by LMS men, perhaps to show Stanier how co-operative Crewe drawing office were; the cylinders were more original in design and were done by Willcocks, a clever young Horwich-trained man, who went to the Ministry in World War II and never came back to the railway. As originally

* *Compilers' Note*: On the smaller GWR engines such as pannier tanks, which were generally steam-braked, the vacuum retaining valve (referred to by Langridge as the isolating valve) was not fitted, but no problems were reported with the driver's brake valve being unable to overcome the extraction of the pump. It is suggested this is due to the GWR driver's brake valve being slightly larger than the LMS one, together with the smaller pumps used on the smaller steam-braked GWR engines being less likely to over-create the vacuum.

turned out, the steam pipe casings outside the smokebox sloped backwards, and as the smokebox front was so far forward, the effect of the boiler having overshot the frame was created. Later a broad vertical casing was fitted, and this made the front look more stable. Derby locomotive drawing office knew nothing of this job until it appeared; Chambers could hardly have been consulted about the details.

Euston had produced a line diagram of a 2-8-0 using the class '5' boiler, but when Coleman's men went into the weight distribution (the job had been given to him), they found it 'back heavy' although the diagram followed the GWR layout. So they produced a revised scheme which brought the boiler forward and, in order to clear the third coupled axle, upward: this Stanier had no alternative but to accept.

By mid-1934 Metro-Vickers had started manufacture of their parts for the 'Third 4-6-2', the 'Turbomotive', as it became to be known in later years. For it a 'spare' new boiler was built, specified to be nickel steel rolled plates and mild flanged ones. The new weights from Metro-Vicks, plus actual weights of the roller bearings as weighed at Crewe brought the estimated distribution to: bogie 19t. 2c. 3q., leading coupled 24t. 0c. 3q., intermediate coupled 24t. 4c. 2q., trailing coupled 24t. 3c. 2q., trailing truck 19t. 16c. 2q.; this did not seem to scare the powers that be, and so the job went forward. Willie Armin got on with his frame, wide hornblocks for the roller bearings and drillings for the two turbines - forward on the left, backward on the right. The forward one was permanently coupled to the driving shaft in the centrally-mounted gearbox supplied by Metro-Vicks; the backward could be coupled up mechanically (as always, an Achilles heel in mechanical devices) as required, when a cooling steam jet would play on the reverse running blades of the forward turbine. The final drive end of the gear case embraced the leading axle of the locomotive, and the spider of this drive was coupled to the two arms forged on the axle. The drive appeared to be solid from turbine to wheel tread.

In the absence of Jack Francis (back at Crewe), I was given the design of the boiler. The specification I received said: nickel steel rolled plates, mild steel flanged plates, three rows of large tubes and a 'combustion' chamber. It was well known that GWR designers had always advocated vertical tubeplates: on this new boiler for No. 6202 and in all subsequent 4-6-2 boilers this prejudice was overcome and this so-called 'combustion chamber' introduced. There was an idea that this should follow the lines of the many-jointed affair of the proposed 'Fowler' ill-fated compound 4-6-2, but after drawing out one or two schemes, Chambers got HQ agreement to a deep flanged plate idea which would avoid any extra joints and all 'scarfing', i.e. thinning down of plate at joint. It all depended on what the plate presses at Crewe could handle, so I was told to go to Crewe and measure the gap, etc. available. It was found possible, after allowing for the depth of the shaping blocks themselves, to press a plate to approximately 3 ft 0 in. depth, allowing a 1 ft 6 in. chamber, shortening the original 4-6-2 tube length by that amount. It thus became possible not only to reduce the tube lengths to a more manageable figure of 19 ft 3 in. (from the original 20 ft 9 in.) but, what was of greater value, to increase the firebox volume and its surface subject to radiant heat from the firegrate, and I got out a sketch and pieces of paper shewing how the plates would overlap for Chambers to submit to Stanier. He came back and told me to get a scale model in wood made

LMS 'Turbomotive' 4-6-2 No. 6202 as built.   *SLS Collection*

LMS 'Turbomotive' 4-6-2 No. 6202 at Shrewsbury.
Kidderminster Railway Museum Trust Collection / W. Potter

by Hunt, Derby pattern shop foreman, and a sheet of lead to represent the plate being flanged. Hunt made a nice job, painted and varnished, and the model plate came out 'as planned'. I was next told to take it to Euston; there I met Cox and Fell, the Crewe boiler shop foreman, who, after explanation, went into the inner sanctum for half an hour with Stanier, while I waited outside. There is no need to describe my feelings: Coleman, having played League Football in his younger days and more used to shop floor methods, would have done a bit of gate crashing. However, it did not matter, I had got my idea accepted and was told to proceed. What made this and subsequent LMS 4-6-2 fireboxes unique was the way in which the semi-cylindrical shape of the throat plate at the boiler barrel end was 'faded out' gradually to suit the flat face at the foundation ring. Normally, when a cylindrical barrel runs into a sloping throat plate one gets a 'hump' on each side, right and left in the firebox, whereas in the design for No. 6202 the radius was specified to be 'constantly changing from that at the barrel end to the flat at the foundation ring. It is very difficult to get this shape across to the reader's mind without a model: and it was equally difficult for the pattern maker constructing the press blocks. In due course I went across to see Dicken who was making the patterns of the blocks; he was making them as if it was a cylinder entering an inclined plate - the usual way - and very naturally too. I had more or less to spokeshave off the 'humps' on his first effort, but after I had demonstrated what was in my mind he made a fine job. He had to get it across to the makers of the corresponding copper plates; the railway always bought these ready flanged but rolled the flat ones. After the boiler was built and stayed there came the problem of how to mark the staying of this curved-both-ways throat plate, so I went across to Crewe and did it myself, not without some misgivings. These stays, like all others in the water space, are required to be at right angles to the copper plate in order to obtain a good seating for the protecting nut, where these are used, and to obtain full screw threads in the copper plate and a good head, in the case of copper or alloy stays, riveted over. The stays in this throat plate were made of Monel metal and had heads riveted over: the only way of obtaining a satisfactory pitching of these on the copper plate was to do the scribing out on the first firebox, but the men were helpful and when the holes had been drilled through without mishap a flexible template was made and used for future, for no more boilers were built to the old '6200' design. It was also awkward for fitting of the brick arch. Normally this butted up against the flat surface of the tubeplate or throat plate. In this case it had to be built up against a constantly changing curved surface. The waist of the firebox also got wider, due to the combined curves, at the point of crossing of the engine main frames. With a slight rounding of the frame top and alteration to ashpan this boiler could go into these two locomotives, and all later 'Princesses' had it. Before leaving this prototype design it should be pointed out that no thinning down or scarfing of steel plates was required except at the lap joint with the foundation ring. The tube arrangement caused some discussion, but finally settled at 114 at $2\frac{1}{4}$ in., 32 at $5\frac{1}{8}$ in. with $1\frac{1}{8}$ in. elements. This design produced a saving in weight, as almost 1 ft 6 in. length of barrel, tubes and water was eliminated. Much later, No. 6202 was given a boiler with 40 large tubes, with regulator in dome. This was built to order BS/1/15.

The first LMS Stanier '5XP' class 4-6-0 No. 5552 as built with a modified old standard design of 3,500 gallon tender. This was used for publicity photographs and was not retained when the locomotive went into service.   *SLS Collection*

My next job was to do the pipe and rod arrangement. The control gear and the valves were supplied by Metro-Vicks. The most interesting thing to me was that the injector (a standard type) delivered water to the boiler after making many passes through a tank heated by steam exhausted from the turbine. The heater was placed at the front at the foot of smokebox. A CME Dept fitter always rode with the locomotive and generally fathered her. She ran off and on up to the early war years and again after; its full history has been written by Bond.

The London to Birmingham service was looked upon by the LNWR and the LMS as of major importance. Readers may remember descriptions in magazines of the City man's express with typist on board (a tribute to the smooth running on the LNWR) running to Broad Street at one time; it had later been worked by LMS 4-4-0 Compounds, and now, in the early 1930s by 'Rebuilt Claughtons'. There were 52 of these so-called 'Baby Scots' by the time the tapered-boilered versions appeared. D.C. Urie was motive power superintendent at this time. The first one, No. 5552, was shown off at Euston on 23rd April, 1934, a good looking locomotive and people wondered why it did not appear on the Euston

LMS 4-6-0 No. 5552 *Silver Jubilee* as decorated for the Jubilee of King George V. This was actually No. 5642.   *SLS Collection*

to Birmingham service fairly soon. The rumour at Derby was that they were not steaming well. Urie refused point blank to put them on this important service until the trouble was cured. Apparently a real row broke out when one, No. 5665 *Lord Rutherford of Nelson*, hauled the special bringing the gentleman of that name to open the new Research Dept building, already mentioned as being next door to the locomotive drawing office, in London Road, and arrived in the siding alongside with 100 lb. pressure on the gauge. There were all the top and lesser 'brass' on board, so that there must have been some leg-pulling that did not go down too well.

Apart from the rumours and the long face of Chambers, the first sign of trouble that the draughtsmen saw were hurried requests for tube comparisons between the parallel and taper boilers, and sketches of proposed repitching, etc. It seems that all and sundry, including Coleman, were asked, 'what should we do?' A boiler was prepared at Crewe with smaller tubes, altered brick arch, etc, and poor *Lord Rutherford* was sent into Crewe shops at once for it to be fitted. But rumour had it that there was a high level inquiry at which Urie, besides complaining about the bad steaming, cited all the vast number of things that had to be maintained: top feed trays to be withdrawn, feed pipes under fiddling casings, smokebox jumper, baffle plates, ashpan damper gear, etc. Some said that Stanier contemplated throwing in his hand; I doubt if we shall ever know the truth of that, but obviously he was a very shaken man. Chambers was even more so, for he had been caught between both sides: what he had had to do and what he felt was the right design (the old LMS). No doubt if there had been a strong reliable lead anywhere things would soon have been settled but Stanier's forces were scattered. He was away up at Euston with a small staff and inspectors, some of whom he had brought with him from Swindon. An unfriendly Motive Power Department was across the road. H. Chambers, his chief technical assistant in charge of the Locomotive, Carriage and Wagon offices at Derby, could hardly see his point of view. T.F. Coleman at Horwich seemed more understanding. There were some 163, three-cylinder taper-boiler 4-6-0s on order: the situation looked grim.

Whether rumour, the lying jade, had dramatized the situation I leave the reader to decide, but the fact is that, hardly had I finished staying the 'Turbo' firebox, than on 19th December, 1934 Chambers came out and said that the next lot of 3-cylinder 4-6-0s were to have a new cylinder design and a new boiler, or at any rate the internal part of it; these were the 1935 programme locomotives.

The outside cylinders were to have 'slap-on' exhaust faces to the frame, the passages to be continued in the inside cylinder casting all joining up to a single-legged blast pipe instead of the three-legged one as hitherto. Better access for tube cleaning was thus obtained.

I put one or two queries to Chambers:

Should we go for straight ports, necessitating moving back valve spindle crossheads, shortening radius rod etc?

Should we use 'Taper Scot' cylinder pattern, boring them out to 17 in. instead of 18 in. as 'Scot'? and a few more.

LMS 4-6-0 No. 6170 *British Legion* as first rebuilt with sloping steam pipe and single chimney.   *SLS Collection*

But the answer was, 'Stick to existing motion. H.C. 21/12/34', with a note from Sanford 'Make saddle and inside cylinder in one piece'. Sanford with his testing section had produced a number of equations giving relative boiler performance derived from grate area and free area of tube ratios. Coleman was more inclined to rely on flair and experience, and was thus in some ways closer to Stanier's outlook. Using Sanford's methods for comparative purposes, Derby DO got out a number of proposed new tubeplates always with more than the Swindon two-row superheater. Criticism had been made of the size of the small tubes - 2⅛ in. - although already used on the successful Crewe-designed parallel boiler, and Coleman - more or less independent of Chambers - had just completed drawings for rebuilding No. 6170 *Fury* as a normal 'Scot' but with taper boiler having 1⅞ in. tubes. But Sanford, following old text books like Perry, and from his own testing, was of the opinion that good steaming came from low resistance boilers. A relaxation of the width of bridge in the firebox tubeplate, permitted by Stanier, allowed a re-arrangement to be brought in on some of the 1934 Crewe batch and Nos. 5642-46 were turned out with 21 flue tubes having 1⅞ in. diameter elements (instead of 1⅜ in. originally) and 130, 2 in. diameter small tubes; but lack of conviction at HQ was shown as the rest of the Crewe batch, Nos. 5647-54 came out with the old two-row flue tube arrangement.

As to the boiler with which I followed in January 1935, the instructions were three rows of elements, increase free area, tube pitch as 'Scot', reduce firebox roof figure (distance between plates) from 2 ft 0 in. (Swindon practice) to 1 ft 8 in. ('Parallel Scot'). I also reduced the width of the water legs, giving us a 31 sq. ft grate, recessed the firebox tubeplate by sloping the throat plate, thus shortening the tube length by 1 ft 0 in. to 13 ft 3 in. Much calculating (no computers then) of boiler resistance and estimated superheat: I gave them nine schemes and for No. 5665 Chambers and Sanford (always keen on a low resistance job) decided on 138 at 2⅛ in., 21 at 5⅛ in. Comparison with the GWR 'Castle' was as follows:

New '5X' free area 4.75 sq. ft   Tube length/bore 85   Almost as old 'G7'
'Castle' free area 4.7 sq. ft   Tube length/bore 85

Before embarking on the next (1935 programme) engines a further look round at what had been done on *Fury* was made, and at the changes in firebox shape on the later 'Princess Royal' boilers. At one time cylinders with straight ports were mooted, but the consequent alterations in length of motion rods were deemed to be too much of a drawback. Improvement on the existing cylinder patterns for the 'Jubilee' was sought by easing out some of the sharp bends and combining in one casting the inside cylinder proper and the smokebox saddle containing all the exhaust passages from inside to outside cylinders.

Evidently differences of opinion existed regarding boiler layout. In any case, its weight had been over-estimated and it was now possible to use mild steel instead of high tensile plates of rather doubtful ductile properties. It was also agreed to reduce the over-generous water leg widths and go in for a sloping throat plate similar to that on the old LNWR Scheme Three and 'Scot' fireboxes. Thus grate area went up from 29.5 to 31 sq. ft; also firebox volume and heating surface changed due to 1 ft recession into the barrel. In conformity with what had been done on other classes the regulator was moved from the smokebox to a dome, necessitating a re-arrangement of internal steam pipes and the abandonment of the Swindon 'trumpet' collector in the firebox. The dome regulator was of the Stroudley pattern but with slides moving in a horizontal plane instead of vertical, being at maximum height above water level. The slides were operated by a one-to-one lever arrangement connected to a crank on the regulator rod which rotated to open or shut in the usual way. The drawings of these boilers were made at Derby but the dome and regulator were designed at Crewe under Coleman's supervision. Thus the shadow of things to come started to spread. This led to more changes in design on future 'Jubilees', Coleman's opinion evidently carrying more weight with Stanier than did Sanford's. Many variations came later as shown in the table on page 182. Unfortunately I have no record of the results. But I know Coleman favoured a small tube diameter (he probably influenced the 5665 'crash decision' boiler), and obviously went for it when he became 'boss'.

LMS 4-6-0 No. 6170 *British Legion* as modified with large straight steam pipe covers but still with single chimney. *SLS Collection*

Table One

Particulars of 3-cylinder 4-6-0 engines with taper boilers (as built) Derby, 22nd September, 1937

Build date	*Loco. Nos.*	*Type of boiler*	*Grate area sq. ft*	*S'heat elements*	*Boiler tubes*	*Bogie w/base*	*Type of sanding*	*Type of blast-pipe*	*Tender*	*Built at*
May 34	5642*	Mild steel straight throat plate	29.5	2 rows of 7, 1⅜″	14, 5⅛″ 160, 2″	6′3″	Hand (trickle)	Three-legged pipe	3,500g, 5½t, rails	Crewe
June 34	5553-5556									
June 34 Apr 35	5557-5606	Nickel steel straight throat plate				6′6″			4,000g, 9t	NB Loco
June-Aug 34	5607-5616	Mild steel straight throat plate				6′3″			3,500g, 7t straight sides	Crewe
Sept-Dec 34	5617-5641								3,500g, 7t curved sides	
Dec 34	5552* 5643-5646			3 rows of 7, 1⅜″	21, 5⅛″ 130, 2″					
Jan-Feb 35	5647-5654			2 rows of 7, 1⅜″	14, 5⅛″ 160, 2″					
Dec 34 Jan 35	5655-5664					6′6″				Derby
Nov 35	5665	Mild steel sloping throat plate and dome	31	3 rows of 7, 1⅛″	21, 5⅛″ 168, 1⅞″			Single leg pipe		Crewe
Nov 35	5666				21, 5″ 138, 2⅛″					
Nov-Dec 35	5667-5676								4,000g, 9t	
Dec 35	5677			4 rows of 7, 1⅛″	28, 5⅛″ 105, 2⅛″					
Dec 35-Mar 36	5678-5694			3 rows of 7, 1⅛″	21, 5⅛″ 138, 2⅛″					
Mar-Apr 36	5695-5701			3 rows of 7, 1¼″	21, 5⅛″ 138, 2⅛″		Steam			
May-Sept 36	5702-5724			3 rows of 8, 1¼″	24, 5⅛″ 159, 1⅞″					
Sept-Oct 36	5725-5730									
Oct 36	5731			3 rows of 8, 1″ triple						
Oct to Dec 36	5732-5742			3 rows of 8, 1¼″						

* No. 5642 was built as No. 5552, but numbers were exchanged on naming of *Silver Jubilee*.
No. 5665 was also fitted with 3 rows of 7 elements, 1¾ in. diameter, and also with a boiler same as No. 5666. Tenders have been extensively changed.

I suppose the most surprising thing about the boiler barrel was that it had a dome housing a regulator. The two slides lay vertical, had prongs in which a long pin fixed to the arm of a lever operated at the opposite end by an arm on the regulator rod from the cab in the usual way. So ended the smokebox regulator.

The 6 ft 6 in. bogie had become standard since the Derby batch, Nos. 5655-64, and the Derby 'Midland' 3,500 gallon tender, despised by all other centres, at last ceased to be built, the Crewe-designed 4,000 gallon and 9 tons tender being fitted to all Crewe-built engines after No. 5666. The narrow 'Midland' tender had never fitted up to any modern engine at all comfortably and would have gone out of production in the Horwich 'Crab' 2-6-0 days if it had not been for Hughes' retirement before the engines were completed. The main snag of this 4,000 gallon tender with closely-pitched wheelbase was that it pushed up the loading on the bridge curve and so could reduce route availability. In some cases the maximum bending moment came under the tender middle axle. Another Swindon 'accessory' that Coleman seemed able to persuade Stanier to drop was the trickle or gravity sanding. From No. 5695 steam sanding was fitted to the 'Jubilees'. An order to fit the original two-row boilers with new tubeplates was issued in 1935. This was an expensive modification but judged to be worthwhile on the 'Jubilees'. The arrangement was the same as for new boilers being built at that time. As time went on all boilers had dome regulators. Top feed removable trays were dropped as well. In due time new inside cylinders combined with smokebox saddle and exhaust passages were also fitted.

We had gone a good way to eliminating Swindon features; some remained - the 'jumper' and the deflector plates in the smokebox, the screwed-on piston heads, were still to go. We were back to where we were before Stanier's arrival in design, having spent a lot of money and time to no purpose. One cannot blame Stanier; it was an error on the part of the very top brass. They appointed a man with a trademark; it suited green engines and he was not to know that it would not work on red ones. He was wise enough to let the old hands have their way when he found out; but the suggestion had to come from the right quarter. Those made by Coleman found favour (the dome just mentioned was done in Crewe drawing office by Jack Francis for him), those from Urie seemed unwelcome. However, he did agree to the fitting of sandguns at Urie's' request; anything more cruel to a man brought up at Swindon cannot be imagined.

Water softening, with which the Research Department had been experimenting for some years, had settled down after many different arrangements and instructions, to a continuous blowdown principle and trays were considered unnecessary. Nevertheless, at times astonishing sludge collection took place in boilers and at other times excessive corrosion caused the CME much trouble. The waste of coal to provide continuous blowdown steam was even more annoying to engine crews than that spent on steam heating. At first we put it through the tender tank to collect a little heat back and clipped the discharge pipe to the rear guard iron. The civil engineer objected on the score of possible broken rail-ends as the drips dropped on his rails, so he said! So we put the pipe end in the ashpan, if my memory holds, where the steam if any might act as a blower. It was supposed to discharge 2½ gallons of hot water per engine mile, equivalent to about 800 gallons on a journey from Euston to Glasgow! I can just imagine, too,

LMS '5XP' 'Jubilee' class 4-6-0 No. 5649 at Bedford shed on 18th April, 1936 before it was named
.   *Online Transport Archive/J.M. Jarvis*

LMS '5XP' 'Jubilee' 4-6-0 No. 5654 *Hood* at Rugby shed, 24th July, 1937.
                                                Online Transport Archive/ J.M. Jarvis

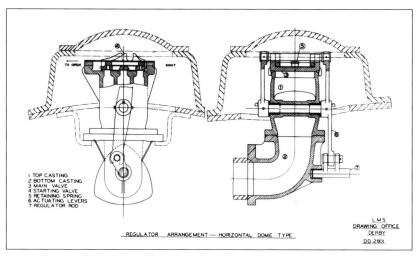

1 TOP CASTING
2 BOTTOM CASTING
3 MAIN VALVE
4 STARTING VALVE
5 RETAINING SPRING
6 ACTUATING LEVERS
7 REGULATOR ROD

REGULATOR ARRANGEMENT — HORIZONTAL DOME TYPE

L M S
DRAWING OFFICE
DERBY
DD. 2801

Stanier dome and regulator, which superseded the smokebox regulator.

J.M. Jarvis Collection

some of our friends in the Middle East during World War II rubbing their hands in satisfaction at the thought of this precious hot water being dumped on the desert sand by the '8F' 2-8-0s in military service! The Motive Power people at one time thought that the leaking joints at the feed pipe to the dome allowed water to drop on to the inside big end as it percolated under the clothing, and they asked for a protection plate to be fitted on the clothing in the region of the big end. I don't know what happened in a thunderstorm in their estimation.

Following the *volte face* there were schedules to be got out for alterations to the 100 or so '5X' engines already built, so that money could be obtained from the Board.

LMS '5XP' 'Jubilee' class 4-6-0 No. 5700 *Britannia* stored new in Crewe stock shed.

Ken Lea Collection

LMS '8F' class 2-8-0 No. 8000, of the series 8000-8012, as built.   *SLS Collection*

LMS '8F' class 2-8-0 No. 8042, of the series 8027-8095 built by Vulcan Foundry with polished wheel rims, smokebox door hinges, buffers, etc.   *SLS Collection*

LMS '8F' class 2-8-0 No. 8041 on freight duty.   *SLS Collection*

Chapter Nine

'Coronations', Diesel Shunters and Wartime

In due course more orders for 2-cylinder 4-6-0s were placed, one for 225 from Armstrong Whitworth, a firm under pushing management, and perhaps with unseen subsidy, that had swept the older builders out of the way, and collected many of their good men as well. 2-8-0s were also built, all to the new pattern boiler design and with shortened tubes. At home, Campbell followed with a taper boiler 2-6-2T, similar to the 2-6-4, only smaller, with motion nearer to that of the Fowler 2-6-4T than to that of his 2-6-2T.

Some moves of personnel were made in 1934/35. Cox was made assistant to the Derby works manager, Chambers was moved to Drummond Street (Euston), perhaps due to poor health; Coleman came to Derby as chief draughtsman, Locomotive, Carriage and Wagon, in his place, and Nicholson moved up to be chief draughtsman, Crewe locomotive drawing office. Sanford remained chief draughtsman, Loco., Derby. One or two men came too; Barraclough who, from his attitude, soon expected to become leading hand. However, although Jock Henderson now lost his authority, a complete outsider appeared on the scene to take over the post of leading hand. Durnford was the new man; he had apparently lost his job in the Argentine (and his pension, due to political changes) and had come home. Stanier took compassion on him for reasons we did not know but could guess. Armin, who had been Jock's No. 1, nominally at least, was naturally disappointed, but anyhow the old idea of leading hands controlling matters of design had been fading for some years in the locomotive drawing office. They came more and more to be concerned with correspondence to do with other works' drawing offices, etc., especially now that Crewe was handling and creating new standard designs.

Meanwhile various ways were tried, in conjunction with the Superheater Co., to increase the steam temperature on the 4-6-2 engines, Nos. 6200 and 6201. These included elements with small tubes down the flue and a large bore return; another with a lagged return tube; others with different sizes of element, mostly using large bore 'downcomers' welded to the elements, and having fixing flanges to the existing header/regulator casting in the smokebox. Finally the boiler originally intended for the 'Turbo' was fitted. Due to the necessity of the plan of the firebox sides to follow the slope of the roof (otherwise there would be a twist in the wrapper plate), and to maintain the 45 sq. ft grate, the width at firebox back is slightly greater on this boiler and required adjustment of platform, etc., here.

Further 'Princess Royal' 4-6-2s were ordered and came out in 1935:

No. 6203	32 elements 1⅛ in. diameter
Nos. 6204-7	24 elements 1¼ in. diameter
Nos. 6208-12	32 elements 1¼ in. diameter

They all had the new boiler type with combustion chamber.

LMS Princess Royal 4-6-2 No. 6209 *Princess Beatrice* under construction in Crewe works erecting shop, 1935.   *Kidderminster Railway Museum Trust Collection/H.G. King*

LMS 'Princess Royal' class 4-6-2 No. 6205 *Princess Victoria* with larger tender at Crewe North shed, 19th July, 1935.   *SLS Collection/W.A. Camwell*

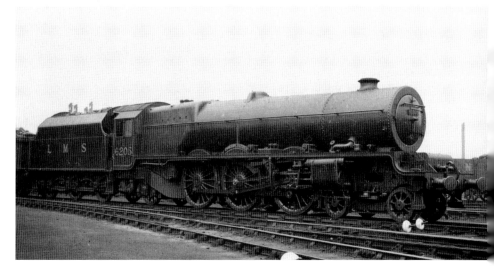

Next, an order for two spare boilers for 4-6-2s provided us with a chance to try to improve the free area ratios. A suggestion to lift the firebox roof level, and so get in more tubes, was turned down as new press blocks would be required; with the Superheater Co.'s standard flue tube it was difficult to improve the balance between gas and steam areas in the elements, and so nothing was done.

All this time Gresley was forging ahead with the LNER 'Silver Jubilee' train in 1935; in various countries locomotives were being designed with a view to high speed trains, e.g. Wagner in Germany and Chapelon in France, and all the LMS could do was to renumber a new '5X' as if it were the first of a new class, decorate it with 'silver' beadings, and call it *Silver Jubilee*. By the end of 1935 the LMS had only 13 4-6-2s. Although Coleman asked Barraclough to see if he could get a larger boiler on the next lot of 4-6-2s, we started ordering up material and marking up drawings 'same as' to use the old MR phraseology, for engines Nos. 6213-17.

Then the powers that be decided to run a fast demonstration train from Euston to Glasgow and return. It was hauled by No. 6201, and did the run at something like 74 mph out and over 70 mph back. Apparently that and the LNER efforts caused a change of heart, for Coleman came out asking for a diagram of a 4-6-2 with 6 ft 9 in. wheels and as big a diameter boiler as we could get in the loading gauge. It was then that E402 was issued; Coleman and one of his senior men at Derby had been working for some time on various schemes for a 'bigger and better design' than the 'Princess'. The reader may well ask, 'Why?' From the designer's point of view, I can only reply that there is always the urge to improve. The true designer wants to be kept busy. Like any other artist he improves with practice. To achieve a change, broadly the old requirements of having the 'right men in the right position at the right time' apply. Also in the early 1930s there seemed to be the urge everywhere to try and advance rail transportation. Apart from detail troubles that could be put right fairly easily, on paper to the discriminating eye the 'Princess' design did not seem to be using material to the best advantage. There were the four valve gears and the spread-out wheelbase, while the boiler seemed to be a long drawn out affair. From the technical press one could see what was happening elsewhere and felt that one could do as well, or better than the others. On the commercial side there was always the publicity value of having 'something new this season'. No doubt the publicity man is apt to be 'the tail that wags the dog' at times and the engineer has to swallow such things as streamlining and smoothing which, in his view, are neither beautiful nor useful. Even in later years the design consultant, so called, had the diesel shunter access doors smoothed over, with the result that the examining fitter could not find the handles on a dark night, and neither would the doors themselves fold back. In achievement little could be finer than the demonstration runs with No. 6201 on the Euston-Glasgow and return runs; yet the thought that the design could be improved persisted and Coleman convinced the 'powers that be'. Undoubtedly every new design is a gamble and perhaps we were luckier than Chambers had been. In his young days Coleman had played football for Stoke FC and perhaps he knew better when to shoot for goal. He asked me to get rid of the inside motion of the 'Princess' design. Sanford with his quick brain at once pointed out

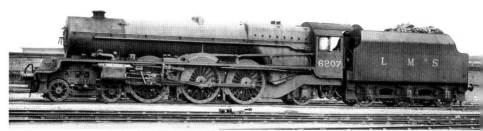

LMS 'Princess Royal' class 4-6-2 No. 6207 *Princess Arthur of Connaught* in Crewe works yard on 3rd July, 1938. The crosshead pump has been removed but the bolt holes are still visible.
SLS Collection/L.W. Perkins

LMS 'Princess Royal' class 4-6-2 No. 6208 *Princess Helena Victoria* on up 'Royal Scot' north of Rugeley in April 1936.   *SLS Collection/P.S. Kendrick*

that if we connected a rocker to an extended outside valve spindle, and drove the rear end of the inside one from the other end of the rocker, the effect of expansion of the spindles would cancel out. I think that was the layout on the Great Southern & Western Railway (Ireland) 4-6-0 built by Watson, who had evidently become enamoured of things GWR when he was manager of Beyer, Peacock just previously. I have never heard the reason for their failure, or for their rebuilding as 2-cylinder locomotives by the next man, J.R. Bazin. I doubt if Sanford had a great knowledge of what had happened elsewhere in the practical locomotive world; his strong point was his sense of development of anything scientific or mathematical.*

I suppose my addiction to what had gone before rather than to original thought made me think of Drummond's 4-cylinder 4-6-0s, where, as I described earlier, he advanced from the staggered pitching of the outside and inside cylinders (as on GWR engines) on his '330' class and old '453' class to his 4-cylinder in-line arrangement on his last '443' class 4-6-0, latterly dubbed 'Paddleboxes', and their arrangement of valve gear. By doing so, he got rid of the racking forces which loosened cylinders and stretchers and which in every example from that day to the 'Kings' and 'Princesses', had taken place with the staggered arrangement. The Drummond arrangement of driving the rocking levers, placed behind the cylinders, involved a die-block, pinned in the outside valve spindle and sliding in a rectangular slot in the end of the rocking lever. This was not much better than the 'Claughton' design, in which the rocking levers were placed forward with the valve spindle cross-heads sliding on the lever ends to take care of the versed sine movement and which really dated back to Webb's 'Alfred the Greats': they were all too full of sliding surfaces. Moreover, on the Drummond design I did not forget having seen a twisted mass which had been the top of the outside combination lever, die block and end of rocking lever, so I did not want to perpetuate that idea. The drawing of the L&YR class '8' appealed to me as the thing, where the rocking lever was driven by a short link having pin joints, one to the outside valve spindle extension and one to the rocker. Coleman, from his earlier position at Horwich, was familiar with this arrangement, so I got out a scheme on those lines. The rear flange of the inside cylinder casting overlapped

* *Compilers' Note*: In March 1980 *Journal* J. Cliffe wrote:

The Irish 400 class came out in 1916 at a difficult period of Irish history and their early years have been shrouded in mystery. Watson, coming from Swindon, based them on the GWR 'Star' but in comparison with the latter, it is generally considered that they suffered from steam pipe expansion and leakage problems, together with a lack of frame stiffness and bracing between the outside cylinders. There does not appear to have been any special advantage over the Swindon arrangement in their rocker drive from the outside, since, unlike the 'Stars' the rocker arms were not cranked to allow for connecting rod angularity.

The success of Bazin's '500' class 2-cylinder 4-6-0 clinched the final rebuilding of the '400s'. Watson, following Maunsell, was intensely disliked at Inchicore, which did not help.

Langridge is slightly in error with E.A. Watson's movements: He moved from Swindon to become works manager at Inchicore in 1911 and was promoted to locomotive, carriage & wagon superintendent in 1913. He was appointed as General Manager at Beyer, Peacock & Co. in 1921, the same year the '400s' were introduced: Ref. *Biographical Dictionary of Railway Engineers*, John Marshall, RCTS 2003.

the front flange of the outside cylinder (with the main frame in between) and fixing bolts went through the three thicknesses. This got rid of the long step between the inside and outside cylinders which always seemed to me to be a bugbear. This scheme had the inside cylinders forward of the bogie centre-line and the outside ones to its rear, with the rocking lever to the inside valve gear at the back of the outside cylinders. In order to keep the outside connecting rod down to 11 ft 0 in. centres the spacing between the first and second coupled wheels had to be reduced from 8 ft 0 in. on the 'Princesses' to 7 ft 3 in. This made the locomotive more compact but did away with the equal length connecting rods and identical valve events which were made a feature of by those who prepared the original 'Princess' layout. This was labelled Scheme 'B' and seemed too revolutionary to be accepted at HQ.

Of course, I also drew out a Scheme 'A' as Sanford had suggested, retaining the GWR pitching of cylinders as on the '6200', i.e. outside cylinders over the rear bogie wheel and the inside ones over the leading bogie wheel centre-line with a rocking lever forward of the outside steam chest and to the rear of the inside steam chest.

With the increased driving wheel diameter of 6 ft 9 in. , I took a little off the top corner of the Belpaire firebox by increasing the corner radius, necessitating riveting over the side row of roof stays, instead of nutting them as was Swindon practice, lifting this up to touch the gauge, and 'pinching' 2 in. off the 2 ft 0 in. (Swindon) figure for distance between inner and outer firebox roofplates. A 6 ft 5½ in. diameter barrel would then just go in with 6 ft 9 in. diameter wheels. An extra liner was put on the barrel above the wheel centre lines so that if full rise of the axleboxes should be taken up, a most unlikely thing, the flanges would not rub a slot in the barrel itself.

Coleman seemed more keen on his big boiler than on the motion schemes, but said he would show them to Stanier: he did not think that Stanier would want to change the former cylinder layout. So I was agreeably surprised when on his return Coleman said, 'He has gone for your layout, get on and cancel the material sheets, we are going to number these 6220-24'. This was a few days before Stanier's departure for India. How nearly we went ahead with more 'Princess Royals' is reflected by the fact that drawings were actually being marked up and material being ordered for 'Eng. Nos. 6213-17' when this last minute effort by Coleman at Euston succeeded in getting the decision reversed, obtaining the agreement to the new cylinder and boiler layouts. It was as a concession to the superstitious that the number 6213 was dropped and the new engines started off at 6220. Stanier had also said that five locomotives must be ready for the 1937 6½ hour London and Glasgow service. In this 'chancy' way history is made.

The design for the 'Coronations' as they came to be called was formulated in the Derby locomotive drawing office, but the detail drawings were prepared partly there and partly in the Crewe LDO, under charge of G.R. Nicholson. The work of detailing the boiler and other parts above the platform was allocated to Crewe and the remainder to Derby.

In the case of the estimated weights for this E402 we were more fortunate than on the parallel boiler 2-6-4T: we had the actual weights of No. 6200, viz. 111 tons 18 cwt. After thinning down castings etc. No. 6201 came out at 108 tons. It was evident that E402 could be kept down to the estimate of 106 tons without much difficulty. In common with all new designs, for the diagram showing the end view of the locomotive in the loading gauge and the points of fouling, a plan of the fixed (coupled) wheelbase and the bogie and pony truck centre pins was drawn out on tracing paper. This was laid on a drawing of the standard, say 6 chain (66 ft) radius, curve which was usually preserved on mounted unshrinkable paper in the DO and drawn out at 3 in. = 1 ft scale. The diagram of bogies wheels and bogie centre, and that of pony truck wheels and pivot arm centre were each drawn out separately to the 3 in. scale. These two diagrams were laid on the main frame diagram in the correct longitudinal positions and the necessary side movements measured off to bring the wheels within the curve. Allowance had to be made throughout for clearance of boxes in guides etc. and for tyre clearance. On E402 the usual thick + thin + thick ARLE profiles were used on the leading, intermediate and trailing coupled wheels respectively, but the pony and bogie tyres had a special thick flange to increase the life before reaching scrapping size. These thick flanges also made the wheels tighter in the gauge and check rails. Taking everything into account it was found that we required 2¾ in. movement at the front bogie centre and 4¼ in. at the pony truck axle centre line, right and left. Most civil engineers would allow some infringement of the loading gauge on curves provided that this was above station platform level. This gave the designer some freedom at cylinders and steam chests where width was valuable.

We then came to the detailing of the boiler. The boiler design as a whole depended on the maximum barrel diameter at the throat plate end. With the water space being carried up from the foundation ring to form an annular space between the steel and copper throat plates, the overall sizes of the firebox tubeplate in all directions were determined. The pitching of the tubes in the plate was governed by the following considerations. Flue tubes were normally supplied by the manufacturers at 5⅛ in. nominal diameter x 7 swg. Small tubes were available in many sizes and the one selected by the designer usually aimed for the ratio of length to diameter of about 100 to 1 (*see Appendix Eight*). Heat transfer increases with gas speed and surfaces exposed to radiant heat are worth their weight in gold. Thus the small tube size selected was 2⅜ in. outside diameter x 11 swg. Each flue tube carried a triple element, i.e. six cross-sections, 1 in. od x 11 swg, the steam making one pass, out and return. The elements finished about 1 ft short of the firebox for the longest and 2 ft 6 in. for the shortest return bend. The a/s ratio for flues was about 1/550 and 1/430 for the tubes. This gives some idea of the proportion of gas passing down each kind of tube. The superheat temperature will bear some relation to these ratios and also to the characteristics of the elements themselves. The search for increasing the amount of superheat went on until the last days of the steam locomotive design. Various types of element were made by the Superheater Company, either to their own ideas or to those of their customers. A few non-Schmidt types were the 'Sinu-flow' having depressions to sine curve shapes along the tube; the 5P4 type; the bifurcated types one of which had the return pipe (a single large diameter) lagged at the smokebox end to prevent heat loss. In E402 the triple element was used.

The pitching of the tubes was then schemed out. The ruling was that the 'bridges', the metal in the tubeplate between each tube, must not be less than ¾ in. The tube hole in the copper tubeplate was ⅛ in. less than the tube nominal size, the tube itself being swaged down before insertion, a practice not allowed in GWR boilers.* Another break-away was in allowing the flue tubes to be more closely pitched at the firebox end than at the smokebox end, entailing the inclination of tapped holes for these in the firebox tubeplate. In setting out the tubes, care was always taken to keep the holes away from the plate corner radii and it sometimes happened, as in E402, that a row of small tubes at the top of the tubeplate was more valuable in using the area economically than in pushing the fluetubes themselves to the top. The scheme adopted in the E402 boiler had 129 tubes at 2⅜ in. od and 40 flues at 5⅛ in. od (nominal). The free areas were:

Through flue tubes	3.66 sq. ft
Through small tubes	3.23 sq. ft
Total free area	*6.89 sq. ft*

This free area is only 13.8 per cent of the grate area, showing how difficult it is to get a high percentage within the British loading gauge for an engine with a large grate. The diameter of the boiler barrel at the front end is dependent on the pitching adopted for the tubes. The LMS figure for the flue tubes transversely was 6¼ in. pitch. This was to accommodate element fixing flanges on the superheated header. Vertically the dimension was reduced to 6 in. The small tubes were pitched as at the firebox tubeplate. Room for about half-a-dozen washout plugs was required, plus a reasonable distance from the flange radius of the drumhead tubeplate. Although it was not disastrous if the tube bank was so high at the smokebox end that it became uncovered by the water on steep inclines or surges, it was felt inadvisable to run the tubes much higher than their firebox level. The drawing office in its scheme had already pointed out the advantages of the truly conical boiler barrel in regard to easy machining and assembly as compared with the previous GWR pattern in which the taper barrel has its bottom plates level, and the true cone arrangement was agreed to. The minimum diameter at the front of the barrel was thus fixed at 5 ft. 8⅝ in. The specified working pressure was 250 psi and the minimum factor of safety was 4.75 (*see Appendix Eight*). Boiler steel plate material was 2 per cent nickel steel. The design of the boiler joints using ⅞ in. diameter rivets in ¹⁵⁄₁₆ in. diameter holes was as normal, i.e. double riveted with an extra reinforcing row through the inside strap and barrel on the longitudinal seams. Following the earlier Pacific boilers, longitudinal stays slung from brackets riveted inside the front ring of the barrel supported the flat portion of the front tube plate, in the same manner as the usual short longitudinal stays supporting the firebox backplate.

Coming to the design of the firebox, the overall dimensions at the cab end were usually settled from a consideration of the height of fittings and other items to be fixed within the loading gauge, such as safety valves, space for lookout forward from the cab between the boiler clothing and the cab side plates, the depth of the ashpan required and the position of the mainframes. Thus the slope of the roof plates could be fixed, bearing in mind that they were to be curved to the usual 18 ft radius for inside and 19 ft 10 in. radius for the

---

* *Compilers' Note*: This appears to have changed sometime after the war, as it clearly became standard practice later on as evidenced by numerous preserved Swindon boilers.

outside plates. The slope of the firebox sides required great care in working out as the wrapper plates had to have a truly plane surface with no twists. As a curved cross-section was also specified, but at the same time a straight-sided (although tapering overall) foundation ring was required for practical reasons such as the assembly of fireboxes etc., one had of necessity to run the line of commencement of radius parallel with the slope of the roof. Above this line all cross-sections were similar, although they increased in width from back to front, where the width of the firebox at the boiler centre matched up with the barrel diameter. Below this line the plates dropped vertically to match the foundation ring face. Joining up the roof with the curvature already mentioned and sides curved as described above was a 9 in. radius on the steel plate, which just brought the clothed boiler within the loading gauge. The inner (copper) wrapper plate could not stand such a large radius, being a weaker material, and therefore had a 5 in. radius in the corner. The radii of the door plate corners and Belpaire front corners were normal: the changing radii of the throat plates were similar to that on the prototype boiler developed for No. 6202 previously described.

The inner firebox at all times had to be designed so that it could be inserted as a unit within the steel one. As design departed from the simple rectangular shape this became more of a problem. LNWR and NER designs reversed the steel back-plate flange. Thus, instead of dropping the inner box through the foundation ring hole, they inserted it through the backplate opening, making the closure by riveting through the exposed back plate flange and wrapper plate, instead of riveting through the foundation ring. Wide grates assist in allowing copper inner boxes to be 'angled' into position. The staying of the copper plate to the steel in the area of the water legs was by means of ¾ in. Monel metal stays on the outside rows and by ⅞ in. special steel stays for the rest of the area. The work of planning the layout of these was a work of patience by the draughtsman concerned. The pitch was determined from the normal formulae by Napier for flat plate staying and, in the case for nutted and/or riveted stays, came out at approximately 3 in. The staying of the copper plate to the roof plate was made by steel stays, nominally ⅞ in. in the body, screwed into inner and outer plates and nutted where possible; otherwise with ends riveted over. The pitching, being governed mostly by the weak copper plate, was similar to that of the water space stays. Transverse steel stays, nominally 1 in. diameter, tied the firebox steel sides together and were screwed into the wrapper plate, which was suitably stiffened in this area by liner plates, thus giving a full thread to the stays. Longitudinal stays from the barrel supported the flat steel firebox backplate. The thickness of the firebox steel plates was decided on largely from experience rather than from strength considerations. Double riveted lap joints were used for all steel lap joints and single riveted ones for copper plate joints. Tapered washout plugs at firebox roof level and washout doors with lead insertion joints were arranged at strategic points just above the foundation ring. Oval holes for washout were better than screwed-in plugs at points where much 'rodding-out' was likely to take place at washout periods. The doors, being inserted from outside and seating inside the plates, were largely self-sealing.

The smokebox wrapper plate, having been drilled and cut to profile in the flat, was rolled to form a cylinder with the ends butting and Vee-welded. In the early streamlined engines the shape was flattened towards the front. It was passed over the distance ring on the boiler front barrel and riveted up, the rivets passing through wrapper distance piece and boiler plate. Considerable weight was saved here by substituting a single riveted ring instead of the GWR double riveted type and also by using a wrapper plate ⅜ in. instead of ½ in. thick. The boiler was far stronger than the frame when considered as a longitudinal beam, and the designer therefore generally used it to support the frame, wheels etc. when the locomotive was being lifted. To this end vertical connections, which may be considered as boiler supports normally (although in lifting they become ties) were arranged at convenient positions. At the smokebox the wrapper was riveted to a small frame stretcher containing exhaust steam passages to the blast pipe. The main front fixing was under the front barrel; there was a sliding support under the rear barrel section; and the main rear support for the boiler was under the front end of the foundation ring.

The boiler mountings in the cab comprised two standard water gauges. The difficulty of reading the water line in these led to various types of reflector being tried. A main steam fountain, with an internal supply pipe from the dome and under the control of a main shut-down valve, had individual valves controlling the supply to the injectors, carriage warming apparatus and the brake ejector, making a cumbersome arrangement high up in the cab. Wire-wound handles of the GWR type had proved too 'finicky' for LMS conditions and wheels with spokes had returned in their place.* The usual centrally-mounted blower valve and operating handles for the hooter were fitted. The firehole door was of the sliding type with hollow doors intended to allow access of secondary air to the fire through grids and slots in the walls. The firehole deflector plate, as usual, depended on the firehole stiffening ring for its location. The regulator handle in its shut position hung some 45° below the horizontal centre line on the driver's side, the driver being on the left. At one time a 'drifting catch' had been fitted corresponding to a 'cracked regulator' position. The usual steam carriage warming services were provided: the reducing valve on the boiler back was a very neat design based on principles enunciated some years previously by D.W. Sanford.

Towards the rear of the firebox top four safety valves of standard LMS short type were mounted on seatings let into the firebox proper, in order to keep their tops within the loading gauge. The dome on the middle barrel provided access to and room for a main regulator with valves working on horizontal faces. The slots and holes in the slides were arranged to give a curve of opening area directly proportional to the movement of the driver's regulator handle in the cab. The mechanism for working the valves themselves from the rotating regulator rod used two forked levers; one on each side of the regulator head, pinned to a shaft which had one lower lever giving a 1 to 1 ratio and connected by a link to an arm on the regulator rod. The forks of the levers meshed with suitable slots in the valve slides themselves. A manhole on the top of the front barrel carried two boiler feed water clack boxes. Due to the newer water

---

* *Compilers' Note*: These wheels were probably too 'finicky' for GWR conditions too, but there they were replaced by turned wooden handles on a steel core, forced tight onto tapered spindles, which gave a far more comfortable feel on the hand and overcame the appalling jangling rattling made by the LMS loose brass handles!

softening arrangements, the former type of so-called removable trays was not fitted: a simple deflector arrangement directed the feed water down the barrel of the boiler.

The 40 flue tubes were screwed into the firebox tubeplate and fitted hard up against the chamfer on the water side. They were beaded over in the firebox after the removal of protruding screw threads and expanded at both ends. It was a practice in Crewe shops to provide one hole slightly larger than standard through which to pass the small tubes. These were finally expanded and beaded over in their holes at the firebox end and in the lower rows at the smokebox; others were simply expanded. Originally Stanier boilers had tubes with a reverse taper at the firebox end, thus holding them extremely tight at that end. The beading of the small tubes in the smokebox followed a very old Crewe practice.

The superheater header was a simple casting fixed to the drumhead tubeplate. It had countersunk facings to suit the superheater element flanges which were fixed by tee-headed bolts slipped into machined slotted ways in the header casting. The 7 in. diameter main internal steam pipe was expanded and ferruled into the front tubeplate and secured by cone joint and bolts in the usual way at the regulator header casting. Saturated steam connections on the superheater header took steam to the atomizer steam valve, mounted outside the smokebox wrapper plate, and to the tube cleaner cock on the smokebox front plate - typical Stanier fittings. Also in the smokebox were the two main steam pipes from the superheater header to tee-pieces mounted low down on the smokebox wrapper, where supplies to inside and outside cylinders divided. This arrangement eliminated the awkward packed glands of previous designs.

As in GWR practice, the smokebox proper is not considered to be another boiler barrel and is therefore of lighter construction. The door had the usual GWR style of fixing: dart with tee-head working in a slot in the cross bar, the end being screwed to take the central fastening handle which provided the necessary tension. The front plate was a pressing with the flanged portion machined to 45° to match up to the door itself, which was likewise machined. An inclined strip caught a projection on the door, as it was being closed, lifting that end of the door so that the whole became central with its hole, thus easing very considerably the work involved in closing and securing this type of door. The cross bar, being a heavy forging, was pivoted at each end. Removal of one of the pins allowed the bar to be swung out of the way through the door opening - a much better design than those of Drummond [or Swindon], where the cross bar had to be lifted out of its brackets. The original chimney was a normal iron casting with a hollow rim. The ejector exhaust ring was bolted on to the chimney bottom. It had a cored passage and a large number of holes drilled at an angle to guide the exhaust up the chimney. This arrangement involved casting a thick ring with its top surface at right angles to the drilled holes, drilling at an angle through this and then turning this ring away out to the chimney bore size - a rather expensive proceeding. Single chimneys were thought by Stanier and most engineers at that time to be sufficiently drastic. An experimental double chimney had been fitted to No. 6201 some time earlier, but the inspector's report was non-committal and the idea faded away. There was a feeling in some quarters that economy could best be obtained by burning as little coal as possible rather than by turning out as much horse-power as possible: it depends on which side of the equation one is interested in. Steam to the blower ring, cored out and drilled as part of the blast pipe cap, came from a fitting in the cab. The blast pipe cap was a plain casting apart from having a cored passage for the blower steam exit up the chimney. The jumper cap had been abandoned on later engines of the previous build. I think it was Sanford who remarked on the poor logic of the argument in its favour, i.e. that it provided a freer exhaust, for before you could get the extra openings the exhaust itself had to lift the weight of the loose cap - about 15 lb.* At one time Swindon's sheet of blast pipe and chimney ratios were worked to, but as they brought in such things as heating surface figures they could only apply to Swindon characteristic designs.† In the case of the locomotives under discussion, Coleman had his own ideas of shape of exhaust cone, etc., and put them into practice. No spark arrestor or deflector plates were installed originally, but later a so-called 'self-cleaning' arrangement was fitted involving expanded metal sheets in frames across the smokebox, with a horizontal table plate and a front skirt, which forced exhaust gases etc. from the tubes to pass through the mesh. This was all part of the scheme to reduce motive power depot costs in ash removal and preparation time. It had not the menace of the original GWR spark deflector plates where careless latching of the inclined plate could allow it to drop onto the blast pipe and cause a 'blow-back'.

To meet the edicts of the commercial department a false clothing, 'streamlining', was fitted to some of the early batches of these locos: its scientific value was small. A model of a streamlined locomotive was made and the final shape determined from experiments made in the Research Dept wind tunnel, supervised by Dr Johansen. An amusing anecdote concerns his name; Sanford was dictating a letter to his typist one day. It came back for his signature addressed to Dr Joe Hansen! The practical disadvantages of closed-in mechanical parts, hidden sandbox lids, mechanical lubricator lids and smokebox doors, together with the necessity of ladders to enable cleaners to wipe down the clothing proved too much of a drawback and in due time the 'streamlining' was removed. This required a great deal of work to be done in fitting normal footplating, etc.

---

* *Compilers' Note*: This may be another case of which side of the equation one is interested in. At lower steaming rates the jumper top in the closed position acted rather like the famous 'Jimmy', an illicit piece of home-made ironmongery which crews would sometimes fit to the blast pipe to sharpen the blast in an effort to improve a poor steaming engine but, unlike the 'Jimmy', the jumper top would indeed lift to provide a freer exhaust at higher steaming rates. In fact ample lifting force is available when the engine is working hard, as evidenced by one occasion in 1985 when the restraining clips came loose on GWR 2-8-0 No. 2857 on the Severn Valley Railway and the jumper top was ejected high into the air, finally coming down among the coals in the tender, to the astonishment of the startled crew!

† For this statement to stand up it is regretted Langridge does not supply more explanation or supporting evidence, though this statement is admittedly less unsatisfactory that his tongue-in-cheek assertion on page 183 that steaming rates were affected by the colour of the paint!

The design of the main frames followed conventional lines. The difference between the design for a 4-6-0 and a 4-6-2 is caused by the widely-spaced longitudinal lifting centres. One endeavours to get these as close as possible in order to minimise the bending moment. In a 2-6-4 tank engine one can drop the lifting slings through the cab roof and pick up the frame just behind the firebox, but in a 4-6-2 the span is bigger, although lifting points are in front of the smokebox and behind the firebox. As mentioned above, the designer uses the boiler strength to reinforce that of the frame. Thus there is a solid fixing on the stretcher, in front of the leading driving axle, and a main sliding support at the front of the foundation ring and behind the trailing driving axle. The latter was drawn out by L. Barraclough. With his North British Locomotive Co. background he got out a typical Contract Shop design used on Indian State and colonial engines, in which the base of the foundation ring rested on a shoe free to slide longitudinally, but not transversely, and also had two retaining lugs keyed to the frame stretcher. The main frame plates were sufficiently strong in the vertical plane to permit being lifted with cross-stretchers *in situ* - minus wheels, axles and hornclips. The ties to the boiler give it the structural stiffness of a beam to resist frame deflection when lifting the locomotive for transfer down the shop, or for wheeling, un-wheeling etc.

Opinion about the design of the frame structure has oscillated between the 'flexible' and the 'rigid' ideas in the horizontal plane. The maintenance investigators at the formation of the LMS decided to cut out the pin-jointed cross stays at the hornblock bottoms (as they did at the centre bearings) used on the LNWR. By Stanier's time many new classes of loco had returned to the ideas of cross-stays, but fixed solid by bolts or studs. Likewise the use of horizontal stays running from front to rear (as far as possible) came and went. Much mathematical and statistical work was done by the rather modestly-sized Research Department of the early 1930s. One cannot determine that it had much effect permanently. A point that seems to have been overlooked in some of the arguments is the fact that, in years gone by, it was customary to have a typically ⅜ in. thick footplate with outside 'running' angle 5 in. x 2½ in. - to quote LSWR practice. When, in later designs, this was cut down by half or more, a lot of horizontal stiffness just disappeared. Again, a few years before, axles had collars against which axleboxes bore and transferred side thrust direct to the main frame concerned, instead of having it passed through frame stretchers from the face of the wheel bearing against the axlebox on the far side, this latter being the case with collar-less axles.* In the case of the 'Coronations' 1⅛ in. thick frame plates in high tensile steel were used. These were tied at the front by the buffer beam, reinforced to resist damage from small collisions in shed yards, but not intended to withstand heavy smashes. Behind this came the solid block of the inside cylinder casting. Then, between the upper sections, was a small cast steel stretcher forming a saddle for the smokebox and having passages for exhaust steam, from each outside cylinder, and one for exhaust steam to the injector. Below, at the base of the frame was the stretcher carrying

---

* *Compilers' Note*: It should be remembered that axle collars can be the source of stress concentration, leading to fatigue problems in the axle, and it for this reason that the practice was abandoned.

the bogie centre pivot and, outside the frames, the brackets transferring vertical weight to the bogie 'spittoons'. Slightly behind, and above, was the vertical inside motion plate carrying the rear of the inside slidebars. From the top of this a line, more or less continuous, of horizontal stretchers ran above the coupled axles. The next vertical stretcher took the main boiler barrel support: its top face carried a liner whose thickness was determined at assembly. The flanges of the bracket on the boiler and on the stretcher were bolted up solid. In designing early Stanier locomotives, the DO had been impressed by an instruction to copy GWR practice in regard to the tops of frame stretchers, and when they saw photographs of GWR tank engines in particular, they were puzzled at the way in which the top of the stretcher between the outside motion plates disappeared within the bottom of the boiler clothing. They were told that this was done to provide 'support if the boiler dropped'. How the boiler was to 'drop' they could not guess, but wishing to be co-operative, the stretchers on the '5Xs' and 2-6-4Ts duly had the top beading of their stretchers disappearing within a pocket in the clothing within about 2 in. of the boiler and curved to match the radius of the boilerplate.* The next stretcher, between leading and intermediate driving axles was in line with the rear of the outside motion girder and the next, between driving and trailing coupled axles carried the rear barrel support at the top and a base plate for the brake cylinder fixing at the base. Behind the trailing coupled axle each of the main 1⅜ in. frames was joined to two hind frame plates. The inner pair were bent inwards and were fixed to the hind dragbox and buffer beam. The outer pair were bent outwards, but stays tied them to the inner frames and provided seatings for brackets transmitting vertical weight to the pony truck 'spittoons'. The joint in these plates was made by turned rivets, a driving fit in the holes and riveted over cold. At this joint was also the stretcher providing the base for the support at the foundation ring, already described and, underneath, a base for the pony truck pivot pin buckle and bracket. The openings in the frames for the axlebox guides had a large radius in the top corners and the plate edges were fully rounded in order to eliminate any marks in this highly stressed portion from which flaws might start. The guides themselves were bolted to the main frames. The frames might well have been spaced to come on the centre-line of the bearings: the figure of 4 ft 1½ in. was more in line with narrow firebox designs where one squeezes the frame between the backs of the tyres (about 4 ft 5½ in.) and the firebox outside plates (about 4 ft 0½ in. width). However, I doubt personally whether there was all that in the 'in-line' fashion associated with the name of Bulleid.

The coupled springs were manufactured from ribbed sectioned alloy steel and were assembled more on a machine shop basis than that of the smith shop outlook. The plates were locked in the buckles by packing pieces and tapered wedge piece seal-welded in position. The span of Stanier springs was longer than previously: a softer ride and lower stresses were hoped for. J-brackets and screwed spring links were specified although the earlier GWR-style of equalizing beams was not proceeded with. Various types of rocking washers between link and spring end were tried over the years, from those with a sharp

---

* *Compilers' Note*: This provision on GWR 2-cylinder locomotives was due to the potential weakness in the event of a serious collision of the bar-frame extensions supporting the cylinders and, as Langridge suspected, would have been largely a waste of time on the LMS plate frame designs.

V seat to those having a large radiused seat which was supposed to allow the two members to roll on each other. All this was due to persistent breakage of spring links. The shape of thread varied from 'Whitworth' to 'Knuckle' for the same reason. Compression links were disliked in many quarters, but they had many advantages over the tension type, chiefly in the matter of accessibility. Going back to my apprenticeship days, a fitter and I had the job of getting an Adams 0-4-4T ready for un-wheeling. Adams' engines all had screwed links in tension and J-brackets, and to get the engine ready for lifting we had to remove nuts on links, drop hornblock stays and also the motion. We spent all one afternoon on one pair of spring links: the lock nuts came off easily - evidently they had not been doing their job - but the main nuts refused to budge in spite of a long tube on a three-foot spanner. Heating up the nuts had no effect. We finally had to split the nuts with cold chisel and flogging hammer. Even if all goes well the lifting requires the springs to be angled to get them in and out of position - a most exasperating job. Drummond engines had 'he and she' screwed compression links, the MR solid compression links, but both required the engine weight to be taken off to adjust them. On Urie's engines, Finlayson used links in compression but screwed to have nut and washer bearing on the spring end shoe and these could be adjusted under load. The type appeared for a short time on LMS locomotives. The whole argument depends on how frequently adjustment is made: the answer is probably only at main shoppings, which would have favoured MR fixed link practice. Of course, in days gone by, case hardening of ends was common: discontinuance of this on spring links (and on motion parts) due to expense would cause maintenance costs to rise - another case of 'gaining on the swings and losing on the roundabouts'. One further disadvantage of the tension link set-up was the bending and twisting on the J-bracket itself. This loosened the rivets in the end. Axlebox hornblock or guide clips were another feature causing much worry to designers. Whether to clip the frame or the guide foot or both seemed to have been the question, and how to prevent the clips coming loose. In the 'Coronations' ordinary horizontal clips with lips clipping to the guide foot were used.

The manufacture of the frames followed normal practice; levelling, profiling and drilling in batches with the use of jigs. Being small orders, Crewe shops did not have a fixed frame stand or jig as they had for the building of Horwich 'Crab' 2-6-0s, which was one of Beames' impressive ideas, but built the frames and stretchers up on adjustable stands. The frames were lined up, with hornclips in position, stretchers added etc. The axlebox guide faces were checked up for transverse alignment and squareness with the cylinder centres. The cylinder front faces were checked by fixed length gauge and trammels, with a straight edge giving true axlebox centre-line positions. Jig drilling simplified the correct positioning of the larger details and minimized constructional errors. It was important that the motion plate and brackets carrying the motion girder ends were true and square. At the same time the motion plate and valve spindle guide castings had to line up with the incline of the cylinders. Across the two frame plates the faces for the reversing shaft brackets had also to be checked. Two other sets of fixed points required careful checking: the brackets transmitting vertical weight at the bogie and at the pony truck. In order to save time in scribing the centre-line of axles in the horn gaps at repair, datum buttons on the horizontal centre-line and at a standard distance to right and left of the hornblock or guide were fitted on the main frames. The line scribed on them was centre-popped and used as a reference point at repairs. Thus, either the liner on the axlebox guide or the face of the axlebox itself could be machined or ground to bring the axlebox back central again.

The 4-wheeled bogie was specified to be the same as for 'Princess Royal'. It was, of course, pure GWR style, but only on the 4-6-2s did the LMS use it. It is strange to note in passing that, later on, Swindon design became 'LMS-ised' on the Hawksworth 'Counties' to the extent of having the LMS 2-8-0 boiler flanged plates, plate frame bogie, 'slap-on' outside cylinders and the main frame plates running through to the front buffer beam, and that this started before 'Nationalization' started injecting 'foreign' personnel. The bogie for the 'Coronation' had top and bottom bar frames with axlebox guides bolted to their inside faces acting as spacers. Across, and fixed to, the two top bars was the cross stretcher on which the centre slide moved, as operated by the projecting centre pin attached to the engine main frame stretcher. Its transverse movement was resisted by the slide and the bogie cross stretcher having, as already stated, to accommodate a movement of 2¾ in. each way Weight transfer from the loco main frames was by the brackets already mentioned into 'spittoons' sliding on the top face of the bogie cross stretcher. Thence the weight was passed to an inverted laminated spring whose buckle was located by a spigot into the underside of the bogie cross stretcher and thence, by links, to pins in the equalizing beam whose ends rested on the axlebox tops. It was a very neat, compact design with only one drawback, which was that due to the laminated spring buckle having a spherical end, the bogie frame did at times run crabwise, 'up' against the axlebox bottom at the front and 'down' against the top at the back. The substitution of a square face instead of the spherical end cured this. It is incredible to think that Swindon used to have a vacuum brake cylinder and blocks on both sides of the wheels on this bogie too. A masterpiece of designing!* The LMS practice was also to fit Ferobestos liners under the 'spittoons' to stop bogie hunting.

The two-wheeled Bissel truck in essentials followed examples given in the *American Locomotive Dictionary*, a volume found in many DOs. Its design had originally been prepared for the 4-6-2 Compound proposed during Fowler's regime, and seemed heavy and cumbersome. In the 'Coronation' a feature was made of transmitting vertical loads to 'spittoons' with Ferobestos liners directly above the axlebox centres. Likewise, control springs for side movement were on line of axle. Laminated bearing springs had rocking washers, rubber pads and screwed links.

The amount and arrangement of side control spring loading on bogies and pony trucks received much attention, both theoretical and practical. A lot of test runs took place on the now lost Hassop/Bakewell curves, which were specially super-elevated for 75 mph running, by an LMS 2-6-4T fitted up with so called flange force recorders. One difficulty in assessing results was to separate flange force from tread friction. The point of the exercise and of theoretical investigation was to find a correct control spring value which would ensure that guiding by bogies etc. was really carried out and side forces on coupled wheels

---

* *Compilers' Note*: Langridge is slightly misleading here; the blocks were on one side of the wheels only on the 'Star' bogie.

reduced.* Actually during World War I we ran one of Drummond's larger 4-4-0s (the '463s') with one side control spring only, as we could not get the bits and pieces to repair the other for a week: the usual loading in those days was 1 ton initial, 2 tons final. Latterly they have been as high as 5 and 6 tons respectively. On a 4-6-2 it appears contrary to control the Bissel which is operating against the loading at the bogie. Experience seems to indicate that all axles should be controlled from 'wandering' on the straight. As already stated, bogie side movement was 2¾ in. each way and loading was usually given as 4 tons initial, 5 tons final loading, and for the pony truck 4¼ in. each way with 1.44 tons initial and 2.96 tons final.

All wheels had the stiff triangular section of rim, shrunk-on tyres and Gibson retaining rings. They were pressed on to the axles in the usual way, with the coupled wheels being keyed on in addition. The axles themselves were bored hollow to save weight and the wheel seat positions were greater in diameter than the journal in order to keep any flaws from developing therein unseen. The crank axle was of the built-up type. Crank pins were also pressed in to the wheels, care being taken that the angle of the driving pin was correct for the attachment of the return crank. For wheel balancing weights were attached to each crank pin to simulate those of the coupling rods etc. The decision concerning reciprocating weights - pistons, part of the connecting rod, etc. - was to balance 50 per cent. The drawing office worked out what was required from information given by the wheel shop of the weights - in the form of steel plates fixed by nuts and bolts - which they found necessary to attach to the wheels to secure freedom from vibration of the wheel-and-axle assembly on the balancing machine. Finally lead was run into pockets formed by plates riveted across the spokes.

The axleboxes for the coupled wheels were steel castings with pressed-in brasses, white metal lined. A feature was that lubrication came from grooves at practically the horizontal centre-line and oil pads below. The oil feed was at the box top and passed through passages at the back of the brass to these grooves. The keeps containing the oil pads were removable by sliding out of the axlebox horizontally. The spring hangers were placed below out of the way. The bearing centre-line was also that of the guide face; the axlebox flanges here were chamfered to allow the engine to roll. Faces to the wheel centres were large and white-metalled, as were those bearing against the guides. The axleboxes for the carrying wheels were conventional alloy castings with removable under-keeps and oil pads; no mechanical or top lubrication was provided. Dust shields were fitted on the open sides of all axleboxes. Endeavours were made to seal the gap on the opposite side, but nothing materialized. The vertical loading on the carrying axles was between 150 and 200 psi and this would increase with wear. For the same reason the stress was kept low and failure of axles on rare occasions was usually due to flaws being set up.

*   *Compilers' Note*: It is unclear from the above if this work was done before or after Stanier's investigations into similar problems in India, which were concurrent with the design work on the 'Coronations'. A memo concerning these curving tests is among the papers in the Langridge file at the National Railway Museum and is dated April 1951, which would suggest that at least some, if not all, of this research came after both the Committee's work and the design of the 'Coronations'. Also E.S. Cox indicates in *Locomotive Panorama, Volume 2*, Ian Allan 1966, that fore-knowledge of the problem within the Indian 'Pacific Locomotive Committee' was absolutely minimal.

The early scheme had a general idea as to the layout of the valve motion. In most designs there was a lack of space, horizontally and transversely. One usually set up on the drawing board one or two cross-sections showing guide, mainframes, springs, wheels, crank pins and coupling rods. On a Walschaert gear the expansion link and its bearings were often a tight squeeze within the loading gauge. One also had to watch that the off-sets of rods when viewed from above were kept to a minimum. It was a good rule to keep the swing of the expansion link down to 45°; although this may have meant a longer link, it kept the slip of the die block down. A curious feature of Walschaert's gear seemed to be that more equal readings of events at front and back strokes of the piston was obtained with the radius rod working at the top of the link, and it was for this reason that the SECR 2-6-0s and 2-6-4Ts of Maunsell's era had their 'foregear' position thus, whereas normally one preferred to have a straight through drive with the radius rod in the lower half of the link. On the 'Coronations' a horizontal 1 to 1 lever with arms at 180° transmitted the valve motion from the outside gear to the inside valve spindle by means of a long rod inside and two 5 in. links on the outside valve spindle extension. Rocking levers were more common working in the vertical plane, e.g. with piston valves placed above cylinders with Stephenson valve gear, and were usually with arms at 180°. Those working in a horizontal plane were also usually at 180° but the GWR had theirs 'off-set'. When the 'Coronation' gear was set up on the valve motion model various off-sets were tried but one could not see much advantage in the valve readings in so doing and therefore the 180° position was adopted. The 'kick' from the die block to the radius rod in the 'Royal Scots' had caused it to strike the expansion link on occasion - possibly due to drivers running the gear down to 'full gear' when coasting - but also due to spring in the reversing shaft. The valve motion on the 'Coronations' was a different layout from that on the 'Princesses' and nearer that of the outside 'Scot' motion: therefore a better design than the 'Scot' was required now.

A young man, D.M. Wilcox, was given the job of designing the reversing gear. Like other 'bright young men' from Horwich, he soon left railway employment for something more promising. He proposed a much lighter pattern girder with plummer blocks carrying the expansion link. At the back end a reversing shaft of large diameter, but hollow-bored, was arranged with a bell-crank at the left-hand end, one arm carrying the sliding block in the radius rod extension, the other connected to the reversing screw. At the right-hand end, there was one arm only, for the sliding block connection. The shaft was in two portions for ease of assembly, with flanged and spigotted couplings. On the last engines the reversing screw and its bracket were placed on a support bracket in front of the wide firebox, where all reacting forces would be absorbed, leaving only a rotating tube connecting to the wheel in the cab to be required. This was far superior to the arrangement on the 'Princesses' where an intermediate shaft was necessary to allow the reversing rod to pass the wide firebox and all vibrations finally being passed to a conventional screw and bracket mounted on a non-too-stiff cab toolbox.

The slidebars, being supported near their centres, departed from the previous 'crocodile' style and were rectangular and fluted. The crossheads had no separate slippers but were castings white-metalled on their wearing surfaces. The piston rod coned end was solid-bottomed into the crosshead, i.e. with no draw, and cottered with the small end of the cotter to the outside. The box-type expansion link and the valve gear generally followed LMS practice; also the return crank fixed on the crank pin end by four studs. True, this had a spigot, but it may seem remarkable that, although it had to be removed whenever the connecting and/or coupling rods were to be taken down, apparently no case of any working loose on any of the hundreds of LMS locos using this feature took place. The two departures from previous designs were in the fact that the coupling rods were fluted instead of the hitherto rectangular section and that the valve spindle slides were carried on a frame bracket instead of being supported from below on the back steam chest cover. This arrangement made for easy adjustment when wear had taken place.

Higher boiler pressures, large steam chest volumes and streamlining of passages were 'the thing' at this time. The cylinders were iron castings; they had straight ports, beloved of the theorists but a worry for the foundry. The straight walls, as compared with those slightly curved, were apt to become highly stressed between the body of the cylinder and that of the steam chest as they cooled off after casting, and flaws were not unknown. During the designing the vertical centre-lines of the inside cylinders were kept as close together as possible, bearing in mind the removal of the cylinder cover and piston head, so keeping down the clearance volume. The bridge pieces across the ports at the liner bore were shaped to help direct the flow of steam and the port shape itself was designed so that its area grew in relation to the feeding area of the liner ports. The liner bores were slightly different in diameter, the far one being slightly smaller than the nearer one. The piston valves were similar and so one did not have to drive the valve spindle and valves through two bores one after the other. The passages to the saddle were easily arranged to decrease evenly in cross-section in the outside cylinder but this was not so easy on the inside cylinder due to lack of space. The piston valve head was also 'streamlined' in the body with a shaped false cover on the outer sides. It had the usual six narrow rings.

The valve motion itself was designed for valves having 1¾ in. lap, a maximum opening to steam port also of 1¾ in. and a lead of ¼ in. This required a travel in full gear of 7 in. By the time the gear was 'notched up' to about 50 per cent the travel would have come down by a third, the opening to steam by two-thirds, and the exhaust port would just be fully used, i.e. its 1¾ in. width fully open. It is interesting to see how the lead opening increased in value as the gear was 'notched up' - for which reason the writer advocated ⁵⁄₁₆ in. lead; and also that by widening the valve head and port width in sympathy an even better opening to exhaust was obtainable at mid and long cut-offs. Earlier Stanier locomotives had run with ¼ in. clearance between piston head and cylinder cover. This had proved too much a policy of perfection for the LMS and the 'Coronations' had the more usual ⅜ in. clearance. The piston head itself, however, still had the tapered screwed GW type fixing. The percentage cut-offs were indicated by a pointer to figures marked on a rotating drum, part of the driver's reversing screw assembly in the cab.

Whether streamlining was fitted or not the cab had a 'peaked' front plate. Side windows of ample size were a feature of Stanier locomotives and the front ones were inclined, so cutting out reflections. All opened to facilitate cleaning. A sliding ventilator was fitted in the roof and no more than the necessary gauges were fitted. A normal fall-plate and cab doors were also fitted.

One consequence of the LMS programme for mechanizing routine work at running sheds was the necessity to design drop grates and hopper ashpans. These appeared on the 'Coronations' and suffered much change in design in order to try and provide equipment that would stand up to rough usage and much abuse. Perhaps the design could have been done better by a steel works or agricultural machinery office than by a locomotive office, except for the fact that weight and accessibility were at a premium - old friends of the LDO. A drop grate, with a removable lever in the cab, was provided and ultimately two ashpan hopper doors, arranged at an angle to help ash and fire clearance, were fitted. Two doors for air admission in the usual way were fitted, one at the front and one at the back. Other more congenial 'self-service' features included atomized mechanical lubrication to valves and cylinders; plain mechanical lubrication to axleboxes and grease lubrication to motion parts. Also fitted were steam sanding to the coupled wheels and steam cylinders operating the cylinder drain cocks, and these had appeared on other Stanier designs in place of hand-operated gear.

The tender ran on roller bearing axleboxes. It was large for a 6-wheeled chassis and intended to carry 10 tons of coal. A coal pusher was mounted on the top of the rear tank. This was another piece of rough machinery that never seemed to reach successful development, probably due to a wish to keep it simple, whereas the problem to be solved demanded complicated movements. Another LMS practice was the fitting of a steam brake on the engine and tender. The braking of guiding wheels had been considered 'dangerous' in the 1920s, but double blocks were now fitted on one side of the coupled wheels.

My notebook records that diagram C34016 of a Kylchap arrangement was sent from Derby LDO to Crewe LDO on 8th July, 1943 and the works manager there, R.C. Bond, would decide which locomotive to fit. There was no member of the experimental staff available - there was a war on! - so I doubt if any records exist. The explanation of the 'C' in the drawing number comes from the fact that in 1942 a re-arrangement of DO staff brought G.R. Nicholson from Crewe to Derby as chief draughtsman with many of his senior men, some of whom had already been moved from Horwich and Glasgow. He brought 'C' and 'H' (Horwich) drawings of so-called standard engines with him and I would guess that the Kylchap arrangement had been copied from a drawing prepared by the makers and sent to Derby by Euston (or The Grove, it being wartime) and added to the original blast pipe drawing. Again, it should be remembered that Crewe did the boiler and above the footplate drawings while Derby did the frames and below the footplate drawings for the 'Coronations'. Lastly, critics should remember that in those days railways aimed at keeping working and were not branches of a Research Laboratory; at that time Rudgard was just about taking over from D.C. Urie as motive power superintendent and both carried on the LNWR tradition in that department.*

For the first time, men from the drawing offices were invited to a preview of No. 6220 in Crewe paint shop, and the press handout said 'designed by the drawing office staffs at Crewe and Derby'. As a matter of fact this remark was very true for Stanier (and his aide) had been in India on a commission from the authorities there, looking into riding and other troubles with Indian locomotives. Thus, the drawing offices could plough their own furrow undisturbed. For some reason or other, the design of this locomotive went through the offices with enthusiasm and little argument. Possibly this was due to the feeling that, for once, it was made up of the DO's own ideas and, with Coleman on the spot and Stanier in India, they 'pleased themselves' to a greater extent.

Some readers may have heard of the American exploits into the two- and three-cylinder compound designs, illustrated in our *Railway Engineer*; one, a 2-8-0, was named *James Archbald*. A former fellow apprentice at Eastleigh, who finally became CME of the Central Argentine Railway, became an enthusiastic supporter of the 2-cylinder idea after Beyer, Peacock built some 2-8-0s to his specification. The LMS people must have noticed a Baltimore & Ohio locomotive, illustrated in the press, fitted with a style of water tube boiler, with the result that I was told to work out something like it for the LMS 4-6-2.

One scheme had a normal barrel; top and bottom headers with side water tubes formed the firebox; there was a throat plate and back plate. Large bore pipes connected the bottom drums with the underside of the barrel, and these were the 'Achilles heel' of the scheme. For some reason I cannot remember, Prof. Cave-Browne-Cave of Southampton University was consulted on water and gas flow. Readers may remember him being consulted on Bulleid's cylinder design a few years later. I started off with 350 psi and 45 sq. ft grate, but weight and loading gauge clearance made me reduce both figures.

Coleman was not very interested in the job; he had no love of working for Euston, at second-hand particularly, and in due course the job was dropped. It

---

* *Compilers' Note*: In the September 1974 *Journal* Mr P.J. Coster wrote:

LMSR drawing No. C34016 contains the details of a 1K/1C Kylchap double blast pipe assembly used on No. 6245. The design is larger than those of the LNER Pacifics, with 5½" diameter orifices instead of 5", although the sizes of the 'barrettes' or knife-edge blocks in the blast pipe orifice are not specified. I tried to ascertain whether the performance of 6245 differed from that of her sisters, but all that could be elicited was that the equipment was non-standard and was removed. It was felt that it would obstruct tube cleaning. If that represents the limit of engineering thought at the time it is disappointing, but surely there was more to it than that?

Mr T.G. Dentith then continued in the same issue:

I was in Crewe Drawing Office at the time this locomotive was completed at Crewe Works at the end of June 1943, streamlined and painted black. I rode on its footplate working the mid-morning West of England train between Crewe and Shrewsbury on 2nd July that year, on what was possibly its first train working after the initial few days of light engine trials. I shall always remember the hoarse but nevertheless sharp beat on that occasion which was characteristic of an engine fitted with a Kylchap blast pipe.

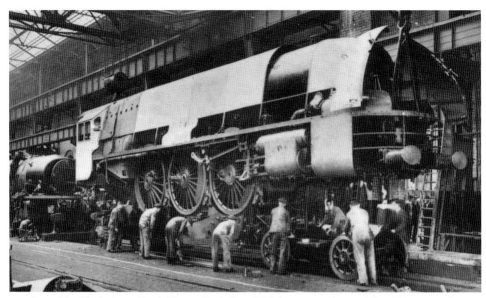

An unidentified streamlined 'Coronation' class 4-6-2 in course of assembly at Crewe works, *c.*1939. *Kidderminster Railway Museum Trust Collection*

LMS 4-6-2 No. 6220 *Coronation* only a few weeks old stands at the head of an Anglo-Scottish express at Euston. The photographer's son is among the members of the public looking on. *Kidderminster Railway Museum Trust Collection/Frank Carrier*

is possible that it might have been revived if war and political troubles had not changed the whole railway outlook. A more conventional proposal which he put me on to was to increase the 2-6-4T superheat and grate area, which we calculated would be 600°F and 26.7 q. ft. This meant new sloping backplates (MR style) and three rows of flues. This boiler went on to new engines; on old ones it required frame stretchers, etc., moving. I do not remember any reports that this made a better locomotive than the old Fowler one.

Higher boiler pressures were becoming the thing in 1935, and my next job was to work out a 275 psi 'Scot' boiler. Once again a lot of calculations done, but nothing materializing.

In pursuing matters of design I have tended to pass by the effects on it of the work of other departments and outside firms. In my LSWR days (1912/19) the storekeeper appeared to place orders for material outside, and unless the CME made complaints all was well. One lot of steel castings for Urie engines, I remember, from the Scottish Steel Co., were so full of blow-holes, which came to light when being machined, that the firm was wiped off the list of suppliers, and we drew out fabrications, made up of plate and angle, to enable the building of the locomotives to proceed: but that was unusual. Mixtures for brass boxes, etc., were the CME's concern; a very cheap one on Urie's 9 in. x 12 in. axleboxes, and a very expensive one for MR and early LMS ones. Drummond had, mostly, brasses fitted into mild steel boxes, lubricated from two grooves either side of the vertical centre line in accord with Beauchamp-Tower's findings, but they were not free from heating so we are told, whereas Urie fed oil on to the top groove right on the centre line, and never ran hot. Perhaps the capacity to absorb heat saved them.

The MR, as I have already mentioned, had its Central Materials Inspection Bureau; it also had a separate chemistry laboratory (in Calvert Street, Derby, until my retirement). Archbutt made a name for himself - his son was the last superintendent of the S&D - and dealt with oil and water matters. Water softening plants had been looked after by them before Stanier's arrival; later, things got involved when others argued in favour of 100 per cent softness; committees were set up and one '4F' class came in with scale up to the top of the front tube plate, falling away to the bottom at the firebox! In yet later years they had to deal with regular sampling of diesel oil, and their head, Bairstow, became the LMS (and I think the BR) chief chemist.

Sanders, the technical chief of one of the large spring makers supplying the railways, in addition to their home supply, was an authority who wrote much on the subject, and got into hot water with his criticism of some LMS designs, to the extent of having his paper unpublished. After the derailment of one of the 2-6-4Ts, Sanford suggested the friction discs fitted to the swing links of the Bissel trucks, which became standard practice. Although I have not seen detail drawings nor a close-up of the actual thing, it looks as if the modern Schlieren carriage bogies have had to have them fitted in spite of having fluid shock absorbers.*

---

* *Compilers' Note*: The 'modern' bogies produced by Metro-Cammell under licence from the Swiss company Schlieren for the diesel 'Blue Pullmans' in 1959 were not entirely successful due to rough ride. While no data has been found on the addition of a friction damper, the very similar 'B4' and 'B5' bogies developed by BR at around the same time were fitted with friction dampers in parallel with the hydraulic dampers and so this may well have been a solution adopted for the Schlieren bogies too.

LMS 4-6-2 No. 6224 *Princess Alexandra* on a local train at the north end of Crewe station below the works footbridge, when new in 1937.   *SLS Collection/W.H. Whitworth*

LMS 4-6-2 No. 6220 *Coronation* leaving Euston with the 'Coronation Scot'.

SLS Collection/C.L. Turner

Looking back, it is strange that the locomotive drawing office was almost completely ignorant of electrical matters; if only someone had had some foresight the office might not have fallen into oblivion. Of course, Fred Onions had fitted up the 'Scot' for America with an electric headlight, and he and Andrew Rankin worked on the Hudd Automatic Train Control (ATC), but mostly away at Bow. The locomotive drawing office only had the job of arranging the equipment on the engines.

But to resume my tale; Price, the C&W chief draughtsman since MR days, situated on the first floor, had retired, and Gilbert had been appointed in his place. When some new coaches were required for the Royal Train Coleman, in his capacity as chief draughtsman of this office as well as of the locomotive drawing office, decided to move some men 'upstairs'! Evidently he was not impressed with the C&W designing people, although the experimental men like Arnold Moon could not be faulted. Anyhow, he put Teddy Fox, who had grown up under him at Stoke (NSR), and Bill Featherstone, who had come down from Horwich LDO soon after the amalgamation, and one or two more onto the bogies and underframes for these vehicles. They were very good men and made an impressive job.

The next job was new stock for the Liverpool and Southport electric line. For this Fox designed bogies whose unique spring arrangement reappeared later on diesel-electric locomotive No. 800 (BR No. 10800), built by the North British under contract for the LMS to their approval. (Other contractors were BTH Rugby and Davey Paxman.) The C&W office had an electric section under Tailby, who were au fait with the modest electric requirements on coaches of that time, but the power equipment came from the English Electric Co. The stock was built at Derby, and represented the first really modern lightweight coaches with sliding doors that the LMS had introduced.

This showed the power of the 'electric section', so called. Fairburn (ex-English Electric) had already been appointed electrical assistant, LMS. He had inherited complete charge of electric trains and the power stations supplying the current, and as we shall see was not the sort of man to let the grass grow under his feet. Beardmore's had equipped four ex-L&YR coaches with diesel-electric power and run them experimentally on the LMS under the electrical engineer's supervision, thus adding strength to his prestige, without a murmur, apparently, from the CME.

The only counter to this were various low-powered diesel-mechanical shunters, looked after by Tommy Hornbuckle and the CME inspectors at Euston, with little interest from his steam-minded superiors. The first of these was 0-6-0 shunter No. 1831, described earlier. Hornbuckle had been assistant to the works manager, Derby (i.e. J.E. Anderson) in MR days, about 1920. A Whitworth scholar with a fine brain and also a practical engineer, but retiring withal, he became chief technical assistant, Euston, LMS. To one who could see the future advantages of using the diesel engine, it must have been very frustrating to work later under a CME whose sympathies were all-out for steam and whose knowledge of diesel railcars was limited to a few maintained under contract to AEC at Southall. A few years later, just before the war, he got approval to order a diesel-mechanical train articulated on his own design of articulation. This used an ingenious system of triangulated links which was

Southport-Liverpool emu No. M28323M in BR blue and grey livery at Blundellsands & Crosby, 30th March, 1979.   *N.R. Knight*

Leyland diesel-hydraulic articulated 3-car set No. 80000-2.   *SLS Collection*

proposed also for ordinary coaching stock as a sort of counter to Gresley's stock. The weights of the coaches were carried on a bolster in the usual way, but the pivoting was arranged on the ends of a parallelogram-like framework, which had the effect of bringing the pivots closer together than the weight-carrying centre pins, thus reducing the throw-over on curves. The train itself was powered by diesel engines and torque converters. The engines were from the original Leyland Motors Co., whose factory, design office, etc. was situated in the town of Leyland, south of Preston, and for whom in those days I had a great respect. Dr Haworth was the brain on their side; he used Lyshoim-Smith converters. A paper was given to the ILocoE by Dr Haworth and T. Hornbuckle describing the train. In some ways it was the forerunner of the BR torque-converter railcars in the same way as the 4-car Beardmore-engined train tried out on the Preston-Blackpool line in 1925 was the forerunner of the BR(SR) Hastings-Charing Cross trains. However, it suffered the fate of being a one-off job, without enough enthusiastic backing in the top quarters. The operating people used it on many branches, notably the Oxford to Cambridge former LNWR cross-country route for quite a time, and were apparently very pleased with it, and from what the CME representatives told me its work was quite impressive. Not so Fairburn - it was not an English Electric production and that was enough to damn it in his view - nor was Sanford interested in it. In fact Fairburn let it lie about and it was finally scrapped soon after his death, an act which caused strong feelings to arise in some people whether diesel-minded or not. Some of the vehicle underframes together with the bogies and power units were incorporated into an overhead equipment construction vehicle in 1949 which worked on electric lines in the Manchester area. '*Sic transit ...*'

On the steam side I have a note of a proposed 2-6-0, with some figures. It came to nothing and, remarkably, '4F' class to the old MR design were built instead. So they could not have been all that bad after all.*

Costs were to the fore of course; welding was coming in and seams on boilers were now sealed in this way to a limited extent instead of caulking. A comparison between fabrications and steel castings for the 'Coronations', including costs and finished weights, makes interesting reading, but is too long to reproduce here. An example is, stretcher between pony frames: weight saved by fabrication 15 cwt, saving in cost 53 per cent.

Another question of costs arose with Peat Marwick & Co. (for the steel makers), and the railway over axle forging costs, and the allowance accepted over drawing size. It meant a pleasant day as honoured guest in VIP company at Sheffield. I had to agree that the large radius on the axle body was impractically awkward for the smith to work to within 2 per cent. It was an old MR practice that had come down through the ages: other people used a parallel body, as I remembered the old LSWR had.

Down the years it was customary to hold an office dinner at the New Year; we provided our own entertainment, songs and topical monologues, and a menu card with cartoons and libellous matter on the back. Not all the Scottish leading hands attended, but most people took the jibes in good humour. The

* *Compilers' Note*: The following batches were built under Stanier: Nos. 4562-4576 at Crewe in 1937; Nos. 4577-4596 at Derby in 1939; Nos. 4597-4604 at Derby in 1940; Nos. 4605-4606 at Derby in 1941.

chief draughtsman took the chair, and in 1936 Chambers came down as our guest. One or two other former members were usually invited also. On this particular occasion Chambers looked a very sick man, very different from the sprightly person of my early Midland days.

I myself felt again that I was getting nowhere, and when I heard that Finlayson was retiring at Eastleigh, I made some inquiries as to what was likely to happen there. Although the new chief draughtsman was hopeful that I might get taken on as his assistant, Turbett, who was acting as CME pending the appointment of a successor to Maunsell, was unwilling to agree to anything definite. As I heard later there were big decisions being taken at high level resulting in the appointment of Bulleid as CME, and until he arrived nothing could be settled among the small fry. Ten to one he would bring in a completely new design staff and ex-LMS men would not be at all welcome. I gathered from C.S. Cocks many years later that Eastleigh men in the drawing office brought up in the old traditional way were soon put on the shelf. So far as I was concerned the matter died without trace.

The year 1937 was also the time of the high speed run which almost came to grief at Crewe. Riddles was on the footplate and Francis A. Lemon, Crewe works manager, on the train, plus the various outside press people. More sensible tests were made with a 'Coronation' on a 6½ hour Euston-Glasgow schedule. This was the first instance I have note of when a cathode ray indicator was used.

Herbert Chambers died in 1937 at a comparatively early age; he was honest and straightforward, probably not tough enough, and unlucky in some ways. Ivatt was moved to Euston to be principal assistant to Stanier; Riddles took his place at St Rollox. Bond was appointed engineer at the Rugby test plant (then on paper), Sanford moved into a newly-created post, development assistant, and had a few picked men as draughtsmen. He came under Coleman and his offices were near him. Their job was to examine ideas, e.g. loose wheels on axles, without any pressure to produce anything practical. None of them could have been very happy with these changes; Ivatt had patrician blood in his veins and liked to go his own independent pace managing men, leaving technical matters to others. Riddles, up from the shop floor, preferred to be close to HQ, and Bond has written of his disappointment at leaving the promotion line to CME. Sanford was also being side-tracked to some extent, for earlier when Coleman was off sick for a few days, he had found Nicholson sitting in the chief's chair dealing with the correspondence and 'crossing it out' to those concerned.

Owen (ex-Furness Railway) was moved up to take Sanford's place as chief locomotive draughtsman Derby, Durnford was appointed assistant chief, and the writer himself became 'leading hand new design'. Actually that meant anything that Owen or Coleman liked to give my section to do.

We cleared off the 1938 2-6-4Ts with dome and sloping backplate, altered one of the 4-6-2s, No. 6207, to have inside valves worked by rocker attached to front of outside extended spindle and with rectangular section slidebars in place of the crocodile type. We started some trials with needle roller bearings in a 2-6-4T in the small end of the connecting rod (they lasted for many years), and then altered details of 'Coronation' motion to take them also. With grease lubrication it was hoped to save preparation time. For some years a ball bearing (in usual cage) had been used on return crank pins, but needle bearings had no cage to hold them together should the inner or outer races be removed intentionally or accidently. Nevertheless, Doncaster had written good reports of thier experience with Ransome and Marles type and it was decided to fit Hoffman's type on the 'Coronations'. In the early design the needles were held in a cage which was pressed in as a unit into the hole in the detail concerned. Then the pin was pushed in through the fork of the other detail, and fixed as usual by collar and pin. In some positions, i.e. the die block in the expansion link, space was so small that no inner race could be provided. Here the needles bore straight on to the pin. Thus the pin had to be hardened and ground to be a working fit within the needles, a push fit in the jaws of the other detail - a policy of perfection. When the inevitable wear took place, usually more at one end than the other, due to the motion not being 100 per cent stiff in plan, the unit had to be replaced together with its pin. At piston and valve examinations, etc., perhaps a needle would fall out, or more likely all the needles scattered far and wide, and that meant another unit replacement. Some attempt was made to arrange oversize replacements, but obviously the complications rule out this idea. So we went over to a large unit comprising inner and outer races with needles. As the normal motion is designed for wearing surface rather than strength the size of pin could be reduced, and the hole in the jaws of the fixed detail likewise.

Needle bearings were first tried on one of the next lot of 4-6-2s, Nos. 6225-34, that we started to order. Very soon after the outbreak of World War II any bearings of this sort were unobtainable for civilian jobs and the former style of bronze bushes with oiling rings on the motion links became standard once more. The second five locomotives of the lot were non-streamlined, but this did not mean much work for us at Derby as Crewe had done all the drawings for parts above the platform. However, with both Derby and Crewe drawing offices having produced drawings for Stanier locomotives, and the necessity of keeping all copies in line, both office and shop, the correspondence that the leading hand had to handle took up too much of his time, and one could only supervise the senior men's work, leaving them to see to detail. Nicholson at Crewe was not exactly helpful. Of course he had works' queries on the one hand and our alterations on the other, so perhaps it was excusable for him to lose his temper at times. In effect, we were clearing the Stanier designs of all the GWR detail which was unnecessary and expensive to maintain; much of this had been foreseen by LMS men, I am sorry to say.

An unusual break came when Stamp 'invited draughtsmen Chidlow (C&W) and Langridge (CME)' to be present at the lunch he was giving at Euston as a send off to America of the 'Coronation' locomotive and train. We duly went and listened to his flowery speech after the meal, mentioning us, amongst others, as having made contributions to this wonderful example of railway enterprise. Amongst the people at the top table was the motive power superintendent, D.C. Urie. I made it my business to have a word with him for I had not seen him since Eastleigh days. He had not many years to go by that time, and he seemed quite an old man; he retired in 1943.

LMS 4-6-2 No. 6226 *Duchess of Norfolk* in red livery at Shrewsbury when new in 1938.
SLS Collection/W.H. Whitworth

LMS 4-6-2 No. 6229 *Duchess of Hamilton* in grey livery. The engine went into traffic in this condition in September 1938 and ran in grey livery until it returned to Crewe later in the year, when it was fitted with a headlamp and bell, and repainted in red livery and to assume temporary number 6220 and name *Coronation* in readiness for display at the New York World Fair in 1939.
SLS Collection/W.H. Whitworth

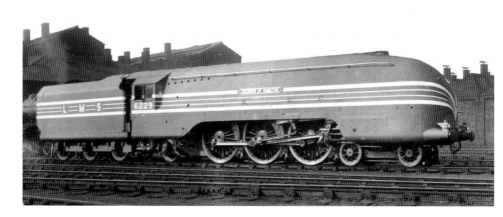

The first LMS non-streamlined 'Princess Coronation' 4-6-2 No. 6230 *Duchess of Buccleugh* when new at Crewe North shed on 3rd July, 1938.   *SLS Collection/L.W. Perkins*

After the final shake-down of the Electrical and CME Departments had taken place on the LMS as a result of the 1923 amalgamation the position became more or less stable so that the CME had an electrical assistant. According to the personalities and first love interests of these people, so the electrical or mechanical side took priority. Dating from MR days the electrical assistant had always had charge of power generating stations and a diesel-electric locomotive thus came under his total supervision. Incidentally, his responsibility for electrically-powered stock also gave him command over cables, conductor rails or wires and the gantries etc.; so he became a very powerful officer. Thus a rivalry grew up on the LMS between diesel-electric and diesel-mechanical, and everyone connected with it fell into one camp or the other. In contrast this did not happen on the SR due to the more gradual and ever-increasing use of electric-operated trains over some decades.

By 1938, Fairburn had won his contention that diesel-electric shunters were cheaper than steam locomotives, and my section were given the job of getting out the design for what was then thought to be the future standard. Fairburn, as electrical engineer, LMS, became assistant to Stanier for this work, ousting Hornbuckle. Two contractors' designs had been tried out by the supply of 10 engines built by Hawthorn, Leslie with two of English Electric's nose-suspended motors and electrical equipment, and 10 built by Armstrong Whitworth with a single traction motor and their own gear and jack-drive. Drawings of the mechanical parts had been supplied to us. The Armstrong-Whitworth team had produced an extremely well laid-out detail design. Armstrong's had gained a lot of valuable experience with locomotives working in South America and was led by notable figures like Blacklock and McArd. English Electric was more spread out geographically - diesel engines at Rugby, electric motors at Bradford and

LMS diesel 0-6-0 No. 7058 built by Armstrong Whitworth in 1933 in Derby works yard, 9th November, 1947.   *Kidderminster Railway Museum Trust Collection*

LMS diesel 0-6-0 No. 7069 built by English Electric and Hawthorn, Leslie outside Crewe South shed, August 1938.   *Kidderminster Railway Museum Trust Collection/W. Potter*

assembly and mechanical design at Preston. To have served at either of these firms was as good as an Oxbridge degree in diesel locomotives, as was a period at North British for steam design. My remit was to use jackshaft drive but with English Electric electric motor which would be finalized by them in association with us. The diesel engine was to be designed and built at the English Electric's Rugby works. Thus commenced a most interesting period of my life. The standard diesel shunter was built in large numbers using the Armstrong-Whitworth type chassis and engine mountings etc., and Englsh Electric type axle-hung motors. The drawings were made in the Derby LDO. Co-operation with the various English Electric personnel in the design of a main-line diesel-electric locomotive was also undertaken, though the development of the 16-cylinder engine by English Electric at Rugby was taking some time.

At that date the companies forming English Electric were still individual concerns. The engineer at Rugby, G.H. Paulin, an Australian I believe, was developing the 450 hp diesel engine which was later used on the SR demus. He was a very knowledgeable man, quite unassuming; he showed me his two-cylinder engine in the test house, which was the guinea pig on which to try out ways of improving performance, etc. They built the final engines there, shipped them to Bradford, where the generators were designed and made and coupled up. The traction motors were also that works' responsibility and were the HQ of the whole English Electric concern then.

As the railway was building the locomotives to their own design, we three offices had to work together. The electrical section people with F.A. Harper, etc. of Ivatt's office came in with us in the mechanical section. As we were also the people who actually produced the drawings to the shops it made for a complicated set-up. I suppose I was given this charge as the older men could hardly be expected to change their spots so late in life. And anyhow Coleman disliked the intrusion of diesel traction and kept out of it as far as possible. For my part I found the contacts with quite-high-ups in this field very interesting - it's never too late to learn - and I have never found it impossible to do that from the most unlikely people. There were also some railway enthusiasts amongst them, whose names I have forgotten, so that over the luncheon table one felt we had all basically got the same interest at heart - railway transport. Amongst those at Bradford, handling the job at shop level as you might say, were the Stockings brothers; John, who unfortunately died young, and Dick who later joined British Railways, and whose retirement I recently read of in *BR News*. Like the others they were very good to work with. The purely electric people had of course already worked with the railways on electric multiple units (emu) motors and control gear, and were familiar with the electric section's (Derby) representative, Evans. He was something of a *bête noir* to the English Electric people at Bradford with his refusal to accept anything not exactly to his liking. I could stand by and enjoy the fun; at times tempers got ruffled.

It was a pity that our locomotive drawing office man did not follow the Armstrong Whitworth pipe layout more closely. I could not get him to toe the line without doing the job myself, and I just had not time to do that, so had to accept second best. He had been on the SECR, got to the NSR and then was pushed around until Derby finally had to endure him. I saw his file once later on, and J. Clayton had not a good word to say for him.

In July 1938 I was told to meet Fairburn at Crewe diesel shop (the first time I had come face to face with him) to hear his comments on the limited lifting height there, gear case leakage, accessibility, and so on, on the Armstrong Whitworth-built locomotives. Then came frequent visits to English Electric, Bradford, settling up the mounting of their parts on to our frame. It was not until May 1939 that No. 7080 came out and was weighed: she was 55 tons 1 cwt (weight was wanted in order to make her brake power effective).

My next door neighbour at Ambergate had been in New Zealand and still had an attractive magazine sent over from there. She used to pass them on to me, and perhaps they made me interested in that country. Anyhow, when an advertisement appeared in the technical press for an assistant chief draughtsman, New Zealand Railways, I applied for the job. That was in the late 1930s, and the international situation was deteriorating rapidly, which also made me think a move to the antipodes would not be a bad idea. In due course I was called up to New Zealand House for interview. I had realised that the advertisement had mentioned that some C&W experience would be an advantage, and when it turned out that Featherstone had also applied, and was following me into the interview room, I guessed that my chances were slim. I had also a family to move whereas Bill had no children. So Bill got the job - obviously the better choice so far as the New Zealand people were concerned. I had known Bill for many years as he was a keen violinist, and we had played trios with another friend from the Research Dept for a long time. His departure broke up that partnership and we split up the music between the three of us. I played no more trios until I retired down south and found another partner to fill the gap, my research friend having by that time moved to Ashford, which was not then too far to prevent us meeting once again.

The feeling that industries can get bogged down, particularly ones like that associated with the steam locomotive, caused the LMS to bring in some part-time members, possibly at Board level. One of these gentlemen, named Barker, I believe, came round the Derby locomotive drawing office. We heard afterwards that he thought our drawing tables (which combined long drawers in which to store the office copies on one side and the draughtsman's board on tapered blocks on the other - a stock way of doing things in most locomotive drawing offices) out of date. A sample board on vertical stand and with universal adjustments, which could be moved around anywhere and at any angle, had to be ordered. It is the sort of thing that you see on TV interviews and is, of course, quite right for offices where no reference is required to large drawings, but a lot of these machines in the old locomotive drawing offices would have cluttered the place up. A board did arrive; no one used it, and it disappeared - perhaps upstairs to the C&W office.

The Electrical Engineer's Dept was gaining power and had a modern office built in Melbury Terrace, just round the corner from the CME's office in Drummond Street, Euston. It seemed to emphasize that 'sparks' was up-to-date compared with steam. It may have been Fairburn who realised that the average draughtsman knew little about welding, which was coming practice, and he started classes for them. Actually, at that time, everyone was feeling their way on the finer points, and all we learned about was the preparation of the plates to be joined; we also had a shot at doing a bit ourselves! The electrode had to be held steadily and just at the right distance from the plates, otherwise there was a bang and it had got stuck to the plates itself! However, one got the idea, but it occurred to me that most draughtsmen had not been in a foundry and a lot of bad design could have been averted if they had had a chance to do so.

Draughtsmen in the locomotive drawing office did not have much chance of seeing the result of their labours. The Derby locomotive works were half a mile away by road - it was too dangerous to cross the main lines from their London Road office and, of course, most of the new work was being built at Crewe. Even next door, they knew little of what the Research Dept was up to except from what they heard from some of their former colleagues who had been transferred from the drawing offices to that department. I found their library and periodic notes on what was happening elsewhere useful. We knew that they had developed gauges for stress measurement: they came out with suggestions for improved frame design and so on. One spectacular large-scale experiment was running a class '5' at high revolutions per minute on a well-greased stretch of track outside their office building. The locomotive was anchored, more or less, and the point was to get an idea of the distortion caused by hammer blow from weights in wheels due to different reciprocating balance percentages. They had also done a lot of work on train resistance and Johansen's formulae are often referred to nowadays. This involved testing in their small wind tunnel as well as on the road.

A well-known product of the Research Dept was the Mobile Test Unit. Dr H.I. Andrews was closely associated with this venture; it has been described in Inst. Loco. Engineers proceedings and, when fully completed after the war, comprised two mobile test units to cover all conditions of speed, and a dynamometer car in which were housed, besides the normal recording facilities, a smokebox gas analysis unit; a wind-resistance recorder measuring from the apparatus mounted on the front of the locomotive, and an electric indicator continuously working from the locomotive cylinder recording the diagram to a large scale. Behind it all was the idea that one got a truer picture of what was happening on the actual railway line, and by testing at constant speed one variable factor was eliminated.

I remember seeing a report of an experiment, before the war when only one of the MTU vehicles had been built, of a non-stop run which had been arranged from Derby to Derby, out via the Bristol line, back via the London line. Perhaps we shall see some of these early proving runs if they are found in the NRM archives. The 'Horwich' dynamometer car was used on this occasion and the date could be fixed roughly as D.W. Sanford was in charge and M. Henstock on the footplate. One of the latter's jobs was to try and get the same amount of fire on the grate at the finish and in the same condition as at the start. Obviously with the Horwich car the facilities for recording were very limited and these runs were made, I presume, only to try out the possibilities of MTU testing. The other unit and the car were not completed until about 1946.

Although the taper 2-6-2T looked a more handsome job than the Fowler parallel version, and a large number had been built, with its two-row

LMS Stanier 2-6-2T No. 163 rebuilt with larger boiler.   *SLS Collection*

LMS Stanier 2-6-4T No. 2622 at Derby shed, 21st August, 1938 when five weeks old. The smokebox door number plate is in the 1936 style of block lettering, although Derby had reverted earlier in the year to the earlier style of cab and tank side insignia.   *SLS Collection/L.W. Perkins*

superheater, it was not powerful. A reboilering scheme was got out, mostly done by Frank Carrier on Campbell's section, doubling up the number of flue tubes and increasing the boiler diameter and the engine weight. This rebuild was pursued in a rather half-hearted way: Frank wanted to reduce the length of coupled wheelbase, as he did for the 2-6-4Ts, but, in both cases, at that time could not get his idea accepted.

As the threat of the outbreak of war came nearer, the LMS, like the SR, bought their 'house on the hill', The Grove, at Watford, and the chief officers and their skeleton staff moved there from Euston. Stanier's personal assistant, Ivatt, came to Derby, occupying one of the old solid MR blocks - formerly the goods manager's, I believe - just outside the station, alongside the MR hotel. He brought with him his inspectors and the 'Special Drawing Office' (which was later known as the tank office) set up to help on government work in the rearmament programme. So the seed was planted for a rival office to that of the locomotive drawing office with its experimental, statistical, and inspecting branches, for Coleman had been allowed to have a full-time inspector (W. Bramley) with authority to enter all motive power depots, thus by-passing Euston HQ inspectors.

I well remember A.E. Owen coming down the office one bright morning and saying excitedly, 'They have invaded Poland', and thinking, 'Great Scot! Have we got to go through all that lot again?' - not that the first war had injured me a great deal - but one thought of all the horror and wasted time and energy that war would entail. As it happened, things went on in much the same way, with the usual sketches of blackout sheets as an extra. The Local Defence Volunteers (LDV) was formed and some of us did a turn at nights, 'guarding' the C&W works area in which our office was situated. One walked round the perimeter and perhaps looked in one or two of the shops, and came back to sit by the phone in the messenger's lobby in the main office entrance waiting for the air-raid signal. One night, Vic Stockton brought along a rifle and to while away the time we rigged up a range on the length of the corridor. No doubt it was all quite illegal, but no one got hurt! And little damage was done to the walls. When the LDV got a little more organized and became the Home Guard, with parades, I opted out in favour of the Auxiliary Fire Service near home at Allestree - but more of that anon.

War means restrictions and I was sent down to Hoffmann's, Chelmsford, in a hurry one day to get as many sets of needle bearings as I could before they dried up. Materials did not get into short supply until the Ministry of Supply got busy, and then railways had to make do without things like rubber and special steels. Paper got short and one found on the reverse of typed letters some MR private correspondence at times!

As to locomotive building, diesel-electric shunters were an obvious 'must'. By using thinner frames, and cutting out boring of axles, costs were reduced. The 1940 building programme included 10 'Coronations', 80 2-8-0s at Crewe, and 2-6-4Ts and some old 0-6-0 '4Fs' at Derby (as no agreement had yet been come to on the proposed 2-6-0 '4F' design). Fairburn, always keeping his eye on the diesel-electric shunters, noticed the time taken to change bearing springs and asked for a simple coil spring arrangement to be drawn out. An engine was fitted but complaints of too lively riding soon came in. A jack-shaft drive makes for a waddling ride and

LMS '4F' 0-6-0 No. 4562 built during the Stanier era with tall Stanier-pattern chimney and tender with coal rails originally fitted to a 'Royal Scot' and later to a 'Jubilee'.   *Ken Lea Collection*

Former LMS '4F' class 0-6-0 No. 4604 as BR No. 44604 at Saltley on 13th August, 1949. The high-sided tender is from the 'Jubilee' class 5607-16 series.   *R.J. Essery Collection*

the coil springs made things worse; no doubt things could have been improved with dampers, but nothing further came of the idea. In any case Fairburn wanted to get nose-suspended motors into the design as soon as they were proved satisfactory for rough work (electrically as well as mechanically.)

War also meant the closing of the Development Office under D.W. Sanford: he went across to Nelson Street as a technical assistant; his staff went to the special drawing office there or to the Ministry of Supply. Most never came back to locomotive design again. Work on the Rugby test plant was suspended and Bond went up to Scotland to fill the job vacated by Riddles' departure to the Ministry of Supply.

Riddles soon got busy on wartime locomotives, mostly to be built by the North British. They were made as simply as possible using cast iron where possible, and had round-topped fireboxes. Saddle tank (steam) shunters were also designed and later 2-10-0s supplemented the first 2-8-0s. A few of our Derby locomotive drawing office men were lent to the North British to help with the jobs.

One day during the war I was ordered to meet a distinguished CME man at York and be prepared to talk about boilers to a Mr Henderson of ICI. After sharing a bedroom with such high company in a rather scruffy Darlington station hotel, we went out to Eaglescliffe, and heard from some Canadian gentlemen that the problem was how to expand tubes in a heat exchanger, part of the equipment they were erecting at, it might be, a chemical plant or an oil refinery, I don't know which. In the end they gave me the sizes of the drum and asked for a drawing showing our suggestions. Back home Edleston did the job. A sequel was a visit to Heysham where the same people were doing the same sort of job and required another drawing, the sizes being different. I had visions of a night at Lancaster but suddenly thought of the Midland line to Leeds and just caught the connecting train. That is the only time I went through the northern Clapham Junction - and that in the dark. Why ICI could not contact local steam engine builders puzzled me: but that is wartime efficiency, I suppose.*

Fairburn had always been keen on breaking into the main line locomotive field, and from time to time had sent further diesel engine drawings as developed by English Electric (Rugby) to the Derby locomotive drawing office for them to include in Co-Co designs. English Electric were slow in getting up their rated horsepower, and weight was also a problem. Coleman had given the job to Fox, keeping a somewhat distant interest in it himself, sufficient to enable him to be able to discuss things at Fox's board when Fairburn paid us a visit to see how things were progressing.

Stanier was given a full-time job under the Government and Fairburn was then appointed acting CME, as well as being chief electrical engineer, and could thus put more of his ideas into practice. He is reputed to have been sarcastic over much steam locomotive design. Why, for instance, did we not put a decent cab on the 2-6-4T? He favoured closed-in cabs, and he had a cooking stove and duplicate controls put in the next diesel-electric shunters, hoping to get one-man-operation and long periods between refuelling.

He also disliked the large drawings common to steam practice and asked for a unit drawing system to be put into operation. This was on the lines of the English Electric's way of doing things, with which he had been familiar. One

---

* *Compilers' Note*: It is suggested that probably ICI considered that the LMS were the local steam engine builders!

Class '8F' WD 2-8-0 BR No. 90335 at Crewe 4th April, 1959.   *SLS Collection/W.H. Whitworth*

Class '8F' WD 2-8-0 BR No. 90369 on a freight at Derwydd Road, 30th June, 1953.
                                            Midland Railway Trust/R.G. Jarvis Collection

had a series of small sheets each showing one part only: thus, instead of, say, a sanding and blower valve being drawn out on one large sheet, one had the bits and pieces individually spread over perhaps half-a-dozen sheets. I got out an elaborate scheme, too elaborate, at first, I am afraid, and drawings for current building programmes were dealt with in this way as far as time permitted. Orders and quantities previously shown on the drawing now appeared on specification sheets. This work previously done in the works offices now became the drawing office's job.

A day I shall not forget was on 11th June, 1940. I was told to go to Buxton to ride on a '3F' class, which had been fitted with a special spark-arrester. Its job was to haul train loads of covered wagons up the hill to Harpur Hill, where caves had been adapted to be a storehouse of bombs. It was a brilliant bright day, and sitting in the engine cab, looking over that wonderful country scene, it seemed absurd to worry about spark throwing, war and the rest. Over lunch in the town I heard of the fall of France, and that brought one back to realities. In the end, three Buxton engines were fitted with this arrester, which, I believe, was to a Swindon design.

A notable loss occurred in April 1941, when Stamp was killed by enemy action in his home at Petts Wood. He had so many contacts that his passing inevitably left a gap at the top. Little has been written of his work on the railway, and it is probably too late now to gauge the extent of it. Wood followed in his post, quite a different sort of personality.

I cannot remember how it was that Coleman had the idea of putting the 'Scot' boiler on the '5X' chassis; it may be that he thought that it would cut out one class of boiler - the '5X' - and, at the same time, give the '5X' class that little bit of boost that sometimes they lacked. However that may be, he came out one day with the order to see if it could be done and what sort of weights we should get. I gave Edleston the job to look at in detail and between us the best we could do without alteration to frames, etc., was practically nil. So we took the bull by the horns, and suggested lopping a bit off the taper 'Scot' barrel and making a new cylinder pattern to suit. When Coleman said, 'Cut up the taper 'Scot' inside cylinder pattern', I said to him, 'What if 6170 wants a new cylinder?' He just said, 'Don't worry about that'; I thought he had gone out of his mind! However, that is what we did: it was a bit rough on the '5X' frame to load it up with a large boiler, but as only two were to be tried out I thought we might improve things later if the re-boilering was successful. Cutting 1 ft 3 in. off the sloping barrel meant an odd diameter smokebox, and 3 in. on the firebox length reduced the firing space. The weight went up but, rather to our surprise, it was still given '5X' route availability. I never understood why Coleman did not give this job to Crewe drawing office: the staff there had done the 6170 rebuild (as I have already recounted) when Coleman was chief draughtsman there, and G.R. Nicholson, now in charge, had done the boiler drawings. True, Wilcox was no longer there and he had made a very good job of the cylinder design, refusing to follow the original North British effort. Incidentally, Wilcox was a Horwich production, and when he was transferred to Derby drawing office, whilst we were doing the 'Coronation' design, he drew out a reversing shaft with a high torsional resistance to overcome the twisting that took on the solid 'Scot' type.

BR 4-6-0 No. 46170 *British Legion* at Rugby shed, 4th February, 1949. Originally experimental high pressure compound No. 6399 *Fury* it was rebuilt in 1935 and classed as a rebuilt 'Royal Scot'. *Online Transport Archive/J.M. Jarvis*

LMS 4-6-0 No. 5736 *Phoenix* as rebuilt with larger boiler. *SLS Collection*

Former LMS 4-6-0 No. 5735 *Comet* as BR No. 45735 in lined black livery. *Ken Lea Collection*

He also did a neat motion girder for the same locomotive, in which the assembly of the expansion link and brackets was much simplified compared with what had gone before. Wilcox had gone on to join D.W. Sanford in the Development Office and, when that closed down at the beginning of the war, had joined the Ministry of Supply, and never came back to the railway - a very good man lost.

And so No. 5736 left Crewe shops in 1942 with a '2A' boiler followed later in the year by No. 5735. New cylinders using the taper 'Scot' patterns had been fitted. Because existing sizes of piston rod, crosshead and bearings prevented any increase of piston load the new cylinders were bored out only to the standard '5Xs' diameter of 17 in. which, with the working pressure of 250 lb., gave a nominal tractive effort at 85 per cent boiler pressure of around 29,600, some 3,000 more than the standard 'Jubilee'. They retained the 'stock' motion from the 2-6-4T design giving 6⅜ in. travel in full gear, but we had played about with the motion from the combination lever which gives 'lap + lead' to give more to the lead than to the lap. This should help to keep the pressure line on the diagram higher with 'notched-up' working, although it probably gave a more uncomfortable ride lower down the scale.

Coming out at a bad time during the war, probably no CME inspector reported on the performance of these locomotives, but it came back by word of mouth that the motive power people found them 'strong' engines, and liked them very much. Why, I am afraid I do not know. The little extra bit of grate could hardly have been the cause: was it the extra radiant surface in the firebox, or the shorter barrel and smaller tubes? Or the 250 lb pressure? And if they were good, why were no more '5Xs' altered? Maybe the existing boiler shells were good for many years, although the mortality of the inside cylinders was fairly high. However, these two engines remained the only rebuilds, whatever the reason, possibly that Riddles stopped it in favour of his 2-cylinder standard engine range.

There was, nevertheless, an off-shoot. The original 'Scots' had run all this time in their as-built condition with their old parallel boilers, etc., and, as the '2A' boiler had turned out to be a good steamer, it seemed logical that the time had come to bring them up to date. It would be interesting to find the minute authorizing this work. Edleston was a fellow-conspirator with me in getting this rebuild through for Coleman during World War II. Everyone seems anxious to claim credit for this and tell us how it was that the new 'front end' (whatever that means?) did wonders. Fairburn was acting CME when we started on the drawings, and he was full CME by the time that the first locomotive was rebuilt. So, in the old parlance, it had been 'designed' by C.E. Fairburn! However, Fairburn had the name for disliking anything steam, and popular opinion has always given the credit to Stanier.

The old frames had to be welded up to take the longer springs and J-brackets: some badly cracked ones were replaced, bogie bolsters added and new cylinders cast from the patterns we had used for Nos. 5735/6, but bored out to 18 in. as their bearings, etc. were bigger than the 'Jubilees'. The tractive efforts remained at 33,000 lb. odd for the 'Scots' and 29,600 lb. for the 'Jubilees'. Box pistons were fitted, of course, but the old four-bar crosshead was retained,

LMS 'Royal Scot' class 4-6-0 No. 6121 *H.L.I.* rebuilt with taper boiler, leaving Crewe. This was later re-named *Highland Light Infantry, City of Glasgow Regiment*   *Ken Lea Collection*

LMS rebuilt 'Royal Scot' 4-6-0 No. 6131 *The Royal Warwickshire Regiment* leaving Manchester London Road on the 2.10 pm to Euston, 16th September, 1947.   *SLS Collection*

rather than the two-bar type used on the '5Xs'. Also I cannot be precise about the sort of coupling rods at the rebuild: it had been the policy to replace the Vibrac (thin flanges) rods 'as and when possible' with manganese steel rods, and likewise to use wheels with triangular section rims, but photographs show all sorts and conditions (*see Appendix Ten for notes on Vibrac*). They did have double chimneys, as No. 5736, but, compared with the 6170 rebuild, had no top-feed trays, just clacks forward of the dome housing the regulator with vertical slides.

This rebuild turned out to be the most successful LMS effort in popular eyes. It must have been good if J.F. Harrison, riding on one at the interchange trials, could say that it was the best 4-6-0 in the country, he being a Gresley man.

One day there seemed to be a lot of to-ing and fro-ing going on outside Mr Owen's office: he was in a bad temper saying something to the effect that Coleman had treated him badly and that he was moving down the passage. On the following Monday G.R. Nicholson appeared and took up his stance in the chief draughtsman's office vacated by Owen. He informed me that he had been appointed chief, and that I should be his assistant on standard engine matters and that Durnford would be the same on other work, and that we should both be 'parked' in the room adjoining his. All this was rather a surprise, the more so when he said that several of the senior men from Crewe would be coming too, and that our locomotive drawing office would have to house office copies of drawings to do with the then Standard engines, i.e. Stanier designs, Horwich 'Crab', and one or two of the MR. So in November 1942, I was more busy finding room for this influx and sorting the men out amongst the different sections than in any design work. Some of the newcomers took the matter philosophically, but one in particular, Gawthorne, went off ill for long periods.

Rebuilt 'Royal Scot' class 4-6-0 with interim BR number No. M6138 *The London Irish Rifleman* at Crewe Works 5th December, 1948.   *SLS Collection/L.W. Perkins*

LMS rebuilt 'Royal Scot' class 4-6-0 No. 6115 *Scots Guardsman*. This was the first rebuild
to be fitted with smoke deflectors.   *J.M. Jarvis Collection*

Most had to put up with daily 'commuting' from their homes in Crewe -
making it a 12-hour day.

Horwich had a way of producing characters and one of them was now given
charge of the senior section. Tom Wright was the elder brother of Wilfred, who
had come straight from Horwich with others at the start of the amalgamated
offices 'under the clock'. Tom's idiosyncrasy was the keeping of a diary (which
if it had been passed on to some library would have settled many queries) with
a note of every decision made, with a remark - 'Mr So and So said this'. This was
not done out of spite, it was just one of those things Tom had always done.
Nicholson was not the sort of man one could get close to. At Derby he appeared
always very smart. He strode into his office a quarter of an hour late and left
early with his head held high. Evidently he was sure of staying and bought a
house in a pleasant northern suburb. He had no car. He treated me fairly, but
passed out most of his letters for me to draft replies to, and came round the
office and dealt in a rather superior manner with his senior men. Tom Wright
said, 'He is like that', and I suppose they had got used to his manner at Crewe:
but he was a very different man from Owen. What impressed Coleman when
he took on Nicholson at Horwich must have been his self-assurance, I presume,
and that he could get on with a job quickly. He was not a neat draughtsman,
such as Coleman had been, and as was Fox, a point that appealed usually to
Coleman. Once he had been taken on, Nicholson must have asserted himself
over the other two men taken on at the same time by sheer personality and his
determination to get to the top.

The most notable event of 1944 was the retiral of Stanier. As he had been
away on war work it passed by without much notice, but, seeing that his
successor was to be Fairburn who had acted for Stanier during his absence, the
consequences could be vital. For the first time the LMS was going to have an
electrical man as CME as well as CEE.